A-Level

Mathematics

for AQA Core 3

The Complete Course for AQA C3

Contents

Chapter 5

Integration

Chapter 6

Numerical Methods

Chapter 7

Proof

Reference

About this book

In this book you'll find...

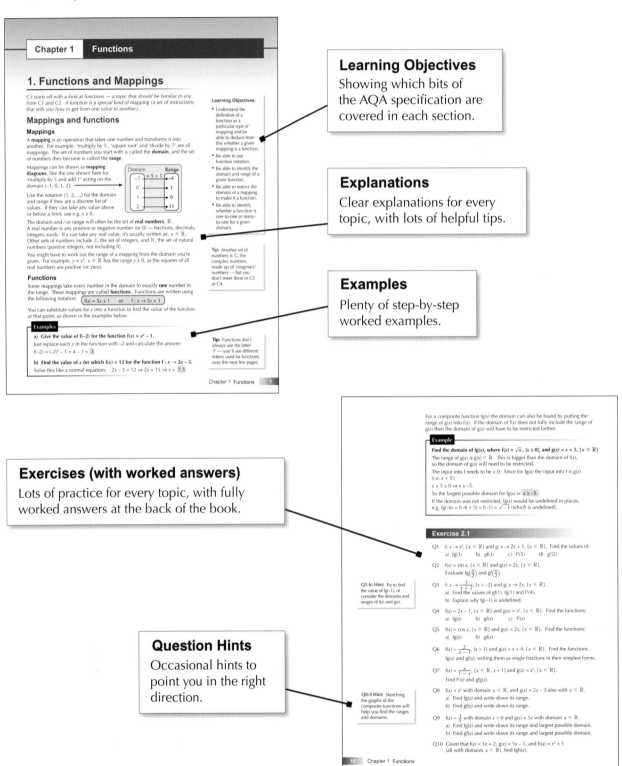

Learning Objectives
Showing which bits of the AQA specification are covered in each section.

Explanations
Clear explanations for every topic, with lots of helpful tips.

Examples
Plenty of step-by-step worked examples.

Exercises (with worked answers)
Lots of practice for every topic, with fully worked answers at the back of the book.

Question Hints
Occasional hints to point you in the right direction.

Review Exercise — Chapter 1

Q1 For the following mappings, state the range and say whether or not the mapping is a function.
If not, explain why, and if so, say whether the function is one-to-one or many-to-one.
a) $f(x) = x^2 - 16$, $x \geq 0$
b) $f : x \to x^2 - 7x + 10$, $x \in \mathbb{R}$
c) $f(x) = \sqrt{x}$, $x \in \mathbb{R}$
d) $f : x \to \frac{1}{x-2}$, $x \in \mathbb{R}$

Q2 $f(x) = \frac{5}{2x+1}$ defines a map.
a) Evaluate f(0) and f($\frac{1}{2}$).
b) Draw the mapping diagram for the domain $\{x \in \mathbb{N}, x < 6\}$ and list the range.
c) Is the map a function for the domain $x \in \mathbb{Z}$? If not, explain why not.
d) Is the map a function for the domain $x \in \mathbb{R}$? If not, explain why not.

Q2 Hint: $\mathbb{Z}$ is the set of integers (positive and negative), and $\mathbb{N}$ is the set of natural numbers (positive integers, not including 0).

Q3 a) Sketch the graph of the function
$f(x) = \begin{cases} x^2 - 2 & -2 < x < 2 \\ 2 & \text{otherwise} \end{cases}$
b) State the range of the function.

Q4 For each pair of functions f and g, find fg(2), gf(1) and fg(x).
a) $f(x) = \frac{2}{x}$, $x > 0$ and $g(x) = 2x + 3$, $x \in \mathbb{R}$
b) $f(x) = 3x^2$, $x \geq 0$ and $g(x) = x + 4$, $x \in \mathbb{R}$

Q5 $f(x) = \log_{10} x$ and $g(x) = 10^{x-1}$.
a) Find the values of fg(1), gf(1), f²(10) and g²(-1).
b) Explain why f²(1) is undefined.

Q6 $f(x) = 3x$ and $g(x) = x + 7$, both with domain $x \in \mathbb{R}$.
Find the composite functions fg(x), gf(x) and g²(x).

Q7 $f(x) = 4x$ with domain $x \geq 2$, and $g(x) = x + 3$ with domain $x \leq 12$.
a) Find the domain and range of fg(x).
b) Find fg(x) and sketch the graph.
c) Find the domain and range of gf(x).
d) Find gf(x) and sketch the graph.

Q8 A one-to-one function f has domain $x \in \mathbb{R}$ and range f(x) $\geq$ 3.
Does this function have an inverse? If so, state its domain and range.

Q9 Using algebra, find the inverse of the function $f(x) = \sqrt{2x - 4}$, $x \geq 2$.
State the domain and range of the inverse.

Review Exercises
Mixed questions covering the whole chapter, with fully worked answers.

Exam-Style Questions — Chapter 1

1 In words, describe what happens to the curve $y = x^3$ to transform it into the curve $y = 2(x - 1)^3 + 4$.
(3 marks)

2 The functions f and g are given by: $f(x) = x^2 - 3$, $x \in \mathbb{R}$ and $g(x) = \frac{1}{x}$, $x \in \mathbb{R}, x \neq 0$.
a) Find an expression for gf(x).
(2 marks)
b) Solve $gf(x) = \frac{1}{6}$.
(3 marks)
c) The function $f^{-1}(x)$ does not exist.
(i) Explain why.
(1 mark)
(ii) Suggest a restricted domain for f(x) so that the function $f^{-1}(x)$ exists.
(1 mark)

3 For the functions f and g, where
$f(x) = 2^x$, $x \in \mathbb{R}$ and $g(x) = \sqrt{3x - 2}$, $x \geq \frac{2}{3}$,
find:
a) fg(6)
(2 marks)
b) gf(2)
(2 marks)
c) (i) $g^{-1}(x)$
(2 marks)
(ii) $fg^{-1}(x)$
(2 marks)

4 a) On the same axes sketch the graphs of $f(x) = |x + 1|$ and $g(x) = x^2 - 4x - 12$.
(2 marks)
b) Hence solve the equation $x^2 - 4x - 12 = |x + 1|$.
Leave your answers in surd form.
(4 marks)
c) Hence solve the inequality $x^2 - 4x - 12 > |x + 1|$.
(2 marks)

Exam-Style Questions
Questions in the same style as the ones you'll get in the exam, with worked solutions and mark schemes.

Formula Sheet
Contains all the formulas you'll be given in the C3 exam.

Glossary
All the definitions you need to know for the exam, plus other useful words.

Practice Exam Papers (on CD-ROM)
Two printable exam papers, with fully worked answers and mark schemes.

A-Level Mathematics for AQA
C3
Exam Practice Papers & Worked Answers
CGP

Published by CGP

Editors:
Mary Falkner, Paul Jordin, Simon Little, Matteo Orsini Jones, Caley Simpson, Charlotte Whiteley, Dawn Wright.

Contributors:
Katharine Brown, Margaret Darlington, Dave Harding, Frances Knight, Barbara Mascetti, James Nicholson, Charlotte O'Brien, Andy Pierson, Rosemary Rogers.

ISBN: 978 1 84762 804 6

With thanks to Mona Allen and Glenn Rogers for the proofreading.

www.cgpbooks.co.uk

Printed by Elanders Ltd, Newcastle upon Tyne.
Clipart from Corel®

1. Functions and Mappings

C3 starts off with a look at functions — a topic that should be familiar to you from C1 and C2. A function is a special kind of mapping (a set of instructions that tells you how to get from one value to another).

Mappings and functions

Mappings

A **mapping** is an operation that takes one number and transforms it into another. For example, 'multiply by 5', 'square root' and 'divide by 7' are all mappings. The set of numbers you start with is called the **domain**, and the set of numbers they become is called the **range**.

Mappings can be drawn as **mapping diagrams**, like the one shown here for 'multiply by 5 and add 1' acting on the domain {–1, 0, 1, 2}:

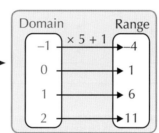

Use the notation {1, 2, ...} for the domain and range if they are a discrete list of values. If they can take any value above or below a limit, use e.g. $x \geq 0$.

The domain and / or range will often be the set of **real numbers**, $\mathbb{R}$. A real number is any positive or negative number (or 0) — fractions, decimals, integers, surds. If x can take any real value, it's usually written as: $x \in \mathbb{R}$. Other sets of numbers include $\mathbb{Z}$, the set of integers, and $\mathbb{N}$, the set of natural numbers (positive integers, not including 0).

You might have to work out the range of a mapping from the domain you're given. For example, $y = x^2$, $x \in \mathbb{R}$ has the range $y \geq 0$, as the squares of all real numbers are positive (or zero).

Functions

Some mappings take every number in the domain to exactly **one** number in the range. These mappings are called **functions**. Functions are written using the following notation:

$$\boxed{f(x) = 5x + 1 \quad \text{or} \quad f : x \rightarrow 5x + 1}$$

You can substitute values for x into a function to find the value of the function at that point, as shown in the examples below.

Examples

a) Give the value of f(–2) for the function f(x) = x^2 – 1.

Just replace each x in the function with –2 and calculate the answer:
$f(-2) = (-2)^2 - 1 = 4 - 1 = \boxed{3}$

b) Find the value of x for which f(x) = 12 for the function f : $x \rightarrow 2x$ – 3.

Solve this like a normal equation: $2x - 3 = 12 \Rightarrow 2x = 15 \Rightarrow x = \boxed{7.5}$

Learning Objectives:

- Understand the definition of a function as a particular type of mapping and be able to deduce from this whether a given mapping is a function.
- Be able to use function notation.
- Be able to identify the domain and range of a given function.
- Be able to restrict the domain of a mapping to make it a function.
- Be able to identify whether a function is one-to-one or many-to-one for a given domain.

Tip: Another set of numbers is $\mathbb{C}$, the complex numbers, made up of 'imaginary' numbers — but you don't meet these in C3 or C4.

Tip: Functions don't always use the letter 'f' — you'll see different letters used for functions over the next few pages.

Functions can also be given in **several parts** (known as '**piecewise**' functions). Each part of the function will act over a different domain. For example:

$$f(x) = \begin{cases} 2x + 3 & x \le 0 \\ x^2 & x > 0 \end{cases}$$

So f(1) is $1^2 = 1$ (because $x > 0$), but f(–1) is $2(–1) + 3 = 1$ (because $x \le 0$).

If a mapping takes a number from the domain to **more than one** number in the range (or if it isn't mapped to any number in the range), it's **not** a function.

Examples

Tip: For the first example, even though each value in the domain maps to only one value in the range, the reverse is not true. This is called a 'many-to-one' function — there's more about these on page 7.

The mapping shown here **is a function**, because any value of x in the domain maps to **only one** value in the range.

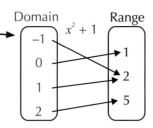

The mapping shown here is **not a function**, because a value of x in the domain can map to **more than one** value in the range.

Exercise 1.1

Q1 Draw a mapping diagram for the map "multiply by 6" acting on the domain {1, 2, 3, 4}.

Q2 $y = x + 4$ is a map with domain $\{x \in \mathbb{N}, x \le 7\}$. Draw the mapping diagram.

Q2 Hint: $x \in \mathbb{N}$ just means that x is in the set of natural numbers (positive integers, not including 0). The $x \le 7$ means that the domain must be the integers 1-7.

Q3 Complete the mapping diagram on the right and state the range.

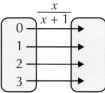

Q4 Complete the mapping diagram below and state the domain.

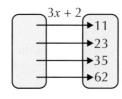

Q5 For the function $f(x) = 3x + 1$, write down the values of f(2) and f(–1).

Q6 Hint: 'Evaluate' is just another way of asking you to 'find the value of'.

Q6 For the function $g : x \to \dfrac{1}{2x + 1}$, $x > -\dfrac{1}{2}$, evaluate g(0) and g(2).

Q7 The function h is such that $h(x) = \sin x$, $-\pi \le x \le \pi$. Find $h\left(\dfrac{\pi}{2}\right)$ and $h\left(\dfrac{5\pi}{6}\right)$.

Q8 f defines a function $f : x \rightarrow \dfrac{1}{2 + \log_{10} x}$ for the domain $x > 0.01$.
Evaluate $f(1)$ and $f(100)$.

Q9 State whether or not each of the mapping diagrams below shows a function, and if not, explain why.

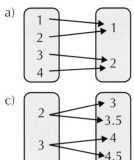

a)

b)

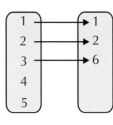

c)

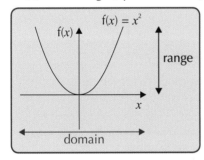

Graphs of functions

Mappings and functions with a **continuous** domain (such as $x \in \mathbb{R}$, i.e. not a discrete set of values) can be drawn as **graphs**. Drawing a graph of, say, $f(x) = x^2$ is exactly the same as drawing a graph of $y = x^2$. For each value of x in the **domain** (which goes along the horizontal x-axis) you can plot the corresponding value of $f(x)$ in the **range** (up the vertical y-axis):

Tip: If you've got a discrete set of values that x can take (e.g. $x \in \{1, 2, 3\}$) then draw a mapping diagram instead of a graph.

$$f(x) = x^2$$

range

domain

Drawing graphs can make it easier to **identify functions**, as shown below.

Examples

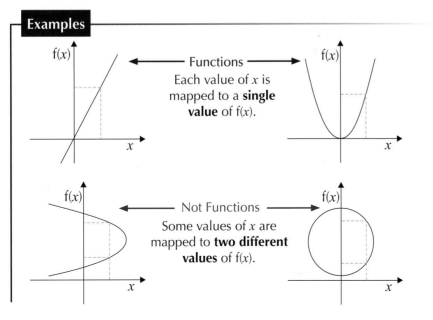

Functions
Each value of x is mapped to a **single value** of $f(x)$.

Not Functions
Some values of x are mapped to **two different values** of $f(x)$.

Tip: This could be turned into a function by restricting the domain to $x \geq 0$ — see page 5.

The graph on the right isn't a function because f(x) is **not defined** for $x < 0$. This just means that when x is negative there is no real value that f(x) can take.

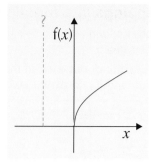

Finding ranges and domains using graphs

Sketching a graph can also be really useful when trying to find limits for the domain and range of a function.

Examples

a) **State the range for the function f(x) = $x^2 - 5$, $x \in \mathbb{R}$.**

The smallest possible value of x^2 is 0.

So the smallest possible value of $x^2 - 5$ must be -5.

So the range is $f(x) \geq -5$.

This can be shown clearly by sketching a graph of the function:

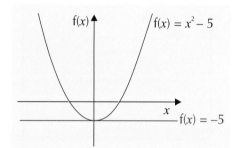

b) **State the domain for f(x) = $\sqrt{(x - 4)}$.**

There are no real solutions for the square root of a negative number.

This means there is a limit on the domain so that $x - 4 \geq 0$.

This gives a domain of $x \geq 4$.

Again, this can be demonstrated by sketching a graph of f(x) = $\sqrt{(x - 4)}$:

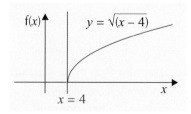

Turning mappings into functions

Some mappings that aren't functions can be turned into functions by **restricting their domain**.

For example, consider the graph of the mapping $y = \frac{1}{x-1}$ for $x \in \mathbb{R}$:

The mapping $y = \frac{1}{x-1}$ for $x \in \mathbb{R}$ is **not** a function, because it's not defined at $x = 1$.

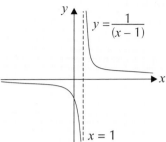

But if you change the domain to $x > 1$, the mapping is now a function, as shown:

You could also restrict the domain by giving values that x can't be equal to, e.g. $x \in \mathbb{R}$, $x \neq 1$. In this case the graph would be in two parts like in the first diagram.

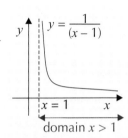

domain $x > 1$

Exercise 1.2

Q1 State whether or not each of the graphs below shows a function, and if not, explain why.

a)

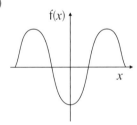

b)

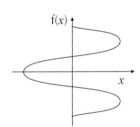

Q2 For each of the following functions, sketch the graph of the function for the given domain, marking relevant points on the axes, and state the range.

a) $f(x) = 3x + 1$ $x \geq -1$

b) $f(x) = x^2 + 2$ $-3 \leq x \leq 3$

c) $f(x) = \cos x$ $0 \leq x \leq \pi$

d) $f(x) = \begin{cases} 5 - x & 0 \leq x < 5 \\ x - 5 & 5 \leq x \leq 10 \end{cases}$

Q2 d) Hint: Sketch the function $f(x) = 5 - x$ over the domain $0 \leq x < 5$, and the function $f(x) = x - 5$ over the domain $5 \leq x \leq 10$.

Q3 State the domain and range for the following functions:

a)

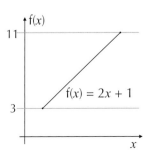

$f(x) = 2x + 1$

b)

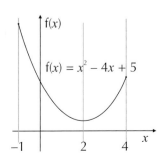

$f(x) = x^2 - 4x + 5$

Q3 Hint: Use the given functions to work out the domain from the given range, or the range from the given domain.

Q4-5 Hint: Use the functions to work out where the asymptotes lie. The range (or domain) will lie on one side of the asymptote.

Q4   The graph below shows the function $f(x) = \dfrac{x+2}{x+1}$, defined for the domain $x \geq 0$. State the range.

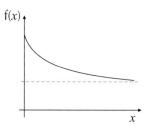

Q5   The diagram shows the function $f(x) = \dfrac{1}{x-2}$ drawn over the domain $x > a$. State the value of a.

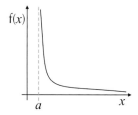

Q6 Hint: $9 - x^2$ cannot be negative, as you can't take the square root of a negative number, so work out the values of x for which $9 - x^2 \geq 0$ and use these as the domain.

Q6   The diagram shows the function $f(x) = \sqrt{9 - x^2}$ for $x \in \mathbb{R}$, $a \leq x \leq b$. State the values of a and b.

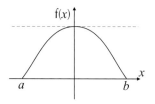

Q7 $h(x) = \sqrt{x + 1}$, $x \in \mathbb{R}$.
Give a restricted domain which would make h a function.

Q8 $k : x \rightarrow \tan x$, $x \in \mathbb{R}$.
Give an example of a domain which would make k a function.

Q8-9 Hint: Sketch a graph of each one first and identify where any asymptotes might be.

Q9 $m(x) = \dfrac{1}{x^2 - 4}$.
What is the largest continuous domain which would make m(x) a function?

Q10   The diagram on the right shows the graph of $y = f(x)$.
a) Explain why f is not a function on the domain $x \in \mathbb{R}$.
b) State the largest possible domain that would make f a function.

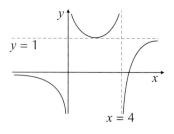
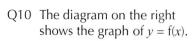

Types of function

One-to-one functions

> A function is **one-to-one** if each value in the **range**
> corresponds to **exactly one** value in the **domain**.

Tip: Sketching a graph is a good way to help you identify the type of function.

Example

The function $f : x \rightarrow 2x$, $x \in \mathbb{R}$ is one-to-one, as every value of x
is mapped to a unique value in the range (the range is also $\mathbb{R}$).

You can see this clearly on a sketch of the function:

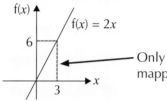

Only 3 in the domain is
mapped to 6 in the range.

Many-to-one functions

> A function is **many-to-one** if some values in the **range**
> correspond to **more than one (many)** values in the **domain**.

Remember that no element in the domain can map to more than one element
in the range, otherwise it wouldn't be a function.

Tip: There are also mappings known as 'one-to-many' and 'many-to-many', but neither of these types are functions.

Example

The function $f(x) = x^2$, $x \in \mathbb{R}$ is a many-to-one function, as two elements
in the domain map to the same element in the range, as shown:

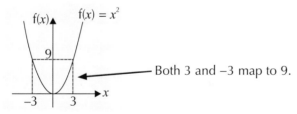

Both 3 and -3 map to 9.

Exercise 1.3

Q1 State whether each function below is one-to-one or many-to-one.

a) $f(x) = x^3$ $x \in \mathbb{R}$

b) $f : x \rightarrow \sin 2x$ $-\pi \leq x \leq \pi$

c) $f(x) = \log_{10} x$ $x > 0$

d) $f(x) = \begin{cases} x + 2 & -2 \leq x < 0 \\ 2 - x & 0 \leq x \leq 2 \end{cases}$

e) $f(x) = \begin{cases} 2^x & x \geq 0 \\ 1 & x < 0 \end{cases}$

2. Composite Functions

Learning Objectives:

- Be able to combine two or more functions into one composite function.
- Know that fg means 'do g first, then f'.
- Be able to solve equations involving composite functions.

When one function is applied to another it makes a different function. This is known as a composite function.

Composite functions

- If you have two functions f and g, you can combine them (do one followed by the other) to make a new function. This is called a **composite function**.
- Composite functions are written fg(x). This means 'do g first, then f'. If it helps, put brackets in until you get used to it, so fg(x) = f(g(x)).
- The order is really important — usually fg(x) ≠ gf(x). If you get a composite function that's written $f^2(x)$, it means ff(x). This just means you have to do f **twice**.

Tip: Composite functions made up of three or more functions work in exactly the same way — just make sure you get the order right.

Examples

If $f(x) = x - 2$ and $g(x) = 3x$, then find:

a) fg(6):

First substitute 6 into g(x).
Then substitute the value that comes out into f(x), as shown below:

$$6 \xrightarrow{\quad g(6)\quad} \boxed{3 \times 6} \longrightarrow 18 \xrightarrow{\quad f(18)\quad} \boxed{18 - 2} \longrightarrow 16$$

So fg(6) = 16.

b) gf(6):

This time substitute 6 into f(x) first.
Then substitute the value that comes out into g(x):

$$6 \longrightarrow \boxed{6 - 2}^{f(6)} \longrightarrow 4 \longrightarrow \boxed{3 \times 4}^{g(4)} \longrightarrow 12$$

So gf(6) = 12.

Tip: Comparing the answers to a) and b) you can see that fg(x) ≠ gf(x).

c) fg(x):

This time leave everything in terms of x. Do g first, then f:

$$x \longrightarrow \boxed{3x}^{g(x)} \longrightarrow 3x \longrightarrow \boxed{(3x) - 2}^{f(3x)} \longrightarrow 3x - 2$$

So fg(x) = 3x – 2.

d) gf(x):

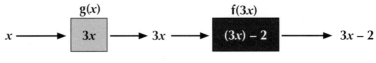

$$x \longrightarrow \boxed{x - 2}^{f(x)} \longrightarrow x - 2 \longrightarrow \boxed{3(x-2)}^{g(x-2)} \longrightarrow \begin{matrix} 3(x - 2) \\ \text{or} \\ 3x - 6 \end{matrix}$$

So gf(x) = 3x – 6.

The key to composite functions is to work things out in steps. Set out your working for composite functions as shown in the examples below.

Examples

For the functions f : $x \to 2x^3$ {$x \in \mathbb{R}$} and g : $x \to x - 3$ {$x \in \mathbb{R}$}, find:

a) fg(4)   **b)** fg(0)   **c)** gf(0)   **d)** fg(x)   **e)** gf(x)   **f)** f²(x).

a) $fg(4) = f(g(4))$
$\qquad = f(4 - 3) = f(1)$
$\qquad = 2 \times 1^3 = 2$

b) $fg(0) = f(g(0))$
$\qquad = f(0 - 3) = f(-3)$
$\qquad = 2 \times (-3)^3 = 2 \times -27$
$\qquad = -54$

c) $gf(0) = g(f(0))$
$\qquad = g(2 \times 0^3) = g(0)$
$\qquad = 0 - 3 = -3$

d) $fg(x) = f(g(x))$
$\qquad = f(x - 3)$
$\qquad = 2(x - 3)^3$

e) $gf(x) = g(f(x))$
$\qquad = g(2x^3)$
$\qquad = 2x^3 - 3$

f) $f^2(x) = f(f(x))$
$\qquad = f(2x^3)$
$\qquad = 2(2x^3)^3 = 16x^9$

Tip: Don't forget the 2^3 when expanding $(2x^3)^3$ in part f).

Domain and range of composite functions

Two functions with given domains and ranges may form a composite function with a **different** domain and range.

Example

Give the domain and range of the composite function fg(x), where:
f(x) = $2x^2 + 1$, domain $x \in \mathbb{R}$, range f(x) $\geq$ 1
g(x) = $\dfrac{1}{x + 3}$, domain $x > -3$, range g(x) > 0

- First work out the composite function in terms of x:
  $$fg(x) = f(g(x))$$
  $$= f\left(\frac{1}{x + 3}\right) = 2\left(\frac{1}{x + 3}\right)^2 + 1$$

- Next, consider the graph of the composite function over the domain and range of the original functions:

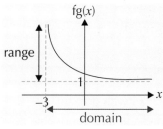

As g(x) is restricted to $x > -3$, so the domain of fg(x) is also restricted to $x > -3$.

Tip: Working out the domains and ranges of composite functions can be tricky — but sketching a graph always helps.

Since $\dfrac{1}{x + 3}$ is always > 0 for the domain $x > -3$,

$2\left(\dfrac{1}{x + 3}\right)^2 + 1$ must be > 1. So the range is fg(x) > 1.

For a composite function fg(x) the domain can also be found by putting the range of g(x) into f(x). If the domain of f(x) does not fully include the range of g(x) then the domain of g(x) will have to be restricted further.

Example

Find the domain of fg(x), where f(x) = $\sqrt{x}$, {x ≥ 0}, and g(x) = x + 5, {x ∈ ℝ}

The range of g(x) is g(x) ∈ ℝ. This is bigger than the domain of f(x), so the domain of g(x) will need to be restricted.

The input into f needs to be ≥ 0. Since for fg(x) the input into f is g(x) (i.e. x + 5):

$x + 5 \geq 0 \Rightarrow x \geq -5$.

So the largest possible domain for fg(x) is $x \geq -5$.

If the domain was not restricted, fg(x) would be undefined in places, e.g. fg(–6) = f(–6 + 5) = f(–1) = $\sqrt{-1}$ (which is undefined).

Exercise 2.1

Q1 f: x → x², {x ∈ ℝ} and g: x → 2x + 1, {x ∈ ℝ}. Find the values of:
a) fg(3)   b) gf(3)   c) f²(5)   d) g²(2)

Q2 f(x) = sin x, {x ∈ ℝ} and g(x) = 2x, {x ∈ ℝ}.
Evaluate fg($\frac{\pi}{2}$) and gf($\frac{\pi}{2}$).

Q3 b) Hint: Try to find the value of fg(–1), or consider the domains and ranges of f(x) and g(x).

Q3 f: x → $\frac{3}{x + 2}$, {x > –2} and g: x → 2x, {x ∈ ℝ}.
a) Find the values of gf(1), fg(1) and f²(4).
b) Explain why fg(–1) is undefined.

Q4 f(x) = 2x – 1, {x ∈ ℝ} and g(x) = x², {x ∈ ℝ}. Find the functions:
a) fg(x)   b) gf(x)   c) f²(x)

Q5 f(x) = cos x, {x ∈ ℝ} and g(x) = 2x, {x ∈ ℝ}. Find the functions:
a) fg(x)   b) gf(x)

Q6 f(x) = $\frac{2}{x - 1}$, {x > 1} and g(x) = x + 4, {x ∈ ℝ}. Find the functions fg(x) and gf(x), writing them as single fractions in their simplest forms.

Q7 f(x) = $\frac{x}{1 - x}$, {x ∈ ℝ, x ≠ 1} and g(x) = x², {x ∈ ℝ}.
Find f²(x) and gfg(x).

Q8-9 Hint: Sketching the graphs of the composite functions will help you find the ranges and domains.

Q8 f(x) = x² with domain x ∈ ℝ, and g(x) = 2x – 3 also with x ∈ ℝ.
a) Find fg(x) and write down its range.
b) Find gf(x) and write down its range.

Q9 f(x) = $\frac{1}{x}$ with domain x > 0 and g(x) = 5x with domain x ∈ ℝ.
a) Find fg(x) and write down its range and largest possible domain.
b) Find gf(x) and write down its range and largest possible domain.

Q10 Given that f(x) = 3x + 2, g(x) = 5x – 1, and h(x) = x² + 1 (all with domains x ∈ ℝ), find fgh(x).

Solving composite function equations

If you're asked to solve an equation such as fg(x) = 8, the best way to do it is to work out what fg(x) is, then rearrange fg(x) = 8 to make x the subject.

Example 1

For the functions f: $x \to \sqrt{x}$ with domain {$x \geq 0$} and g: $x \to \dfrac{1}{x-1}$ with domain {$x > 1$}, solve the equation fg(x) = $\dfrac{1}{2}$. Also, state the range of fg(x).

- First, find fg(x): $fg(x) = f\left(\dfrac{1}{x-1}\right) = \sqrt{\dfrac{1}{x-1}} = \dfrac{1}{\sqrt{x-1}}$

- So $\dfrac{1}{\sqrt{x-1}} = \dfrac{1}{2}$

- Rearrange this equation to find x:
  $\dfrac{1}{\sqrt{x-1}} = \dfrac{1}{2} \Rightarrow \sqrt{x-1} = 2 \Rightarrow x - 1 = 4 \Rightarrow x = 5$

- To find the range, draw the graph of fg(x).

- From the graph you can see that the domain of fg(x) is $x > 1$ (though the question doesn't ask for this) and the range is fg(x) > 0.

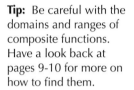

$y = fg(x)$

Tip: Be careful with the domains and ranges of composite functions. Have a look back at pages 9-10 for more on how to find them.

Example 2

For the functions f: $x \to 2x + 1$ {$x \in \mathbb{R}$} and g: $x \to x^2$ {$x \in \mathbb{R}$}, solve gf(x) = 16.

- Find gf(x): $\qquad gf(x) = g(2x + 1) = (2x + 1)^2$
- Now solve gf(x) = 16: $(2x + 1)^2 = 16$
  $\qquad\qquad\qquad (2x + 1) = 4 \text{ or } {-4}$
  $\qquad\qquad\qquad 2x = 3 \text{ or } {-5}$

- So $x = \dfrac{3}{2}$ or $x = -\dfrac{5}{2}$.

Exercise 2.2

Q1 $f(x) = 2x + 1$ and $g(x) = 3x - 4$. Solve the equation fg(x) = 23.

Q2 $f(x) = \dfrac{1}{x}$ and $g(x) = 2x + 5$. Solve the equation gf(x) = 6.

Q3 $f(x) = x^2$ and $g(x) = \dfrac{x}{x-3}$. Solve the equation gf(x) = 4.

Q4 $f(x) = x + 3$ and $g(x) = x^2 - 1$. Solve the equation gf(x) = 3.

Q5 $f(x) = x^2 + 1$ and $g(x) = 3x - 2$. Solve the equation fg(x) = 50.

Q6 $f(x) = 2^x$ and $g(x) = 2x + 1$. Solve the equation fg(x) = 32.

Q7 $f(x) = \log_{10}x$ and $g(x) = 3 - x$. Solve the equation fg(x) = 0.

Q8 $f(x) = 2^x$ and $g(x) = x^2 + 2x$. Solve the equation fg(x) = 8.

Q9 $f(x) = \dfrac{x}{x+1}$ and $g(x) = 2x - 1$. Solve the equation fg(x) = gf(x).

Q10 $f(x) = 2^x$ and $g(x) = x + 1$. Solve the equation fg(x) = gf(x).

3. Inverse Functions

Learning Objectives:

- Understand which functions will have inverses.
- Know that $f^{-1}f(x) = ff^{-1}(x) = x$.
- Be able to find the inverse of a function, and find its domain and range.
- Be able to draw and interpret graphs of functions and their inverses.

Inverse functions 'undo' functions. So if a function tells you to do a certain thing to x, the inverse of that function tells you how to get back to the start.

Inverse functions and their graphs

- An **inverse function** does the **opposite** to the function. So if the function was '+ 1', the inverse would be '− 1', if the function was '× 2', the inverse would be '÷ 2' etc.
- The inverse for a function f(x) is written **f⁻¹(x)**.
- An inverse function maps an element in the **range** to an element in the **domain** — the opposite of a function. This means that only **one-to-one** functions have inverses, as the inverse of a many-to-one function would be one-to-many, which isn't a function.

Tip: See page 7 for more on the different types of functions.

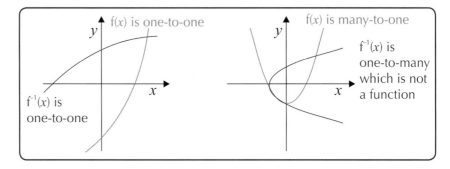

- For any inverse $f^{-1}(x)$:

$$f^{-1}f(x) = x = ff^{-1}(x)$$

Tip: $f^{-1}f(x)$ is a composite function. It just means 'do f then f^{-1}' (see page 8).

Doing the function and then the inverse...

...is the same as doing the inverse then doing the function — both just give you x.

- The **domain** of the inverse is the **range** of the function, and the **range** of the inverse is the **domain** of the function.

Example

A function f(x) = x + 7 has domain x ≥ 0 and range f(x) ≥ 7. State whether the function has an inverse. If so, find the inverse, and give its domain and range.

The function f(x) = x + 7 is one-to-one, so it does have an inverse.

The inverse of +7 is −7, so $f^{-1}(x) = x − 7$.

$f^{-1}(x)$ has domain x ≥ 7 (the range of f(x)).

It has range $f^{-1}(x) ≥ 0$ (the domain of f(x)).

Tip: Check that this is correct by seeing if $f^{-1}f(x) = x$:
$f^{-1}f(x) = f^{-1}(x + 7)$
$= (x + 7) − 7 = x$
So it's correct.

For simple functions (like the one in the example above), it's easy to work out what the inverse is just by looking at it. But for more complex functions, you need to **rearrange** the original function to **change the subject**.

Finding the inverse of a function

Here's a general method for finding the inverse of a given function:

- Replace f(x) with y to get an equation for **y in terms of x**.
- **Rearrange** the equation to make x the subject.
- Replace x with $f^{-1}(x)$ and y with x — this is the **inverse function**.
- **Swap** round the **domain** and **range** of the function.

Tip: It's easier to work with y than f(x).

Example 1

Find the inverse of the function f(x) = $\sqrt{2x - 1}$, with domain $x \geq \frac{1}{2}$ and range f(x) $\geq$ 0. State the domain and the range of the inverse.

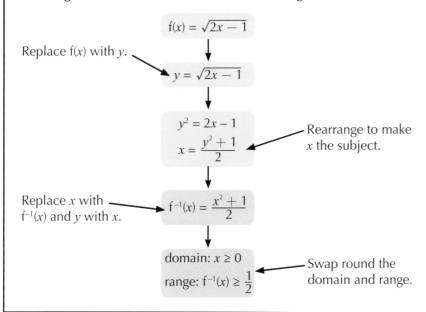

Replace f(x) with y.

$$f(x) = \sqrt{2x - 1}$$

$$y = \sqrt{2x - 1}$$

$$y^2 = 2x - 1$$
$$x = \frac{y^2 + 1}{2}$$

Rearrange to make x the subject.

Replace x with $f^{-1}(x)$ and y with x.

$$f^{-1}(x) = \frac{x^2 + 1}{2}$$

domain: $x \geq 0$

range: $f^{-1}(x) \geq \frac{1}{2}$

Swap round the domain and range.

Tip: Breaking it into steps like this means you're less likely to go wrong. It's worth doing it this way even for easier functions.

Example 2

Find the inverse of the function f(x) = $3x^2$ + 2 with domain $x \geq 0$, and state its domain and range.

$$y = 3x^2 + 2.$$

Replace f(x) with y.

Rearrange to make x the subject.

$$y - 2 = 3x^2$$
$$\frac{y - 2}{3} = x^2$$

$$x = \sqrt{\frac{y - 2}{3}}$$

$x \geq 0$ so you don't need the negative square root.

Replace x with $f^{-1}(x)$ and y with x.

$$f^{-1}(x) = \sqrt{\frac{x - 2}{3}}$$

The range of f(x) is f(x) $\geq$ 2, so $f^{-1}(x)$ has domain $x \geq 2$.

The domain of f(x) is $x \geq 0$ and so the inverse has range $f^{-1}(x) \geq 0$.

Tip: If you're not given the domain and / or the range of the function you'll need to work this out first. In this example where x is always at least 0, f(x) must always be at least 2.

Graphs of inverse functions

The inverse of a function is its **reflection** in the line $y = x$.

Example

Sketch the graph of the inverse of the function $f(x) = x^2 - 8$ with domain $x \geq 0$.

- **Step 1:** Draw $f(x)$.

- **Step 3:** Reflect $f(x)$ in $y = x$ to get $f^{-1}(x)$.

- **Step 2:** Draw $y = x$.

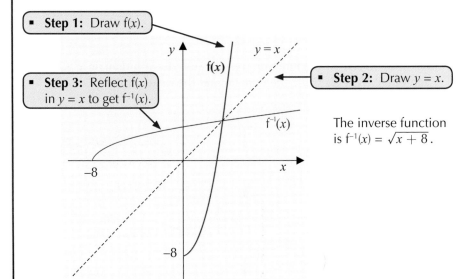

The inverse function is $f^{-1}(x) = \sqrt{x + 8}$.

It's easy to see what the domains and ranges are from the graph — $f(x)$ has domain $x \geq 0$ and range $f(x) \geq -8$, and $f^{-1}(x)$ has domain $x \geq -8$ and range $f^{-1}(x) \geq 0$.

Exercise 3.1

Q1 Does the function shown on the right have an inverse? Justify your answer.

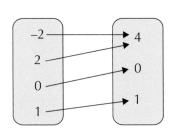

Q2 Does the function shown in this mapping diagram have an inverse? Justify your answer.

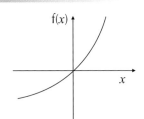

Q3 $f(x) = \sin x$ with domain $x \in \mathbb{R}$.
Does the inverse function $f^{-1}(x)$ exist? Justify your answer.

Q4 Function f(x) is defined on the domain $x \in \mathbb{R}$, where $f(x) = x^2 + 3$.
Does the inverse function $f^{-1}(x)$ exist? Justify your answer.

Q4-11 Hint: If in doubt, sketch a graph of the function to check domains and ranges.

Q5 $f(x) = (x - 4)^2$, $\{x \geq 4\}$. Does $f^{-1}(x)$ exist? Justify your answer.

Q6 Find the inverse of each of the following functions, stating the domain and range:

a) $f(x) = 3x + 4$, $\{x \in \mathbb{R}\}$. b) $f(x) = 5(x - 2)$, $\{x \in \mathbb{R}\}$.

c) $f(x) = \dfrac{1}{x + 2}$, $\{x > -2\}$. d) $f(x) = x^2 + 3$, $\{x > 0\}$.

Q7 $f(x) = \dfrac{3x}{x + 1}$, $\{x > -1\}$.

a) Find $f^{-1}(x)$, stating the domain and range.

b) Evaluate $f^{-1}(2)$.

c) Evaluate $f^{-1}\left(\dfrac{1}{2}\right)$.

Q7-8 Hint: The range of f(x) is quite tricky to find — you might find it helpful to think about what happens to f(x) as $x \to \infty$ and sketch the graph.

Q8 $f(x) = \dfrac{x - 4}{x + 3}$, $\{x > -3\}$.

a) Find $f^{-1}(x)$, stating the domain and range.

b) Evaluate $f^{-1}(0)$.

c) Evaluate $f^{-1}\left(-\dfrac{2}{5}\right)$.

Q9 $f(x) = \log_{10}(x - 3)$, $\{x > 3\}$. Find the domain and range of $f^{-1}(x)$.

Q10 $f(x) = 4x - 2$, $\{1 \leq x \leq 7\}$. Find the domain and range of $f^{-1}(x)$.

Q11 $f(x) = \dfrac{x}{x - 2}$, $\{x < 2\}$. Find the domain and range of $f^{-1}(x)$.

Q12 $f(x) = 2x + 3$, $\{x \in \mathbb{R}\}$. Sketch $y = f(x)$ and $y = f^{-1}(x)$ on the same set of axes, marking the points where the functions cross the axes.

Q13 $f(x) = x^2 + 3$, $\{x > 0\}$.

a) Sketch the graphs of f(x) and $f^{-1}(x)$ on the same set of axes.

b) State the domain and range of $f^{-1}(x)$.

Q14 $f(x) = \dfrac{1}{x + 1}$, $\{x > -1\}$.

a) Sketch the graphs of f(x) and $f^{-1}(x)$ on the same set of axes.

b) Explain how your diagram shows that there is just one solution to the equation $f(x) = f^{-1}(x)$.

Q14 Hint: The functions are equal where the two graphs cross.

Q15 $f(x) = \dfrac{1}{x - 3}$, $\{x > 3\}$.

a) Find $f^{-1}(x)$ and state its domain and range.

b) Sketch f(x) and $f^{-1}(x)$ on the same set of axes.

c) How many solutions are there to the equation $f(x) = f^{-1}(x)$?

d) Solve $f(x) = f^{-1}(x)$.

4. Modulus

- Understand the meaning of the modulus, including modulus notation.
- Be able to write the modulus of a number or function.
- Be able to sketch the graph of $y = |ax + b|$, and the graph of $y = |f(x)|$, given $y = f(x)$.
- Be able to sketch the graph of $y = f(|x|)$, given $y = f(x)$.
- Be able to solve equations and inequalities involving the modulus.

Sometimes in maths you want to work with numbers or functions without having to deal with negative values. The modulus function lets you do this.

The graphs of |f(x)| and f(|x|)

Modulus of a number

The **modulus** of a number is its **size** — it doesn't matter if it's positive or negative. So for a positive number, the modulus is just the same as the number itself, but for a negative number, the modulus is its numerical value without the minus sign.

> The modulus of a number, x, is written $|x|$.
> In general terms, for $x \geq 0$, $|x| = x$ and for $x < 0$, $|x| = -x$.

Example

The modulus of 8 is 8, and the modulus of −8 is also 8.
This is written $|8| = |-8| = 8$.

Tip: The modulus is sometimes called the **absolute value**.

Modulus of a function

Functions can have a modulus too — the modulus of a function $f(x)$ is just $f(x)$ but with any negative values that it can take turned positive.
Suppose $f(x) = -6$, then $|f(x)| = 6$. In general terms:

> $|f(x)| = f(x)$ when $f(x) \geq 0$ and
> $|f(x)| = -f(x)$ when $f(x) < 0$.

If the modulus is inside the brackets in the form $f(|x|)$, then you make the x-value positive **before** applying the function. So $f(|-2|) = f(2)$.

The graphs of |f(x)| and f(|x|)

> - For the graph of $y = |f(x)|$, any negative values of $f(x)$ are made positive by reflecting them in the x-axis.
>
> - This restricts the range of the modulus function to $|f(x)| \geq 0$ (or some subset within $|f(x)| \geq 0$, e.g. $|f(x)| \geq 1$).
>
> - The easiest way to draw a graph of $y = |f(x)|$ is to initially draw $y = f(x)$, then reflect the negative part in the x-axis.

Tip: Don't get the two types of modulus graph mixed up. For some functions $y = |f(x)|$ looks very different to $y = f(|x|)$ — as you'll see in the examples on the next two pages.

> - For the graph of $y = f(|x|)$, the negative x-values produce the same result as the corresponding positive x-values. So the graph of $f(x)$ for $x \geq 0$ is reflected in the y-axis for the negative x-values.
>
> - To draw a graph of $y = f(|x|)$, first draw the graph of $y = f(x)$ for positive values of x, then reflect this in the y-axis to form the rest of the graph.

Example 1

Draw the graphs of $y = |f(x)|$ and $y = f(|x|)$ for $f(x) = 5x - 5$.

$y = |f(x)|$

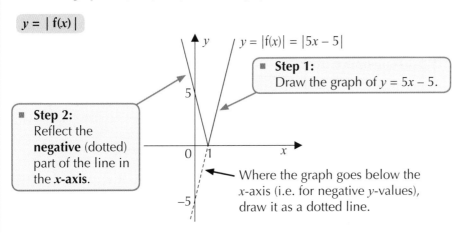

Step 1:
Draw the graph of $y = 5x - 5$.

Step 2:
Reflect the **negative** (dotted) part of the line in the **x-axis**.

Where the graph goes below the x-axis (i.e. for negative y-values), draw it as a dotted line.

$y = |f(x)| = |5x - 5|$

Tip: Always mark on any key points such as the places that the graph touches or crosses the axes.

Tip: The dotted line isn't actually part of the graph — it's just there to help you sketch the reflected bit.

$y = f(|x|)$

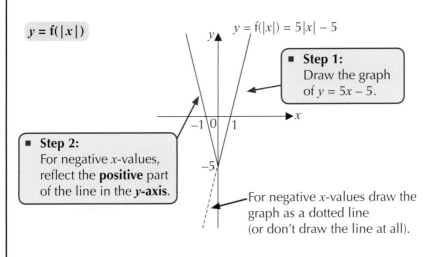

$y = f(|x|) = 5|x| - 5$

Step 1:
Draw the graph of $y = 5x - 5$.

Step 2:
For negative x-values, reflect the **positive** part of the line in the **y-axis**.

For negative x-values draw the graph as a dotted line (or don't draw the line at all).

Tip: For $y = |f(x)|$ graphs you reflect the **dotted** line in the **x-axis**, but for $y = f(|x|)$ graphs you reflect the **solid** line in the **y-axis**.

Example 2

Draw the graphs of $y = |f(x)|$ and $y = f(|x|)$ for $f(x) = x^2 - 4x$.

$y = |f(x)|$

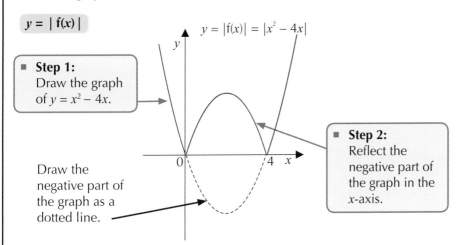

Step 1:
Draw the graph of $y = x^2 - 4x$.

Draw the negative part of the graph as a dotted line.

$y = |f(x)| = |x^2 - 4x|$

Step 2:
Reflect the negative part of the graph in the x-axis.

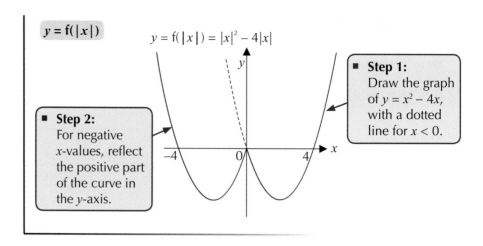

$y = f(|x|)$

$y = f(|x|) = |x|^2 - 4|x|$

Step 1:
Draw the graph of $y = x^2 - 4x$, with a dotted line for $x < 0$.

Step 2:
For negative x-values, reflect the positive part of the curve in the y-axis.

Exercise 4.1

Q1 Hint: Don't forget to label the key points such as where the graphs cross the axes.

Q1 Sketch the following graphs:

   a) $y = |x + 3|$ b) $y = |5 - x|$ c) $y = |3x - 1|$

   d) $y = |x^2 - 9|$ e) $y = |x^2 - 5x|$

Q2 If $f(x) = \sin x$, sketch the graph of $|f(x)|$ for $0 \le x \le 2\pi$.

Q3 If $f(x) = x^3$, sketch the graph of $|f(x)|$.

Q4 If $f(x) = (x - 2)(x + 3)$, sketch the graph of $|f(x)|$.

Q5 Sketch the graphs of $y = f(|x|)$ for the following functions:

   a) $f(x) = 2x + 3$ b) $f(x) = 4 - 3x$ c) $f(x) = x^2 - 3x$

   d) $f(x) = x^2 - 8x + 12$ e) $f(x) = x^3 + 1$ f) $f(x) = 2^x$

   g) $f(x) = \dfrac{1}{x}$ h) $f(x) = x^2 - 7x - 18$ i) $f(x) = x^3 - 4x$

Q6 Match up each graph (1-4) with its correct equation (a-d):

Q6 Hint: Try sketching the graphs from the given functions to see what shape they should be, then compare them in terms of where they cross the x and y axes.

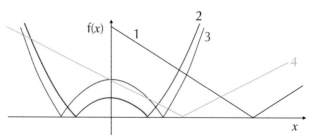

   a) $y = |x^2 - 1|$
   b) $y = |4 - x|$
   c) $y = |x - 2|$
   d) $y = |2 - x^2|$

Q7 For each of the following graphs, copy the graph of $y = f(x)$
and sketch on separate axes the graphs of $y = |f(x)|$ and $y = f(|x|)$:

a)

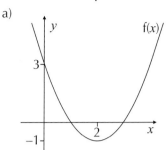

b)

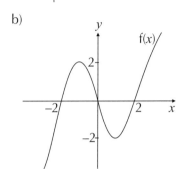

Q8 For the function $f(x) = 3x - 5$:
   a) Draw, on the same axes, the graphs of $y = f(x)$ and $y = |f(x)|$.
   b) How many solutions are there to the equation $|3x - 5| = 2$?

Q8 b) Hint: Read across from 2 on the y-axis to find the number of values of x for which $|3x - 5| = 2$.

Q9 Draw the graph of the function $f(x) = \begin{cases} |2x + 4| & x < 0 \\ |x - 2| & x \geq 0 \end{cases}$

Q10 For the function $f(x) = 4x + 1$:
   a) Draw accurately the graph of $y = f(|x|)$.
   b) Use your graph to solve the equation $f(|x|) = 3$.

Q10 b) Hint: Read across from 3 on the y-axis to find any values of x for which $4|x| + 1 = 3$.

Q11 Match up each graph (1-4) with its correct equation (a-d).

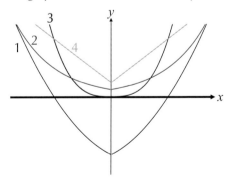

   a) $y = |x|^3$
   b) $y = 2^{|x|}$
   c) $y = 3|x| + 2$
   d) $y = (|x| - 2)(|x| + 4)$

Q11 Hint: If you can't see which graph goes with which equation, try sketching some of the functions yourself and matching it to the graph it looks like.

Solving modulus equations and inequalities

$|f(x)| = n$ and $|f(x)| = g(x)$

The method for solving equations of the form $|f(x)| = n$ is shown below.
Solving $|f(x)| = g(x)$ is exactly the same — just replace n with g(x).

- **Step 1:** Sketch the functions $y = |f(x)|$ and $y = n$ on the same axes. The solutions you're trying to find are where they **intersect**.
- **Step 2:** From the graph, work out the ranges of x for which $f(x) \geq 0$ and $f(x) < 0$: e.g. $f(x) \geq 0$ for $x \leq a$ or $x \geq b$ and $f(x) < 0$ for $a < x < b$. These ranges should 'fit together' to cover **all** possible x-values.
- **Step 3:** Use this to write **two new equations**, one true for each range of x:
  - (1) $f(x) = n$ for $x \leq a$ or $x \geq b$
  - (2) $-f(x) = n$ for $a < x < b$
- **Step 4:** Solve each equation and check that any solutions are **valid**. Get rid of any solutions outside the range of x you've got for that equation.
- **Step 5:** Look at the graph and **check** that your solutions look right.

Tip: The original equation $|f(x)| = n$ becomes $f(x) = n$ in the range where $f(x) \geq 0$, and it becomes $-f(x) = n$ in the range where $f(x) < 0$.

Tip: When sketching the graphs, use a big enough domain so that you can see all the places where the lines cross.

Tip: It's important to work out and label the points where the graphs touch the x-axis so you can easily see where f(x) changes from positive to negative.

Example 1

Solve $|x^2 - 9| = 7$. ◄— This is an example of $|f(x)| = n$, where $f(x) = x^2 - 9$ and $n = 7$.

- First off, sketch the graphs of $y = |x^2 - 9|$ and $y = 7$.

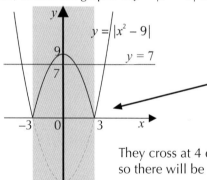

$y = |x^2 - 9|$

$y = 7$

$x^2 - 9 = (x + 3)(x - 3)$, so the curve crosses the x-axis at 3 and −3.

They cross at 4 different points, so there will be **4 solutions**.

- Now use the graph to see where $f(x) \geq 0$ and $f(x) < 0$:
  - $x^2 - 9 \geq 0$ for $x \leq -3$ or $x \geq 3$, and
  - $x^2 - 9 < 0$ for $-3 < x < 3$ (shaded in grey on the diagram)
- Form two equations for the different ranges of x:
  - (1) $x^2 - 9 = 7$ for $x \leq -3$ or $x \geq 3$
  - (2) $-(x^2 - 9) = 7$ for $-3 < x < 3$
- Solving (1) gives: $x^2 = 16 \Rightarrow x = 4, x = -4$
- Check they're valid: $x = -4$ is in '$x \leq -3$' and $x = 4$ is in '$x \geq 3$' — so they're both valid.
- Solving (2) gives: $x^2 - 2 = 0 \Rightarrow x^2 = 2 \Rightarrow x = \sqrt{2}, x = -\sqrt{2}$.
- Check they're valid: $x = \sqrt{2}$ and $x = -\sqrt{2}$ are both within $-3 < x < 3$ — so they're also both valid.
- Check back against the graphs — we've found four solutions and they're in the right places. So the four solutions to $|x^2 - 9| = 7$ are:

$$x = -4, x = -\sqrt{2}, x = \sqrt{2}, x = 4$$

Example 2

Solve $|x^2 - 2x - 3| = 1 - x.$ ◄—— This is an example of $|f(x)| = g(x)$, where $f(x) = x^2 - 2x - 3$ and $g(x) = 1 - x$.

Tip: Remember that you can solve equations of the form $|f(x)| = g(x)$ using the method for solving $|f(x)| = n$ on the previous page.

▪ Sketch $y = |x^2 - 2x - 3|$ and $y = 1 - x$. The graphs cross twice.

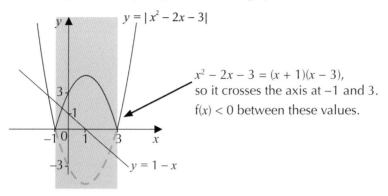

$x^2 - 2x - 3 = (x + 1)(x - 3)$, so it crosses the axis at -1 and 3. $f(x) < 0$ between these values.

Tip: You can see from the graph that there will be one solution in the shaded area where $-f(x) = g(x)$, and one solution in the positive region ($x \leq -1$) where $f(x) = g(x)$.

▪ Looking at where $f(x) \geq 0$ and where $f(x) < 0$ gives:
  (1) $x^2 - 2x - 3 = 1 - x$ for $x \leq -1$ or $x \geq 3$
  (2) $-(x^2 - 2x - 3) = 1 - x$ for $-1 < x < 3$.

▪ Solving (1) using the quadratic formula gives:

$$x = 2.562 \quad \text{and} \quad \boxed{x = -1.562}$$

$x \leq -1$ or $x \geq 3$, so this solution is not valid...   ...but this one is.

▪ Solving (2) using the quadratic formula gives:

$$x = 3.562 \quad \text{and} \quad \boxed{x = -0.562}$$

$-1 < x < 3$, so this solution is not valid...   ...but this one is.

▪ Checking against the graph, there are two solutions and they're where we expected.

$|f(x)| = |g(x)|$

When using **graphs** to solve equations of the form $|f(x)| = |g(x)|$ you have to do a bit more work at the start to identify the different areas of the graph. There could be regions where:

▪ $f(x)$ and $g(x)$ are **both** positive or **both** negative — for solutions in these regions you need to solve the equation $f(x) = g(x)$.

▪ One function is **positive** and the other is **negative** — for solutions in these regions you need to solve the equation $-f(x) = g(x)$.

Tip: Solving $-f(x) = -g(x)$ is the same as solving $f(x) = g(x)$, and solving $f(x) = g(x)$ is the same as solving $-f(x) = g(x)$.

There is also an **algebraic** method for solving equations of this type:

> If $|a| = |b|$ then $a^2 = b^2$.
> So if $|f(x)| = |g(x)|$ then $[f(x)]^2 = [g(x)]^2$.

This is true because squaring gives the same answer whether the value is positive or negative. You'll usually be left with a quadratic to solve, but in some cases this might be easier than using a graphical method.

The following example shows how you could use either method to solve the same equation.

Example

Solve $|x - 2| = |3x + 4|.$ ◄——— This is an example of $|f(x)| = |g(x)|$, where $f(x) = x - 2$ and $g(x) = 3x + 4$.

a) Solving graphically:

- Sketch $y = |x - 2|$ and $y = |3x + 4|$. The graphs cross twice.

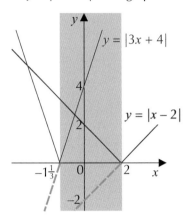

Tip: There is a third region on the graph — where $f(x)$ and $g(x)$ are both positive (for $x \geq 2$). The graphs do not cross in this region though so there won't be a solution.

- There are two regions of the graph that contain a solution (i.e. where the graphs cross):
  (1) where $f(x)$ is negative but $g(x)$ is positive (shaded grey)
  (2) where $f(x)$ and $g(x)$ are both negative (where $x < -1\frac{1}{3}$).

- This means we can form the following equations:
  (1) $-(x - 2) = 3x + 4$ for $-1\frac{1}{3} \leq x < 2$
  (2) $(x - 2) = (3x + 4)$ for $x < -1\frac{1}{3}$

- Solving (1) gives $x = -\frac{1}{2}.$

  This is valid, as it's in the region $-1\frac{1}{3} \leq x < 2$.

- Solving (2) gives $x = -3.$

  This is valid, as it's in the region $x < -1\frac{1}{3}$.

- Checking against the graph, there are two valid solutions and they're where we expected.

b) Solving algebraically:

Tip: For this example the algebraic method involves less work than using graphs.

- $|x - 2| = |3x + 4|$
  Square both sides to give: $(x - 2)^2 = (3x + 4)^2$
  $x^2 - 4x + 4 = 9x^2 + 24x + 16$
  $8x^2 + 28x + 12 = 0$
  $2x^2 + 7x + 3 = 0$

Tip: You can use the quadratic formula to solve it if it won't easily factorise.

- Factorise and solve: $(2x + 1)(x + 3) = 0$

  $x = -\frac{1}{2}$ and $x = -3$

|f(x)| = g(|x|)

You can solve equations of the form $|f(x)| = g(|x|)$ by sketching the graphs (like you did for equations of the form $|f(x)| = |g(x)|$).

- When you sketch the graph, remember that $g(|x|)$ is reflected in the y-axis, so $g(|-x|) = g(x)$.
- This means that the two equations you have to solve are $f(x) = g(x)$ and $-f(x) = g(x)$ (or $f(x) = g(-x)$ and $-f(x) = g(-x)$).

You can also solve equations of the form $|f(x)| = a|x|$ (where a is a constant) by **squaring both sides** of the equation.

This works because $(a|x|)^2 = a^2x^2$, so if $|f(x)| = a|x|$ then $[f(x)]^2 = [ax]^2$.
This **doesn't** work for things like $|f(x)| = a|x| + b$, because squaring both sides doesn't get rid of the modulus signs — so you'd have to use graphs instead.

Tip: It doesn't matter whether you're solving $f(x) = g(x)$ and $-f(x) = g(x)$ or $f(x) = g(-x)$ and $-f(x) = g(-x)$ as you'll get the same pair of solutions for both.

Example

Solve $|3x + 2| = 2|x| + 1$. ← This is an example of $|f(x)| = g(|x|)$, where $f(x) = 3x + 2$ and $g(x) = 2x + 1$.

Solving graphically:

- Sketch $y = |3x + 2|$ and $y = 2|x| + 1$. The graphs cross twice.

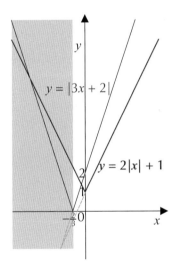

- There are two regions of the graph that contain a solution:
  (1) where $-f(x) = g(-x)$ (shaded grey)   and   (2) where $f(x) = g(-x)$.
- So the equations you need to solve are:
  (1) $-(3x + 2) = 2(-x) + 1 \Rightarrow \boxed{x = -3}$

  and (2) $3x + 2 = 2(-x) + 1 \Rightarrow \boxed{x = -\dfrac{1}{5}}$

Tip: From the graph, you can see that one solution needs to be in the range $x < -\dfrac{2}{3}$ and the other needs to be in the range $-\dfrac{2}{3} < x < 0$.

In this example, you **couldn't** have solved it algebraically as it's of the form $|f(x)| = a|x| + b$. If the original equation had been $|3x + 2| = 2|x|$, you could have solved it by squaring both sides of the equation — you'd be solving $(3x + 2)^2 = (2x)^2$.

Solving modulus inequalities

You might have to deal with a **modulus term** in an **inequality**. Inequalities can be a bit more complicated than equations, so you need to understand what the inequality is telling you.

- $|x| < 5$ means that $x < 5$ **and** $-x < 5$ (which you can rewrite as $x > -5$). Putting these inequalities **together** gives $-5 < x < 5$.

- $|x| > 5$ means that $x > 5$ **and** $-x > 5$ (which you can rewrite as $x < -5$). You **can't** put these inequalities together — you have **two separate ranges**. So in general,

$$|x| < a \text{ means } -a < x < a$$
$$\text{and } |x| > a \text{ means } x < -a \text{ and } x > a$$

- Using this, you can rearrange more **complicated** inequalities such as: $|x - a| \leq b \Rightarrow -b \leq x - a \leq b \Rightarrow a - b \leq x \leq a + b$.

Tip: You need to add a onto each bit of the inequality to get x on its own in the middle.

Examples

a) Solve $|x| > 13$.

- $|x| > 13$ means $x > 13$ **and** $-x > 13$ (or $x < -13$).
- These two ranges don't fit together so you **can't** combine them. So $x < -13$ and $x > 13$.

b) Solve $|3x| \leq 15$.

- First, **rearrange** to get rid of the modulus: $-15 \leq 3x \leq 15$.
- Then **divide** each bit of the inequality by **3**: $-5 \leq x \leq 5$.

c) Solve $|x - 4| < 7$.

- First, **rearrange** to get rid of the modulus: $-7 < x - 4 < 7$.
- Then **add 4** onto each bit of the inequality: $-3 < x < 11$.

d) Solve $|2x + 5| \geq 11$.

- It's a $\geq$ sign, so you're going to end up with **two separate ranges**, so just deal with each bit **separately**.
- The first range is where $2x + 5 \geq 11 \Rightarrow 2x \geq 6 \Rightarrow x \geq 3$.
- The second range is where $-(2x + 5) \geq 11 \Rightarrow 2x + 5 \leq -11 \Rightarrow 2x \leq -16 \Rightarrow x \leq -8$.
- So the ranges that satisfy the inequality are: $x \leq -8$ and $x \geq 3$.

You can also use a **graph** to help you solve modulus inequalities — you just have to work out which bit of the graph you want.

- To do this, plot the graphs of the functions on either side of the inequality and find their **points of intersection**.
- These intersection points are the **limits** of the ranges for which one of the functions is greater than (or less than) the other.

Tip: You'll often come across this type of problem as the last part of a question — after being asked to draw a graph or solve an equation you'll be told to 'hence solve' the inequality.

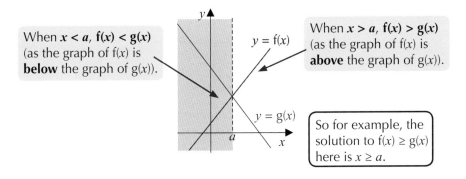

When $x < a$, $f(x) < g(x)$ (as the graph of $f(x)$ is **below** the graph of $g(x)$).

When $x > a$, $f(x) > g(x)$ (as the graph of $f(x)$ is **above** the graph of $g(x)$).

So for example, the solution to $f(x) \geq g(x)$ here is $x \geq a$.

- If the graphs cross in **two places** (say at a and b, with $a < b$), then the values of x that satisfy the inequality will either be in the range $a < x < b$ or in the ranges $x < a$ and $x > b$.

Example

Solve $|x - 2| > |3x + 4|$.

- This is based on the example from page 22 — you know that the graphs cross **twice**, once at $x = -\frac{1}{2}$ and once at $x = -3$.

- Work out which bit of the graph shows the range of x for which $|x - 2| > |3x + 4|$.

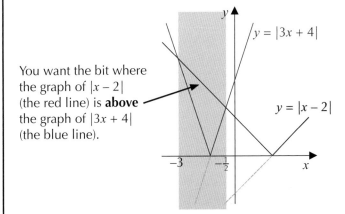

You want the bit where the graph of $|x - 2|$ (the red line) is **above** the graph of $|3x + 4|$ (the blue line).

- You can see from the shaded area on the graph that

$|x - 2| > |3x + 4|$ when $-3 < x < -\frac{1}{2}$.

Tip: For $|x - 2| < |3x + 4|$ you'd want the other bits of the graph: $x < -3$ and $x > -\frac{1}{2}$.

Q1 The diagram below shows a function $y = |f(x)|$.
$y = f(x)$ is shown as a dotted line.

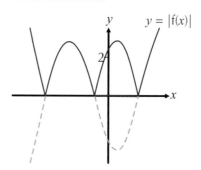

Q1 Hint: Try drawing a line across at $y = 2$, and shading in the different regions of the graph where $f(x)$ is negative.

a) How many solutions are there to the equation $|f(x)| = 2$?
b) How many of the solutions could be found by solving the equation $f(x) = 2$?
c) Explain how the other solutions could be found.

Q2 Solve the equation $|4x + 2| = 10$.

Q3 Solve the equation $2 - |3x - 4| = 1$.

Q4 Solve the equation $|x^2 - 4| = 5$.

Q5 Hint: 'Surd form' just means keeping the roots as roots, but make sure you simplify as much as possible.

Q5 Solve the equation $|x^2 - 2x - 8| = 1$.
Leave your answers in surd form.

Q6 Solve the equation $|2x - 1| = 4|x|$.

Q7 a) Sketch the graph of $y = |x^2 - 16|$.
b) Hence solve the equation $|x^2 - 16| = 3$.
Leave your answers in surd form.

Q8 b) Hint: You can solve this equation algebraically if you prefer, using the squaring method.

Q8 a) Sketch the graphs of $y = |4x - 1|$ and $y = |2x + 3|$.
b) Hence, or otherwise, solve the equation $|4x - 1| = |2x + 3|$.

Q9 Solve the inequality $|4x - 2| \leq 6$.

Q10 a) On the same axes sketch the graphs of $|f(x)|$ and $g(x)$, where:
$f(x) = \dfrac{1}{x}$
$g(x) = x - 1$
b) Hence solve the inequality $|f(x)| \geq g(x)$.

Q11 a) On the same axes sketch the graphs of $|f(x)|$ and $|g(x)|$, where:
$f(x) = x^2 - 5x + 6$
$g(x) = x + 1$
b) Hence solve the inequality $|f(x)| > |g(x)|$.

5. Transformations of Graphs

You should be familiar with transformations from C1 and C2. For C3 you have to know how to put them all together to form combinations of transformations.

Transformations of graphs

The four transformations

The transformations you met in C1 and C2 are translations (a vertical or horizontal shift), stretches or squeezes (either vertical or horizontal) and reflections in the *x*- or *y*-axis. Here's a quick reminder of what each one does:

Learning Objectives:

- Be able to sketch graphs when $y = f(x)$ has been affected by a combination of these transformations:
  $y = f(x + c)$,
  $y = f(x) + c$,
  $y = af(x)$,
  and $y = f(ax)$.

- Be able to interpret transformed graphs, including finding coordinates of points.

Tip: All these graphs use $f(x) = \sin x$.

$y = f(x + c)$

For $c > 0$:

- $f(x + c)$ is $f(x)$ translated c **left**,
- $f(x - c)$ is $f(x)$ translated c **right**.

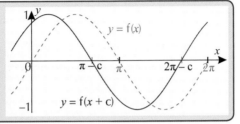

$y = f(x) + c$

For $c > 0$:

- $f(x) + c$ is $f(x)$ translated c **up**,
- $f(x) - c$ is $f(x)$ translated c **down**.

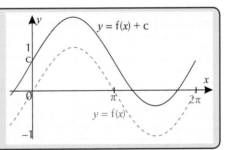

$y = af(x)$

- The graph of $af(x)$ is $f(x)$ **stretched vertically** by a factor of a.
- And if **$a < 0$**, the graph is also **reflected** in the **x-axis**.

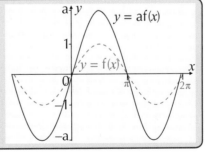

Tip: It might be easier to think of a stretch by a scale factor **$0 < a < 1$** as a 'squash' — but make sure you use the word stretch in the exam.

$y = f(ax)$

- The graph of $f(ax)$ is $f(x)$ **stretched horizontally** by a factor of $\frac{1}{a}$.
- And if **$a < 0$**, the graph is also **reflected** in the **y-axis**.

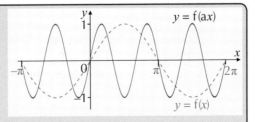

Tip: In this case, the transformation is a stretch when **$0 < a < 1$** and a squash when **$a > 1$**.

Combinations of transformations

Combinations of transformations can look a bit tricky, but if you take them one step at a time they're not too bad. Don't try to do all the transformations at once — break it up into the separate bits shown on the previous page and draw a graph for each stage.

Example 1

The graph below shows the function $y = f(x)$. Draw the graph of $y = 3f(x + 2)$, showing the coordinates of the turning points.

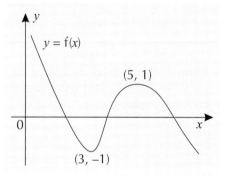

Tip: Make sure you do the transformations the right way round — you should do the bit in the brackets first.

- Don't try to do everything at once. First draw the graph of $y = f(x + 2)$ and work out the coordinates of the turning points:

Tip: Remember —
$y = f(x + c)$ is $f(x)$
translated c to the left.

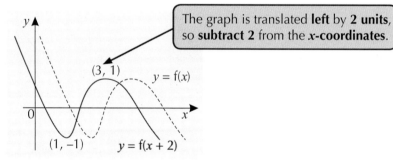

> The graph is translated **left** by **2 units**, so **subtract 2** from the x-coordinates.

- Now use your graph of $y = f(x + 2)$ to draw the graph of $y = 3f(x + 2)$:

Tip: $y = af(x)$ is $f(x)$
stretched vertically
by a factor of a.

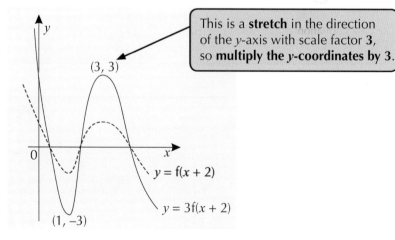

> This is a **stretch** in the direction of the y-axis with scale factor **3**, so **multiply the y-coordinates by 3**.

Example 2

The graph below shows the function $y = \sin x$, $0 \leq x \leq 2\pi$.
Draw the graph of $y = 2 - \sin 2x$, $0 \leq x \leq 2\pi$.

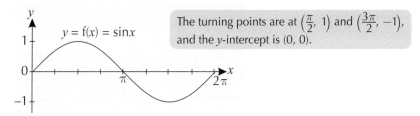

The turning points are at $\left(\frac{\pi}{2}, 1\right)$ and $\left(\frac{3\pi}{2}, -1\right)$, and the y-intercept is (0, 0).

- This is a lot easier to deal with if you rearrange the function from $y = 2 - \sin 2x$ to **$y = -\sin 2x + 2$**. This gets it in the form $y = -f(2x) + 2$. So we need a **horizontal stretch** by a factor of $\frac{1}{2}$, followed by a **vertical stretch** by a factor of **–1**, followed by a **vertical translation** by **2 up** (in the positive y-direction).

Tip: Always try to break it down like this before you start drawing lots of graphs.

- First draw the graph of $y = \sin 2x$, by squashing the graph horizontally by a factor of 2 (i.e. a stretch by a factor of $\frac{1}{2}$).

$y = \sin x$ $y = \sin 2x$

The turning points have been squashed up in the x-direction, so halve the x-coordinates: $\left(\frac{\pi}{4}, 1\right)$ and $\left(\frac{3\pi}{4}, -1\right)$. There are also now an extra two within the domain, each one occurring a further $\frac{\pi}{2}$ along the x-axis: $\left(\frac{5\pi}{4}, 1\right)$ and $\left(\frac{7\pi}{4}, -1\right)$.

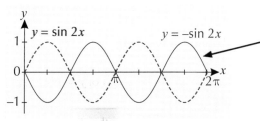

$y = \sin 2x$ $y = -\sin 2x$

- From there, draw the graph of $y = -\sin 2x$, by reflecting in the x-axis.

Tip: A stretch with a factor of –1 doesn't change the size of the graph, you just have to reflect in the x-axis.

This transformation flips the turning points, so multiply the y-coordinates by –1. They're now at $\left(\frac{\pi}{4}, -1\right)$, $\left(\frac{3\pi}{4}, 1\right)$, $\left(\frac{5\pi}{4}, -1\right)$ and $\left(\frac{7\pi}{4}, 1\right)$.

- Finally, translate the graph of $y = -\sin 2x$ up by 2 to get the graph of $y = -\sin 2x + 2$ (or $y = 2 - \sin 2x$).

  Add 2 to the y-coordinates of the turning points to give $\left(\frac{\pi}{4}, 1\right)$, $\left(\frac{3\pi}{4}, 3\right)$, $\left(\frac{5\pi}{4}, 1\right)$ and $\left(\frac{7\pi}{4}, 3\right)$.

  The y-intercept is also translated up by 2: it's at (0, 2).

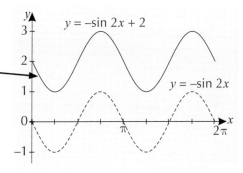

$y = -\sin 2x + 2$

$y = -\sin 2x$

Tip: Having clearly labelled axes makes it easier to read off key points at the end of all the transformations and check your answer.

Example 3

Tip: Have a look back at pages 16-17 to refresh your memory on the modulus function, $y = |x|$ and its graph.

The graph shows the function $f(x) = |x|$.
Draw the graph of $y = 4 - f(x + 1)$,
and give the equation of the transformed graph.

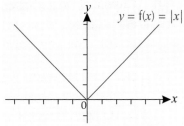

- Again, rearrange the function from $y = 4 - f(x + 1)$ to $y = -f(x + 1) + 4$. So you need to do...

- ...a **horizontal translation left** by **1**...

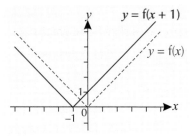

- ...followed by a **vertical stretch** by a factor of **−1** (reflection in the x-axis)...

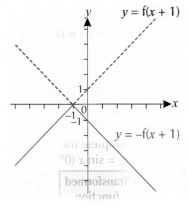

- ...followed by a **vertical translation** of **4 upwards**.

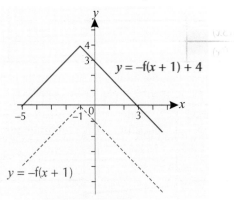

- To find the equation of the transformed graph, just replace $f(x + 1)$ in $y = 4 - f(x + 1)$ with $|x + 1|$. So the equation is:

$$y = 4 - |x + 1|$$

Tip: If you're not sure whether your graph is correct, try putting some numbers into the function and checking them against coordinates on the graph.

Q1 Given that $f(x) = x^2$, sketch the following graphs on the same axes:

a) $y = f(x)$ b) $y = f(x) + 3$ c) $y = f(x - 2)$ d) $y = f(x + 4) - 1$

In each case write down the coordinates of the turning point.

Q2 The graph of $f(x) = x^3$ is translated to form the graph $y = f(x - 1) + 4$.

a) Sketch the graphs of $y = f(x)$ and $y = f(x - 1) + 4$.

b) What is the equation of the graph $y = f(x - 1) + 4$?

> **Q2 a) Hint:** Do this step by step.

Q3 Given that $f(x) = |x|$, sketch the following graphs on the same axes:

a) $y = f(x)$ b) $y = f(x) + 2$ c) $y = f(x - 4)$ d) $y = 2f(x + 1)$

In parts b) - d) describe the transformation from $y = f(x)$ in words.

Q4 Let $f(x) = |2x - 6|$. On the same axes sketch the graphs of:

a) $y = f(x)$ b) $y = f(-x)$ c) $y = f(-x) + 2$

Q5 Let $f(x) = \frac{1}{x}$. On the same axes sketch the graphs of:

a) $y = f(x)$ b) $y = -f(x)$ c) $y = -f(x) - 3$

Q6 a) Let $f(x) = \cos x$. Sketch the graph $y = f(x)$ for $0° \le x \le 360°$.

b) On the same axes sketch the graph of $y = f(2x)$.

c) On the same axes sketch the graph of $y = 1 + f(2x)$.

d) State the coordinates of the minimum point(s) of the graph $y = \cos 2x + 1$, in the interval $0° \le x \le 360°$.

Q7 Complete the following table for the function $f(x) = \sin x \ (0° \le x \le 360°)$.

Transformed function	New equation	Maximum value of transformed function	Minimum value of transformed function
$f(x) + 2$			
$f(x - 90°)$			
$f(3x)$			
$4f(x)$			

> **Q7 Hint:** Try sketching the graphs of the transformed functions first.

Q8 Complete the following table for the function $f(x) = x^3$:

Transformed function	New equation	Coordinates of point of inflection
$f(x) + 1$		
$f(x - 2)$		
$-f(x) - 3$		
$f(-x) + 4$		

> **Q8 Hint:** The point of inflection is the stationary point. For $y = x^3$ the point of inflection is at (0, 0).

Q9 The graph $y = \cos x$ is translated $\frac{\pi}{2}$ to the right and stretched by scale factor $\frac{1}{2}$ parallel to the y-axis.

a) Sketch the new graph for $0 \le x \le 2\pi$. b) Write down its equation.

Q10 Hint: You can also write g(x) as $-\dfrac{1}{x} + 3$.

Q10 a) Sketch the graph of $y = f(x)$ where $f(x) = \dfrac{1}{x}$.

b) Write down the sequence of transformations needed to map $f(x)$ on to $g(x) = 3 - \dfrac{1}{x}$.

c) Sketch the graph of $y = g(x)$.

Q11 Complete the following table:

Original graph	New graph	Sequence of transformations
$y = x^3$	$y = (x-4)^3 + 5$	
$y = 4^x$	$y = 4^{3x} - 1$	
$y = |x + 1|$	$y = 1 - |2x + 1|$	
$y = \sin x$	$y = -3\sin 2x + 1$	

Q12 Hint: Try taking out a common factor (the value of a) before completing the square.

Q12 a) Write $y = 2x^2 - 4x + 6$ in the form $y = a[(x + b)^2 + c]$.

b) Hence list the sequence of transformations which will map $y = x^2$ on to $y = 2x^2 - 4x + 6$.

c) Sketch the graph of $y = 2x^2 - 4x + 6$.

d) Write down the coordinates of the minimum point of the graph.

Q13 Starting with the curve $y = \cos x$, state the sequence of transformations which could be used to sketch the following curves:

a) $y = 4\cos 3x$

b) $y = 4 - \cos 2x$

c) $y = 2\cos (x - \dfrac{\pi}{3})$

Q14 The diagram shows $y = f(x)$ with a minimum point, P, at $(2, -3)$.

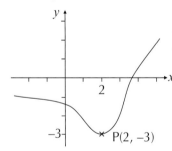

Copy the diagram and sketch each of the following graphs. In each case state the new coordinates of the point P.

a) $y = f(x) + 5$

b) $y = f(x + 4)$

c) $y = -f(x)$

Q15 The diagram shows $y = f(x)$ with a minimum point, Q, at $(-1, -3)$ and a maximum point, P, at $(2, 4)$.

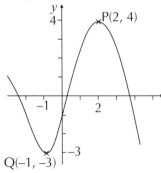

Copy the diagram and sketch, on separate axes, each of the following graphs. In each case state the new coordinates of the points P and Q.

a) $y = f(x - 1) + 3$

b) $y = -f(2x)$

c) $y = |f(x + 2)|$

Review Exercise — Chapter 1

Q1 For the following mappings, state the range and say whether or not the mapping is a function. If not, explain why, and if so, say whether the function is one-to-one or many-to-one.

a) $f(x) = x^2 - 16$, $x \geq 0$

b) $f : x \rightarrow x^2 - 7x + 10$, $x \in \mathbb{R}$

c) $f(x) = \sqrt{x}$, $x \in \mathbb{R}$

d) $f : x \rightarrow \dfrac{1}{x - 2}$, $x \in \mathbb{R}$

Q2 $f(x) = \dfrac{5}{2x + 1}$ defines a map.

a) Evaluate f(0) and $f(\tfrac{1}{2})$.

b) Draw the mapping diagram for the domain $\{x \in \mathbb{N}, x < 6\}$ and list the range.

c) Is the map a function for the domain $x \in \mathbb{Z}$? If not, explain why not.

d) Is the map a function for the domain $x \in \mathbb{R}$? If not, explain why not.

Q2 Hint: $\mathbb{Z}$ is the set of integers (positive and negative), and $\mathbb{N}$ is the set of natural numbers (positive integers, not including 0).

Q3 a) Sketch the graph of the function

$$f(x) = \begin{cases} x^2 - 2 & -2 < x < 2 \\ 2 & \text{otherwise} \end{cases}.$$

b) State the range of the function.

Q4 For each pair of functions f and g, find fg(2), gf(1) and fg(x).

a) $f(x) = \dfrac{3}{x}$, $x > 0$ and $g(x) = 2x + 3$, $x \in \mathbb{R}$

b) $f(x) = 3x^2$, $x \geq 0$ and $g(x) = x + 4$, $x \in \mathbb{R}$

Q5 $f(x) = \log_{10} x$ and $g(x) = 10^{x+1}$.

a) Find the values of fg(1), gf(1), $f^2(10)$ and $g^2(-1)$.

b) Explain why $f^2(1)$ is undefined.

Q6 $f(x) = 3x$ and $g(x) = x + 7$, both with domain $x \in \mathbb{R}$. Find the composite functions fg(x), gf(x) and $g^2(x)$.

Q7 $f(x) = 4x$ with domain $x \geq 2$, and $g(x) = x + 3$ with domain $x \leq 12$.

a) Find the domain and range of fg(x).

b) Find fg(x) and sketch the graph.

c) Find the domain and range of gf(x).

d) Find gf(x) and sketch the graph.

Q8 A one-to-one function f has domain $x \in \mathbb{R}$ and range $f(x) \geq 3$. Does this function have an inverse? If so, state its domain and range.

Q9 Using algebra, find the inverse of the function $f(x) = \sqrt{2x - 4}$, $x \geq 2$. State the domain and range of the inverse.

Q10 $f(x) = \cos x$, $0 \le x \le \frac{\pi}{2}$. Does the inverse function $f^{-1}(x)$ exist? Justify your answer.

Q11 $f(x) = \log_{10}(x + 4)$, $x > -4$. Find $f^{-1}(x)$.

Q12 $f(x) = x + 4$ and $g(x) = \frac{3}{x + 1}$, $x > 0$.
   a) Find $f^{-1}(x)$.
   b) Find $g^{-1}(x)$.
   c) Find $f^{-1}g^{-1}(x)$.
   d) Find $gf(x)$.
   e) Find the inverse of $gf(x)$. What do you notice?

Q13 For the function $f(x) = 2x - 1$ $\{x \in \mathbb{R}\}$, sketch the graphs of:
   a) $|f(x)|$ b) $f(|x|)$

Q14 Solve the equation $|3x - 1| = |4 - x|$.

Q15 Solve the equation $|4x + 3| = 5|x|$.

Q16 Solve the following inequalities:
   a) $|x| \le 17$.
   b) $|x + 8| < 2$.
   c) $|4x + 3| < 5$.

Q17 $f(x) = x^2 - 2x - 8$.
   a) On the same axes sketch the graphs of $|f(x)|$ and $f(|x|)$.
   b) Use your graphs to help you solve the equation $f(|x|) = -5$.
   c) Hence solve the inequality $f(|x|) \ge -5$.

Q17 b) Hint: You can either use the symmetry of the graph of $f(|x|)$ to find the negative solution from the positive solution, or you can use the fact that for $x \ge 0$, $f(|x|) = f(x)$ and for $x < 0$, $f(|x|) = f(-x)$.

Q18 Sketch the graphs of:
   a) $y = 3x + 2$.
   b) $y = |3x + 2|$.
   c) $y = -|3x + 2|$.

Q19 The function $y = f(x)$ is shown on the graph below.
Draw the graph of $y = 2f(x) + 1$.

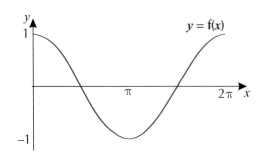

1   In words, describe what happens to the curve $y = x^3$ to transform it into the curve $y = 2(x - 1)^3 + 4$.

(3 marks)

2   The functions f and g are given by: $f(x) = x^2 - 3$, $x \in \mathbb{R}$ and $g(x) = \dfrac{1}{x}$, $x \in \mathbb{R}, x \neq 0$.

    a)   Find an expression for gf(x).

(2 marks)

    b)   Solve $gf(x) = \dfrac{1}{6}$.

(3 marks)

    c)   The function $f^{-1}(x)$ does not exist.

        (i)   Explain why.

(1 mark)

        (ii)   Suggest a restricted domain for f(x) so that the function $f^{-1}(x)$ exists.

(1 mark)

3   For the functions f and g, where

$$f(x) = 2^x, \; x \in \mathbb{R} \qquad \text{and} \qquad g(x) = \sqrt{3x - 2}, \; x \geq \tfrac{2}{3},$$

    find:

    a)   fg(6)

(2 marks)

    b)   gf(2)

(2 marks)

    c)   (i) $g^{-1}(x)$

(2 marks)

        (ii) $fg^{-1}(x)$

(2 marks)

4   a)   On the same axes sketch the graphs of $f(x) = |x + 1|$ and $g(x) = x^2 - 4x - 12$.

(2 marks)

    b)   Hence solve the equation $x^2 - 4x - 12 = |x + 1|$.
        Leave your answers in surd form.

(4 marks)

    c)   Hence solve the inequality $x^2 - 4x - 12 > |x + 1|$.

(2 marks)

5   The graph of the function f(x) passes through points P(1, 2) and Q(3, 6).

   f(x) is first reflected in the y-axis and then translated 3 units up and 2 units right to form a new graph, g(x).

   a)   Write down the equation of g(x) in terms of f(x).

   (3 marks)

   b)   Write down the new coordinates of the points P and Q.

   (2 marks)

6   The function f(x) is defined as follows: $f(x) = \dfrac{1}{x + 5}$, domain $x > -5$.

   a)   State the range of f(x).

   (1 mark)

   b)   (i)   Find the inverse function, $f^{-1}(x)$.

   (2 marks)

      (ii)   State the domain and range of $f^{-1}(x)$.

   (2 marks)

   c)   On the same axes, sketch the graphs of $y = f(x)$ and $y = f^{-1}(x)$.

   (2 marks)

7   The graph below shows the curve $y = f(x)$, and the intercepts of the curve with the x- and y-axes.

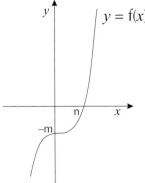

   Sketch the graphs of the following transformations on separate axes, clearly labelling the points of intersection with the x- and y-axes in terms of m and n.

   a) $y = |f(x)|$

   (2 marks)

   b) $y = -3f(x)$

   (2 marks)

   c) $y = f(|x|)$

   (2 marks)

1. Inverse Trig Functions

In Chapter 1 you saw that some functions have inverses, which reverse the effect of the function. The trig functions have inverses too.

Sin⁻¹, cos⁻¹ and tan⁻¹

The inverse trig functions

- **Sin⁻¹** is the inverse of **sin**. You might see it written as arcsine or arcsin.

- **Cos⁻¹** is the inverse of **cos**.
  You might see it written as arccosine or arccos.

- **Tan⁻¹** is the inverse of **tan**.
  You might see it written as arctangent or arctan.

The inverse trig functions **reverse** the effect of sin, cos and tan.
For example, $\sin 30° = 0.5$, so $\sin^{-1} 0.5 = 30°$. You should
have buttons for doing sin⁻¹, cos⁻¹ and tan⁻¹ on your calculator.

Graphs of the inverse trig functions

The functions sine, cosine and tangent **aren't one-to-one** mappings
(see p.7). This means that more than one value of x gives the same
value for $\sin x$, $\cos x$ or $\tan x$. For example: $\cos 0 = \cos 2\pi = \cos 4\pi = 1$,
and $\tan 0 = \tan \pi = \tan 2\pi = 0$.

If you want the inverses to be **functions**, you have to **restrict the domains**
of the trigonometric functions to make them **one-to-one**.

The graphs of the inverse functions are the **reflections**
of the sin, cos and tan graphs in the line $y = x$.

Sin⁻¹

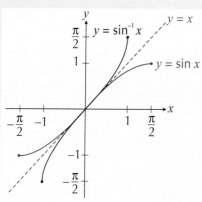

- For $\sin^{-1} x$, limit the **domain**
  of $\sin x$ to $-\dfrac{\pi}{2} \leq \boldsymbol{x} \leq \dfrac{\pi}{2}$
  (the range of $\sin x$ is still
  $\boldsymbol{-1 \leq \sin x \leq 1}$).

- So, the **domain** of $\sin^{-1} x$
  is $\boldsymbol{-1 \leq x \leq 1}$.

- The **range** of $\sin^{-1} x$ is
  $-\dfrac{\pi}{2} \leq \boldsymbol{\sin^{-1} x} \leq \dfrac{\pi}{2}$.

- The graph of $\boldsymbol{y = \sin^{-1} x}$
  goes through the **origin**.

- The coordinates of its **endpoints**
  are $(-1, -\dfrac{\pi}{2})$ and $(1, \dfrac{\pi}{2})$.

Learning Objectives:

- Know that the inverse
  of the trig functions
  sin, cos and tan are
  sin⁻¹, cos⁻¹ and tan⁻¹.

- Recognise and be able
  to sketch the graphs
  of sin⁻¹, cos⁻¹ and
  tan⁻¹, including their
  restricted domains.

- Be able to evaluate
  the inverse trig
  functions.

Tip: Functions are
mappings which have
just one y value for every
x value. There's more on
functions on pages 1-7,
and on inverse functions
on pages 12-14.

Tip: These graphs
show values in radians,
but you might have to
use angles in degrees
too. Remember that
π radians is 180°.

Cos⁻¹

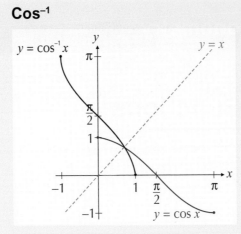

- For $\cos^{-1} x$, limit the **domain** of $\cos x$ to $\mathbf{0 \leq x \leq \pi}$ (the range of $\cos x$ is still $\mathbf{-1 \leq \cos x \leq 1}$.)

- So the **domain** of $\cos^{-1} x$ is $\mathbf{-1 \leq x \leq 1}$.

- The **range** of $\cos^{-1} x$ is $\mathbf{0 \leq \cos^{-1} x \leq \pi}$.

- The graph of $y = \cos^{-1} x$ crosses the **y-axis** at $(0, \frac{\pi}{2})$.

- The coordinates of its **endpoints** are $(-1, \pi)$ and $(1, 0)$.

Tan⁻¹

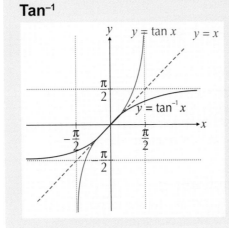

- For $\tan^{-1} x$, limit the **domain** of $\tan x$ to $-\frac{\pi}{2} < x < \frac{\pi}{2}$ (this **doesn't limit** the range of $\tan x$.)

- This means that the **domain** of $\tan^{-1} x$ **isn't** limited (it's $x \in \mathbb{R}$).

- The **range** of $\tan^{-1} x$ is $-\frac{\pi}{2} < \tan^{-1} x < \frac{\pi}{2}$.

- The graph of $y = \tan^{-1} x$ goes through the **origin**.

- It has **asymptotes** at $y = \frac{\pi}{2}$ and $y = -\frac{\pi}{2}$.

Evaluating sin⁻¹, cos⁻¹ and tan⁻¹

If a is an angle within the interval $-\frac{\pi}{2} \leq a \leq \frac{\pi}{2}$ (or $-90° \leq a \leq 90°$) such that $\sin a = x$, then $\sin^{-1} x = a$. So to evaluate $\sin^{-1} x$ you need to find the angle a in this interval such that $\sin a = x$. Using a calculator, this will be the answer you get when you enter "$\sin^{-1} x$" (for a given value of x).

Similarly, to find $\cos^{-1} x$, you need to find the angle a within the interval $0 \leq a \leq \pi$ (or $0° \leq a \leq 180°$) such that $\cos a = x$.

And $\tan^{-1} x$ is the angle a in the interval $-\frac{\pi}{2} < a < \frac{\pi}{2}$ (or $-90° < a < 90°$) such that $\tan a = x$.

When evaluating inverse trig functions, it'll be helpful if you know the **sine**, **cosine** and **tangent** of some **common angles**. Here's a quick recap of the method of drawing triangles from C2 — and **SOH CAH TOA**.

Remember: SOH CAH TOA...

$$\sin x = \frac{\text{opp}}{\text{hyp}}$$

$$\cos x = \frac{\text{adj}}{\text{hyp}}$$

$$\tan x = \frac{\text{opp}}{\text{adj}}$$

The sin, cos and tan of 30°, 45° and 60° can be found by drawing the following triangles and using **SOH CAH TOA**.

Draw an equilateral triangle with 60° angles and sides of 2 and split it to make a right-angled triangle.
Use Pythagoras to work out the length of the third side.

Draw a right-angled triangle where the edges adjacent to the right angle have length 1. Use Pythagoras to work out the length of the third side.

You should already know the sin, cos and tan of 90° and 180°, so you can work out all the values in this table:

$x°$	x (rad)	$\sin x$	$\cos x$	$\tan x$
0	0	0	1	0
30	$\frac{\pi}{6}$	$\frac{1}{2}$	$\frac{\sqrt{3}}{2}$	$\frac{1}{\sqrt{3}}$
45	$\frac{\pi}{4}$	$\frac{1}{\sqrt{2}}$	$\frac{1}{\sqrt{2}}$	1
60	$\frac{\pi}{3}$	$\frac{\sqrt{3}}{2}$	$\frac{1}{2}$	$\sqrt{3}$
90	$\frac{\pi}{2}$	1	0	—
180	π	0	−1	0

Be careful though — the first solution you find might **not** lie within the appropriate domain for the inverse function (see the graphs on pages 37 and 38). To find a solution that **does** lie in the correct domain, you need to use the **graphs** of the functions, or the **CAST diagram** that was introduced in C2. The following examples show how to use these methods.

Tip: You might find it useful to look back at your C2 notes on solving trig equations in a given interval.

Examples

a) **Evaluate, without using a calculator, $\cos^{-1} 0.5$.**
   Give your answer in degrees.

   - First, work out the angle a for which $\cos a = 0.5$.
     Since you're expected to do this without a calculator, it will be a common angle you can find using a right-angled triangle:

    0.5 is $\frac{1}{2}$ which is either sin 30° (if using $\frac{\text{opp}}{\text{hyp}}$ on the triangle) or cos 60° (if using $\frac{\text{adj}}{\text{hyp}}$).

   - We are looking for the inverse of **cos**, so $a = 60°$.
   - Next check that this answer lies in the appropriate domain for cos: $0 \le a \le \pi$ in radians, which is $0° \le a \le 180°$.
     60° lies within this domain, so $\cos^{-1} 0.5 = 60°$.

b) **Evaluate, without using a calculator, $\tan^{-1} (−1)$.**
   Give your answer in radians.

   - Work out the angle a for which $\tan a = -1$, over $-\frac{\pi}{2} < a < \frac{\pi}{2}$.

    ▪ Using this triangle you can see that $\tan \frac{\pi}{4} = 1$. But you need to look at the symmetry of the tan x graph to find the solution for $\tan a = -1$:

Tip: For all of these examples, the values that you need are in the table — it really helps to learn it.

Tip: You could also use the CAST diagram (as shown in the example on the next page) to find any negative solutions — for tan they lie in the 'S' and 'C' quadrants. You will have used the CAST diagram in C2, so check your notes if you can't remember.

- The graph shows that if $\tan \frac{\pi}{4} = 1$ then $\tan\left(-\frac{\pi}{4}\right) = -1$.
- So $\boxed{\tan^{-1}(-1) = -\frac{\pi}{4}}$.

  This answer lies in the appropriate domain for tan, i.e. $-\frac{\pi}{2} < a < \frac{\pi}{2}$.

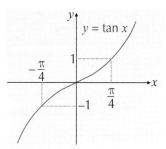

c) **Evaluate** $\sin^{-1}\left(-\frac{1}{\sqrt{2}}\right)$ **without using your calculator. Give your answer in radians.**

- Using the triangle from the previous example: $\sin \frac{\pi}{4} = \frac{1}{\sqrt{2}}$.
- To find the angle a such that $\sin a = -\frac{1}{\sqrt{2}}$, look at the **CAST diagram**:

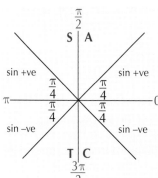

- Positive solutions for $\sin \frac{\pi}{4}$ are found in the quadrants labelled 'S' (for 'sin positive') and 'A' (for 'all positive'). This means that the desired **negative** solutions will be in the 'T' and 'C' quadrants:

  so $a = \pi + \frac{\pi}{4} = \frac{3\pi}{4}$, or $0 - \frac{\pi}{4} = -\frac{\pi}{4}$.

- Only the second of these answers lies within the appropriate domain $\left(-\frac{\pi}{2} \leq a \leq \frac{\pi}{2}\right)$, so $\boxed{\sin^{-1}\left(-\frac{1}{\sqrt{2}}\right) = -\frac{\pi}{4}}$.

Tip: Remember, you start with the top right quadrant and work your way round anticlockwise. If you're not confident with using the CAST diagram you could sketch the sin graph instead and look at the symmetry (as in the previous example).

Exercise 1.1

Q1 Evaluate the following, giving your answer in radians.

    a) $\cos^{-1} 1$ b) $\sin^{-1}\frac{\sqrt{3}}{2}$ c) $\tan^{-1}\sqrt{3}$

Q2 a) Sketch the graph of $y = 2\cos^{-1} x$ for $-1 \leq x \leq 1$.

    b) Sketch the graph of $y = \frac{1}{2}\tan^{-1} x$ and state the range.

Q3 By drawing the graphs of $y = \frac{x}{2}$ and $y = \cos^{-1} x$, determine the number of real roots of the equation $\cos^{-1} x = \frac{x}{2}$.

Q4 Evaluate the following, giving your answers in radians:

    a) $\sin^{-1}(-1)$ b) $\cos^{-1}\left(-\frac{\sqrt{3}}{2}\right)$

Q5 Evaluate the following:

    a) $\tan(\sin^{-1}\frac{1}{2})$ b) $\cos^{-1}(\cos\frac{2\pi}{3})$ c) $\cos(\sin^{-1}\frac{1}{2})$

Q6 Hint: Have a look back at pages 12-13 for a reminder on how to find inverse functions.

Q6 $f(x) = 1 + \sin 2x$. Find an expression for $f^{-1}(x)$.

2. Cosec, Sec and Cot

*There are a few more trigonometric functions to learn. This time
it's the reciprocals of sin, cos and tan — cosec, sec and cot.*

Graphs of cosec, sec and cot

When you take the **reciprocal** of the three main trig functions, sin, cos and
tan, you get three new trig functions — **cosecant** (or **cosec**), **secant** (or **sec**)
and **cotangent** (or **cot**).

$$\operatorname{cosec} \theta \equiv \frac{1}{\sin \theta} \qquad \sec \theta \equiv \frac{1}{\cos \theta} \qquad \cot \theta \equiv \frac{1}{\tan \theta}$$

Since $\tan \theta = \frac{\sin \theta}{\cos \theta}$, you can also think of **cot θ** as being $\frac{\cos \theta}{\sin \theta}$.

> **Examples**
>
> **Write the following in terms of sin and cos only:**
>
> **a) cosec 20°** $\quad \operatorname{cosec} 20° = \dfrac{1}{\sin 20°}$
>
> **b) sec π** $\quad \sec \pi = \dfrac{1}{\cos \pi}$
>
> **c) cot $\dfrac{\pi}{6}$** $\quad \cot \dfrac{\pi}{6} = \dfrac{1}{\tan \dfrac{\pi}{6}} = \dfrac{\cos \dfrac{\pi}{6}}{\sin \dfrac{\pi}{6}}$

Graph of cosec

This is the graph of $y = \operatorname{cosec} x$:

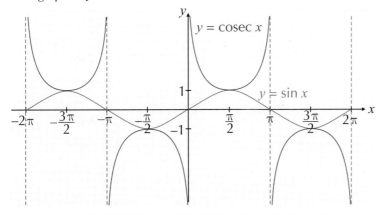

- Since $\operatorname{cosec} x = \dfrac{1}{\sin x}$, $y = \operatorname{cosec} x$ is **undefined** at any point
  where $\sin x = 0$.
- So $y = \operatorname{cosec} x$ has **vertical asymptotes** at $x = n\pi$ (where n is any integer).
- This means that the **domain** of cosec x is $x \in \mathbb{R}, x \neq n\pi$.
- The graph $y = \operatorname{cosec} x$ has **minimum** points at $x = ..., -\dfrac{3\pi}{2}, \dfrac{\pi}{2}, \dfrac{5\pi}{2}, ...$
  (wherever the graph $y = \sin x$ has a **maximum**). At these points, $y = 1$.
- It has **maximum** points at $x = ..., -\dfrac{\pi}{2}, \dfrac{3\pi}{2}, \dfrac{7\pi}{2}, ...$
  (wherever the graph $y = \sin x$ has a **minimum**). At these points, $y = -1$.

Learning Objectives:

- Know that the reciprocals of sin, cos and tan are cosec, sec and cot.
- Recognise and be able to sketch the graphs of cosec, sec and cot.
- Know the domains of cosec, sec and cot.
- Be able to evaluate the reciprocal trig functions.
- Be able to simplify expressions involving the reciprocal trig functions.
- Be able to solve equations involving the reciprocal trig functions.

Tip: The trick for remembering which is which is to look at the third letter — co**s**ec (1/**s**in), se**c** (1/**c**os) and cot (1/**t**an).

Tip: The x-coordinates of the turning points for cosec x are the same as for sin x — but remember a maximum on sin x becomes a minimum on cosec x, and vice versa.

Graph of sec

This is the graph of $y = \sec x$:

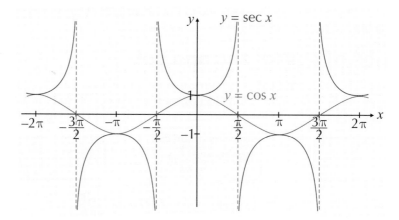

Tip: Just like the graphs of $\sin x$ and $\cos x$, the graphs of cosec x and sec x have a **period** of 2π radians — this just means they repeat themselves every 2π (or 360°).

Tip: The integer n can be negative too, so the asymptotes are at $x = -\frac{\pi}{2}, -\frac{3\pi}{2}, -\frac{5\pi}{2}$... etc, as well as $\frac{\pi}{2}, \frac{3\pi}{2}, \frac{5\pi}{2}$...

- As $\sec x = \frac{1}{\cos x}$, $y = \sec x$ is **undefined** at any point where $\cos x = 0$. So $y = \sec x$ has **vertical asymptotes** at $\boldsymbol{x = \left(n\pi + \frac{\pi}{2}\right)}$ (where n is any integer).

- This means that the **domain** of sec x is $\boldsymbol{x \in \mathbb{R}, x \neq \left(n\pi + \frac{\pi}{2}\right)}$.

- The graph of $y = \sec x$ has **minimum** points at $x = 0, \pm 2\pi, \pm 4\pi$, ... (wherever the graph of $y = \cos x$ has a **maximum**). At these points, $\boldsymbol{y = 1}$.

- It has **maximum** points at $x = \pm\pi, \pm 3\pi$, ... (wherever the graph of $y = \cos x$ has a **minimum**). At these points, $\boldsymbol{y = -1}$.

Graph of cot

This is the graph of $y = \cot x$:

Tip: The graphs of $\tan x$ and $\cot x$ both have a period of π radians.

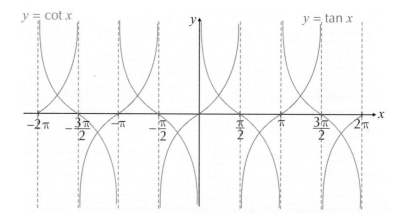

Tip: The asymptotes for $\cot x$ are the $\tan x$ asymptotes shifted horizontally by $\frac{\pi}{2}$.

- Since $\cot x = \frac{1}{\tan x}$, $y = \cot x$ is **undefined** at any point where $\tan x = 0$.
- So $y = \cot x$ has **vertical asymptotes** at $\boldsymbol{x = n\pi}$ (where n is any integer).
- This means that the **domain** of cot x is $\boldsymbol{x \in \mathbb{R}, x \neq n\pi}$.
- $y = \cot x$ **crosses the x-axis** at every place where the graph of $\tan x$ has an asymptote. This is any point with the coordinates $\left(\left(n\pi + \frac{\pi}{2}\right), 0\right)$.

Transformations of cosec, sec and cot

The graphs of the cosec, sec and cot functions can be transformed in the same way as other functions.

Tip: Look back at pages 27-30 for more on transformations of graphs.

Examples

a) Sketch the graph of $y = \cot 2x$ over the interval $-\pi \leq x \leq \pi$.

If $f(x) = \cot x$, then $y = f(2x)$. This transformation is a **horizontal stretch** by a factor of $\frac{1}{2}$ (i.e. the graph is squashed up in the x-direction by a factor of 2).

The x-coordinates of the asymptotes for $y = \cot 2x$ are **half** of those for $y = \cot x$.

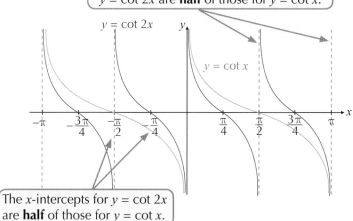

The x-intercepts for $y = \cot 2x$ are **half** of those for $y = \cot x$.

The **period** of the graph is also halved: $y = \cot 2x$ repeats itself every $\frac{\pi}{2}$ radians.

b) Give the coordinates of the maximum point on the graph of $y = \sec(x - 30°) + 1$, between 0 and 360°.

- The graph of $f(x) = \sec x$ has a maximum point at **(180°, −1)**.

- $y = f(x - 30°) + 1$. This transformation is a **horizontal translation right** by **30°**, followed by a **vertical translation up** by **1**.

- The coordinates of the maximum point will be affected by this transformation — the x-coordinate will be **increased by 30°** and the y-coordinate will be **increased by 1**.

- So the coordinates of the maximum point on the transformed graph will be: (210°, 0).

Tip: Make sure you know all the key coordinates on the graphs in both radians and degrees.

c) Describe the position of the asymptotes on the graph of $y = \text{cosec}(x + \frac{\pi}{3})$.

- The graph of $f(x) = \text{cosec } x$ has asymptotes at $x = n\pi$ (where n is any integer).

- $y = f(x + \frac{\pi}{3})$. This transformation is a **horizontal translation left** by $\frac{\pi}{3}$.

- Each asymptote will be translated left by $\frac{\pi}{3}$.

    So there will be asymptotes at $x = n\pi - \frac{\pi}{3}$ (where n is any integer).

Tip: The position of a vertical asymptote is only affected by transformations in the x-direction.

Q1 a) Sketch the graph of $y = \sec x$ for $-2\pi \le x \le 2\pi$.

b) Give the coordinates of the minimum points within this interval.

c) Give the coordinates of the maximum points within this interval.

d) State the range of $y = \sec x$.

Q1 d) Hint: Think about which values are **not** included in the range.

Q2 a) Sketch the graph of $y = \operatorname{cosec} x$ for $0 < x < 2\pi$.

b) Give the coordinates of any maximum and minimum points within this interval.

c) State the domain and range of $y = \operatorname{cosec} x$.

Q3 Hint: Compare the graphs you've drawn for Q1 and Q2.

Q3 Describe the transformation that maps $y = \sec x$ onto $y = \operatorname{cosec} x$.

Q4 a) Describe the transformation that maps $y = \cot x$ onto $y = \cot \frac{x}{4}$.

b) What is the period, in degrees, of the graph $y = \cot \frac{x}{4}$?

c) Sketch the graph of $y = \cot \frac{x}{4}$ for $0 < x \le 360°$.

Q5 a) Sketch the graph of $y = 2 + \sec x$ for $-2\pi \le x \le 2\pi$.

b) Give the coordinates of any maximum and minimum points within this interval.

c) State the domain and range of $y = 2 + \sec x$.

Q6 a) Sketch the graph of $y = 2 \operatorname{cosec} 2x$ for $0° < x < 360°$.

b) Give the coordinates of the minimum points within this interval.

c) Give the coordinates of the maximum points within this interval.

d) For what values of x in this interval is $y = 2 \operatorname{cosec} 2x$ undefined?

Q7 Hint: Work out the transformations from the graph of $y = \operatorname{cosec} x$ first and see how they affect the graph's properties.

Q7 a) Describe the position of the asymptotes on the graph of $y = 2 + 3 \operatorname{cosec} x$.

b) What is the period, in degrees, of the graph $y = 2 + 3\operatorname{cosec} x$?

c) Sketch the graph of $y = 2 + 3\operatorname{cosec} x$ for $-180° < x < 180°$.

d) State the range of $y = 2 + 3\operatorname{cosec} x$.

Evaluating cosec, sec and cot

To **evaluate** cosec, sec or cot of a number, first evaluate sin, cos or tan then work out the **reciprocal** of the answer.

Examples

a) Evaluate 2 sec(–20°) + 5, giving your answer to 3 significant figures.

- First write out the expression in terms of sin, cos or tan.

  $\sec x = \dfrac{1}{\cos x}$, so $2 \sec(-20°) + 5 = \dfrac{2}{\cos(-20°)} + 5$.

- Now use a calculator to find the answer:

  $\dfrac{2}{\cos(-20°)} + 5 = \dfrac{2}{0.93969...} + 5 = \boxed{7.13 \text{ to 3 sf.}}$

b) Evaluate cosec $\frac{\pi}{4}$ without a calculator. Give your answer in surd form.

- $\operatorname{cosec} x = \dfrac{1}{\sin x}$, so $\operatorname{cosec} \dfrac{\pi}{4} = \dfrac{1}{\sin \frac{\pi}{4}}$

- Using the triangle on the right, $\sin \dfrac{\pi}{4} = \dfrac{1}{\sqrt{2}}$.

- So $\operatorname{cosec} \dfrac{\pi}{4} = \dfrac{1}{\left(\frac{1}{\sqrt{2}}\right)} = \boxed{\sqrt{2}}$.

Tip: If you're asked for an answer in surd form, or to give an exact answer, it means you probably have to do it without a calculator. You should be able to solve it by considering angles of 0, $\frac{\pi}{6}$, $\frac{\pi}{4}$, $\frac{\pi}{3}$, $\frac{\pi}{2}$, π or 2π — see p.39.

c) Give the exact value of cot $\left(-\frac{\pi}{6}\right)$.

- $\cot x = \dfrac{1}{\tan x}$, so $\cot\left(-\dfrac{\pi}{6}\right) = \dfrac{1}{\tan\left(-\frac{\pi}{6}\right)}$

- Using the triangle, you can see that $\tan \dfrac{\pi}{6} = \dfrac{1}{\sqrt{3}}$.

- The graph of $y = \tan x$ below shows that if $\tan \dfrac{\pi}{6} = \dfrac{1}{\sqrt{3}}$

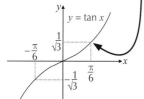

  then $\tan\left(-\dfrac{\pi}{6}\right) = -\dfrac{1}{\sqrt{3}}$.

- So $\cot\left(-\dfrac{\pi}{6}\right) = \dfrac{1}{\left(-\frac{1}{\sqrt{3}}\right)} = \boxed{-\sqrt{3}}$.

Tip: You could use a CAST diagram for this too. $-\frac{\pi}{6}$ is in a negative quadrant for tan, so it is the same as $-\tan \frac{\pi}{6}$.

d) Find cosec 300° without using a calculator.

- $\operatorname{cosec} 300° = \dfrac{1}{\sin 300°} = \dfrac{1}{\sin(360° - 60°)}$.

- The CAST diagram shows that sin 300° is the same size as sin 60°, but it lies in a quadrant where sin is negative.

  So $\sin 300° = -\sin 60° = -\dfrac{\sqrt{3}}{2}$.

- So $\operatorname{cosec} 300° = \dfrac{1}{\left(-\frac{\sqrt{3}}{2}\right)} = \boxed{-\dfrac{2}{\sqrt{3}}}$.

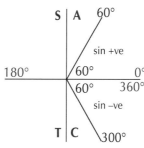

Tip: Get used to spotting angles that are 30°, 45° and 60° either side of 180° and 360° so that you can use the CAST diagram to help find them without a calculator.

Q1 Hint: If you have to give an answer rounded to a certain accuracy it means you'll have to use a calculator for part of it.

Q1 Evaluate the following, giving your answers to 2 decimal places:

a) $\operatorname{cosec} 80°$
b) $\sec 75°$
c) $\cot 30°$
d) $\sec(-70°)$
e) $3 - \cot 250°$
f) $2 \operatorname{cosec} 25°$

Q2 Hint: Don't forget to switch your calculator back to 'radians' for this question.

Q2 Evaluate the following, giving your answers to 3 significant figures:

a) $\sec 3$
b) $\cot 0.6$
c) $\operatorname{cosec} 1.8$
d) $\sec(-1)$
e) $\operatorname{cosec} \frac{\pi}{8}$
f) $8 + \cot \frac{\pi}{8}$
g) $\dfrac{1}{1 + \sec\frac{\pi}{10}}$
h) $\dfrac{1}{6 + \cot\frac{\pi}{5}}$

Q3 Using the table of common angles on p.39, find the exact values of:

a) $\sec 60°$
b) $\operatorname{cosec} 30°$
c) $\cot 45°$
d) $\operatorname{cosec} \frac{\pi}{3}$
e) $\sec(-180°)$
f) $\operatorname{cosec} 135°$
g) $\cot 330°$
h) $\sec \frac{5\pi}{4}$
i) $\operatorname{cosec} \frac{5\pi}{3}$
j) $\operatorname{cosec} \frac{2\pi}{3}$
k) $3 - \cot \frac{3\pi}{4}$
l) $\dfrac{\sqrt{3}}{\cot\frac{\pi}{6}}$

Q4 Hint: Use the table of common values on page 39 if you need to.

Q4 Find, without a calculator, the exact values of:

a) $\dfrac{1}{1 + \sec 60°}$
b) $\dfrac{2}{6 + \cot 315°}$
c) $\dfrac{1}{\sqrt{3} - \sec 30°}$
d) $1 + \cot 420°$
e) $\dfrac{2}{7 + \sqrt{3}\cot 150°}$

Simplifying expressions and solving equations

Simplifying expressions

You can use the cosec, sec and cot relationships to **simplify expressions**. This can make it a lot easier to **solve** trig equations.

Examples

a) **Simplify $\cot^2 x \tan x$.**

$\cot x = \dfrac{1}{\tan x}$, so:

$\cot^2 x \tan x = \left(\dfrac{1}{\tan^2 x}\right)\tan x = \dfrac{1}{\tan x} = \boxed{\cot x}$

b) **Show that $\dfrac{\cot x \sec x}{\csc^2 x} \equiv \sin x$.**

$\cot x = \dfrac{\cos x}{\sin x}$, so:

$\dfrac{\cot x \sec x}{\csc^2 x} = \dfrac{\left(\frac{\cos x}{\sin x}\right)\left(\frac{1}{\cos x}\right)}{\left(\frac{1}{\sin^2 x}\right)} = \dfrac{\left(\frac{1}{\sin x}\right)}{\left(\frac{1}{\sin^2 x}\right)} = \boxed{\sin x}$

> **Tip:** To 'show that' one thing is the same as another, you need to rearrange the expression on one side of the identity until it's the same as the other.

c) **Write the expression $(\csc x + 1)(\sin x - 1)$ as a single fraction in terms of $\sin x$ only.**

- First expand the brackets:

  $(\csc x + 1)(\sin x - 1) = \csc x \sin x + \sin x - \csc x - 1$

- $\csc x \sin x = \left(\dfrac{1}{\sin x}\right)\sin x = 1$, so the expression becomes:

  $1 + \sin x - \csc x - 1 = \sin x - \csc x$

- Using $\csc x = \dfrac{1}{\sin x}$ the expression becomes:

  $\sin x - \dfrac{1}{\sin x}$

  $= \boxed{\dfrac{\sin^2 x - 1}{\sin x}}$

> **Tip:** You usually need to write an expression in terms of only one type of trig function in order to solve an equation.

Solving equations

You can **solve** an equation involving cosec, sec and cot by **rewriting** it in terms of sin, cos or tan and solving as usual. You'll often need to write it in terms of sin, cos or tan **only**. You may also need to use the **CAST diagram** (or the graph of the trig function) to find all the solutions to an equation in a given interval.

a) Solve sec $x = \sqrt{2}$ in the interval $0 \leq x \leq 2\pi$.

- sec $x = \sqrt{2}$, so cos $x = \dfrac{1}{\sqrt{2}}$ ◄ —— Write in terms of cos x by giving the reciprocal.

- The triangle on the right shows that one solution to cos $x = \dfrac{1}{\sqrt{2}}$ is $x = \dfrac{\pi}{4}$. ———►

- Use the **CAST diagram** to find the **other** solution in the interval:

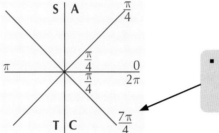

- The other positive solution is in this quadrant, where $x = 2\pi - \dfrac{\pi}{4} = \dfrac{7\pi}{4}$.

- So the two solutions are $x = \dfrac{\pi}{4}$ and $x = \dfrac{7\pi}{4}$.

Tip: If you've learnt the values of the sin, cos and tan of common angles on p.39, you won't need to keep drawing these triangles.

b) Solve $\text{cosec}^2\, x - 3\,\text{cosec}\, x + 2 = 0$ in the interval $-180° \leq x \leq 180°$.

Tip: Make a substitution of $y = \text{cosec}\, x$ and solve as a quadratic in y if you're struggling here.

- First you need to spot that this is a **quadratic equation** in cosec x, which can be factorised as follows:

$(\text{cosec}\, x - 1)(\text{cosec}\, x - 2) = 0$

- This gives **two** equations to solve:

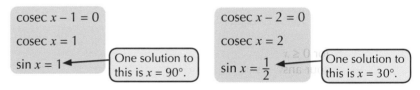

cosec $x - 1 = 0$
cosec $x = 1$
sin $x = 1$ ◄ —— One solution to this is $x = 90°$.

cosec $x - 2 = 0$
cosec $x = 2$
sin $x = \dfrac{1}{2}$ —— One solution to this is $x = 30°$.

- Look at the **graph** of $y = \sin x$ over the interval $-180° \leq x \leq 180°$:

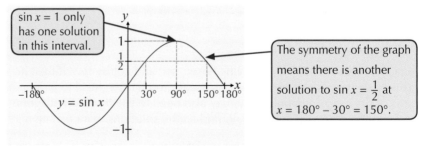

sin $x = 1$ only has one solution in this interval.

$y = \sin x$

The symmetry of the graph means there is another solution to sin $x = \dfrac{1}{2}$ at $x = 180° - 30° = 150°$.

- So the three solutions are $x = 30°$, $x = 90°$ and $x = 150°$.

Exercise 2.3

Q1 Simplify the following expressions:

a) $\sec x + \dfrac{1}{\cos x}$

b) $(\cosec^2 x)(\sin^2 x)$

c) $2 \cot x + \dfrac{1}{\tan x}$

d) $\dfrac{\sec x}{\cosec x}$

e) $(\cos x)(\cosec x)$

f) $\dfrac{\cosec^2 x}{\cot x}$

Q2 Show that:

a) $\sin x \cot x \equiv \cos x$

b) $\sec x - \cos x \equiv \tan x \sin x$

c) $\tan x \cosec x \equiv \sec x$

d) $\dfrac{(\tan^2 x)(\cosec x)}{\sin x} \equiv \sec^2 x$

Q2 Hint: You might find the identity $\sin^2 x + \cos^2 x \equiv 1$ useful — you should have seen it in C2.

Q3 Solve these equations for $0° \leq x \leq 360°$.
Give your answers in degrees to one decimal place.

a) $\sec x = 1.9$

b) $\cot x = 2.4$

c) $\cosec x = -2$

d) $\sec x = -1.3$

e) $\cot x = -2.4$

f) $4 \sec 2x = -7$

Q3 Hint: Use a calculator to find one solution, but then look at the graph or the CAST diagram to find any other solutions in the interval.

Q4 Solve these equations for $0 \leq x \leq 2\pi$, giving your answers in radians in terms of π.

a) $\sec x = 2$

b) $\cosec x = -2$

c) $\cot 2x = 1$

d) $\sec 5x = -1$

Q3-4 Hint: For questions where you're looking for solutions for a multiple of x, such as $2x$, the interval that you'll need to look in will be different. E.g. If $a \leq x \leq b$ then $2a \leq 2x \leq 2b$.

Q5 Solve the equation $\cot 2x - 4 = -5$ in the interval $0 \leq x \leq 2\pi$.
Give your answers in radians in terms of π.

Q6 Solve for $0° \leq x \leq 360°$: $2 \cosec 2x = 3$.
Give your answers in degrees to 1 decimal place.

Q7 Find, for $0 \leq x \leq 2\pi$, all the solutions of the equation $-2 \sec x = 4$.
Give your answers in radians in terms of π.

Q8 Solve $\sqrt{3} \cosec 3x = 2$ for $0 \leq x \leq 2\pi$.
Give your answers in radians in terms of π.

Q9 Solve the following for $0° \leq x \leq 180°$.
Give your answers in degrees.

a) $\sec^2 x - 2\sqrt{2} \sec x + 2 = 0$

b) $\cot^2 x - \dfrac{4}{\sqrt{3}} \cot x + 1 = 0$

Q9 Hint: Factorise or use the quadratic formula — if it helps, make the substitution $y = \cot x$ or $y = \sec x$.

Q10 Solve the equation $(\cosec x - 3)(2 \tan x + 1) = 0$ for $0° \leq x \leq 360°$.
Give your answers to 1 decimal place.

3. Identities Involving Cosec, Sec and Cot

Learning Objective:

- Know, and be able to use, the following identities:
  $\sec^2 \theta \equiv 1 + \tan^2 \theta$
  $\csc^2 \theta \equiv 1 + \cot^2 \theta$

An identity is an equation that's true for all values of a variable. You met some trig identities in C2 — you can build on these to include cosec, sec and cot.

Deriving the identities

You should remember using the following **trig identities** in C2:

$$\cos^2 \theta + \sin^2 \theta \equiv 1 \qquad \qquad \tan \theta \equiv \frac{\sin \theta}{\cos \theta}$$

Tip: The $\equiv$ sign tells you that this is true for all values of θ, rather than just certain values.

You can use them to produce a couple of other identities:

$$\sec^2 \theta \equiv 1 + \tan^2 \theta \qquad \qquad \csc^2 \theta \equiv 1 + \cot^2 \theta$$

You'll need to know how to **derive** these identities from the C2 trig identities.

Deriving $\sec^2 \theta \equiv 1 + \tan^2 \theta$

Start with the identity $\cos^2 \theta + \sin^2 \theta \equiv 1$ and divide through by $\cos^2 \theta$.

$$\frac{\cos^2 \theta}{\cos^2 \theta} + \frac{\sin^2 \theta}{\cos^2 \theta} \equiv \frac{1}{\cos^2 \theta}$$

Tip: Remember that $\cos^2 \theta = (\cos \theta)^2$.

$\tan \theta \equiv \dfrac{\sin \theta}{\cos \theta}$, so $\dfrac{\sin^2 \theta}{\cos^2 \theta} = \tan^2 \theta$

$$1 + \tan^2 \theta \equiv \frac{1}{\cos^2 \theta}$$

The definition of $\sec \theta = \dfrac{1}{\cos \theta}$, so replace $\dfrac{1}{\cos^2 \theta}$ with $\sec^2 \theta$.

$$1 + \tan^2 \theta \equiv \sec^2 \theta$$

Rearrange slightly...

$$\sec^2 \theta \equiv 1 + \tan^2 \theta$$

Deriving $\csc^2 \theta \equiv 1 + \cot^2 \theta$

Start again with $\cos^2 \theta + \sin^2 \theta \equiv 1$ but this time **divide** through by $\sin^2 \theta$.

$$\frac{\cos^2 \theta}{\sin^2 \theta} + \frac{\sin^2 \theta}{\sin^2 \theta} \equiv \frac{1}{\sin^2 \theta}$$

$\tan \theta \equiv \dfrac{\sin \theta}{\cos \theta}$, so $\dfrac{\cos^2 \theta}{\sin^2 \theta} = \dfrac{1}{\tan^2 \theta}$.

$$\frac{1}{\tan^2 \theta} + 1 \equiv \frac{1}{\sin^2 \theta}$$

The definition of $\cot\theta = \dfrac{1}{\tan\theta}$, so replace $\dfrac{1}{\tan^2\theta}$ with $\cot^2\theta$.

$$\cot^2\theta + 1 \equiv \frac{1}{\sin^2\theta}$$

The definition of **cosec** $\theta = \dfrac{1}{\sin\theta}$, so replace $\dfrac{1}{\sin^2\theta}$ with $\operatorname{cosec}^2\theta$.

$$\cot^2\theta + 1 \equiv \operatorname{cosec}^2\theta$$

Rearrange slightly...

$$\boxed{\operatorname{cosec}^2\theta \equiv 1 + \cot^2\theta}$$

Tip: These derivations are examples of direct proof (see page 163), where known or accepted facts are used to prove that other relationships are true. In this case the identities from C2 are the known facts.

Using the identities

You can use identities to get rid of any trig functions that are making an equation difficult to solve.

Example 1

Simplify the expression $3\tan x + \sec^2 x + 1$.

- Use $\sec^2\theta \equiv 1 + \tan^2\theta$ to swap $\sec^2 x$ for $1 + \tan^2 x$:

$$3\tan x + 1 + \tan^2 x + 1$$

- Now rearrange:

$$\tan^2 x + 3\tan x + 2$$

- This is a quadratic in $\tan x$ which will **factorise**:

$$(\tan x + 1)(\tan x + 2)$$

Tip: It's usually best to get the expression all in terms of one thing — in this case $\tan x$. You'll often be asked to simplify an expression in order to then solve an equation involving that expression.

Example 2

Solve the equation $\cot^2 x + 5 = 4\operatorname{cosec} x$ in the interval $0° \le x \le 360°$.

- You can't solve this while it has both cot and cosec in it, so use $\operatorname{cosec}^2\theta \equiv 1 + \cot^2\theta$ to swap $\cot^2 x$ for $\operatorname{cosec}^2 x - 1$.

$$\operatorname{cosec}^2 x - 1 + 5 = 4\operatorname{cosec} x$$
$$\operatorname{cosec}^2 x + 4 = 4\operatorname{cosec} x$$
$$\operatorname{cosec}^2 x - 4\operatorname{cosec} x + 4 = 0 \quad \longleftarrow \text{Rearrange so that one side is zero.}$$

- So you've got a quadratic in $\operatorname{cosec} x$ which will **factorise**.

$$(\operatorname{cosec} x - 2)(\operatorname{cosec} x - 2) = 0$$

- One of the brackets must be equal to zero — here they're both the same, so you only get one **equation**:

$$(\operatorname{cosec} x - 2) = 0$$
$$\Rightarrow \operatorname{cosec} x = 2$$

Tip: If it helps, think of this as $y^2 - 4y + 4 = 0$. Factorise it, and then replace the y with $\operatorname{cosec} x$.

- Now you can convert this into **sin x**, and **solve** it:

$$\sin x = \frac{1}{2}$$
$$\Rightarrow x = 30°$$

- To find the other values of x, draw a quick sketch of the sin curve:

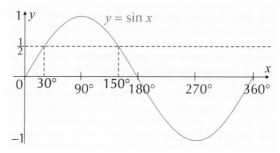

- From the graph, you can see that sin x takes the value of $\frac{1}{2}$ **twice** in the given interval, once at $x = 30°$ and once at $x = 180 - 30 = \boxed{150°}$.

Tip: You could use a CAST diagram here instead.

Example 3

Given that cot $x = \sqrt{8}$, where $0 \leq x \leq 180°$, show how you can use the identity $\operatorname{cosec}^2 \theta \equiv 1 + \cot^2 \theta$ to find the exact value of sin x. Use Pythagoras' Theorem to confirm the result.

- If $\cot x = \sqrt{8}$, then **$\cot^2 x = 8$**.

- $\cot^2 \theta = \operatorname{cosec}^2 \theta - 1$ so: **$\operatorname{cosec}^2 x - 1 = 8$**.

- Rearranging: $\operatorname{cosec}^2 x = 9 \Rightarrow$ **$\operatorname{cosec} x = \pm 3$**

- Since $\operatorname{cosec} x = \frac{1}{\sin x}$, $\sin x = \pm\frac{1}{3}$.

- We're told that **$0 \leq x \leq 180°$**, and sin x is **positive** over this interval, so: $\sin x = \frac{1}{3}$.

Look at the graph of sin x to see why.

- To confirm this using **Pythagoras' Theorem**:
$\cot x = \sqrt{8} \Rightarrow \tan x = \frac{1}{\cot x} = \frac{1}{\sqrt{8}}$.
Now draw a **right-angled triangle** for which $\tan x = \frac{1}{\sqrt{8}}$

(i.e. the opposite has a length of 1 and the adjacent has a length of $\sqrt{8}$):

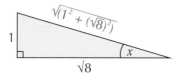

Using Pythagoras' Theorem, the hypotenuse will have a length of $\sqrt{1^2 + (\sqrt{8})^2} = 3$.

So $\sin x = \dfrac{\text{OPP}}{\text{HYP}} = \dfrac{1}{3}$.

Tip: In this example, you're told which identity to use, but this won't always be the case. It takes practice to quickly spot which identity will work best.

Q1 Express $\cosec^2 x + 2\cot^2 x$ in terms of $\cosec x$ only.

Q2 Simplify the following expression: $\tan^2 x - \dfrac{1}{\cos^2 x}$.

Q3 Given that $x = \sec\theta + \tan\theta$, show that $x + \dfrac{1}{x} = 2\sec\theta$.

Q4 a) Show that the equation $\tan^2 x = 2\sec x + 2$ can be written as:
$$\sec^2 x - 2\sec x - 3 = 0.$$
    b) Hence solve $\tan^2 x = 2\sec x + 2$ over the interval $0° \le x \le 360°$, giving your answers in degrees to 1 decimal place.

> **Q4 Hint:** The 'hence' in part b) means that you should use the result of part a) and solve $\sec^2 x - 2\sec x - 3 = 0$. It's a quadratic in $\sec x$.

Q5 a) Show that the equation $2\cosec^2 x = 5 - 5\cot x$ can be written as:
$$2\cot^2 x + 5\cot x - 3 = 0.$$
    b) Hence solve $2\cosec^2 x = 5 - 5\cot x$ over the interval $-\pi \le x \le \pi$, giving your answers in radians to 2 decimal places.

Q6 a) Show that the equation $2\cot^2 A + 5\cosec A = 10$ can be written:
$$2\cosec^2 A + 5\cosec A - 12 = 0.$$
    b) Hence solve $2\cot^2 A + 5\cosec A = 10$ over the interval $0° \le x \le 360°$, giving your answers in degrees to 1 decimal place.

Q7 Solve the equation $\sec^2 x + \tan x = 1$ for $0 \le x \le 2\pi$, giving exact answers.

> **Q7 Hint:** First write out the equation in terms of $\tan x$ only.

Q8 a) Given that $\cosec^2\theta + 2\cot^2\theta = 2$, find the possible values of $\sin\theta$.
    b) Hence solve the equation $\cosec^2\theta + 2\cot^2\theta = 2$ in the interval $0° \le \theta \le 180°$.

Q9 Solve the equation $\sec^2 x = 3 + \tan x$ in the interval $0° \le x \le 360°$, giving your answers in degrees to 1 decimal place.

Q10 Solve the equation $\cot^2 x + \cosec^2 x = 7$, giving all the solutions in the interval $0 \le x \le 2\pi$ in radians in terms of π.

Q11 Solve the equation $\tan^2 x + 5\sec x + 7 = 0$, giving all the solutions in the interval $0 \le x \le 2\pi$ in radians to 2 decimal places.

Q12 Given that $\tan\theta = \dfrac{60}{11}$, and $180° \le \theta \le 270°$, find the value of:
    a) $\sin\theta$ b) $\sec\theta$ c) $\cosec\theta$

Q13 Given that $\cosec\theta = -\dfrac{17}{15}$, and $180° \le \theta \le 270°$, find the value of:
    a) $\cos\theta$ b) $\sec\theta$ c) $\cot\theta$

> **Q14 Hint:** You're told to use this identity so you need to show your working out for this — you can't get away with stating the answer after using a different method.

Q14 Given that $\cos x = \dfrac{1}{6}$, use the identity $\sec^2\theta = 1 + \tan^2\theta$ to find the two possible values of $\tan x$.

Proving other identities

You can also use identities to prove that two trig expressions are the same, as shown in the examples below. You just need to take one side of the identity and play about with it until you get what's on the other side.

Examples

a) Show that $\dfrac{\tan^2 x}{\sec x} \equiv \sec x - \cos x$.

- Start by looking at the **left-hand side** of the identity: $\dfrac{\tan^2 x}{\sec x}$.
- Try replacing $\tan^2 x$ with $\sec^2 x - 1$:

$$\frac{\tan^2 x}{\sec x} \equiv \frac{\sec^2 x - 1}{\sec x} \equiv \frac{\sec^2 x}{\sec x} - \frac{1}{\sec x} \equiv \sec x - \cos x \equiv \text{RHS}$$

Do some rearranging...

...until you get the **right-hand side** of the identity.

b) Prove the identity $\dfrac{\tan^2 x}{\sec x + 1} \equiv \sec x - \cos^2 x - \sin^2 x$.

As before, replace $\tan^2 x$ with **$\sec^2 x - 1$**...

$$\frac{\tan^2 x}{\sec x + 1} \equiv \frac{(\sec^2 x - 1)}{\sec x + 1} \equiv \frac{(\sec x + 1)(\sec x - 1)}{\sec x + 1}$$

...But factorise the $\sec^2 x - 1$ as it's the **difference of two squares**.

$$\equiv \sec x - 1$$

$$\equiv \sec x - (\cos^2 x + \sin^2 x)$$

The right-hand side of the identity has a $\cos^2 x$ and $\sin^2 x$. So use **$\cos^2 x + \sin^2 x \equiv 1$** to replace the '1' here.

$$\equiv \sec x - \cos^2 x - \sin^2 x$$

Tip: Keep checking that you're getting closer to the right-hand side of the identity. As well as using the known identities, there are lots of little tricks you can use — such as looking for the 'difference of two squares', and multiplying the top and bottom of a fraction by the same expression.

Exercise 3.2

Q1 b) Hint: Think about 'the difference of two squares'.

Q1 a) Show that $\sec^2 \theta - \operatorname{cosec}^2 \theta \equiv \tan^2 \theta - \cot^2 \theta$.
   b) Hence prove that
       $(\sec \theta + \operatorname{cosec} \theta)(\sec \theta - \operatorname{cosec} \theta) \equiv (\tan \theta + \cot \theta)(\tan \theta - \cot \theta)$.

Q2 Prove the identity $(\tan x + \cot x)^2 \equiv \sec^2 x + \operatorname{cosec}^2 x$.

Q3 Hint: You'll need to use two identities here.

Q3 Prove the identity $\cot^2 x + \sin^2 x \equiv (\operatorname{cosec} x + \cos x)(\operatorname{cosec} x - \cos x)$.

Q4 Prove the identity $\dfrac{(\sec x - \tan x)(\tan x + \sec x)}{\operatorname{cosec} x - \cot x} \equiv \cot x + \operatorname{cosec} x$.

Q6 Hint: Try multiplying the top and bottom by the same expression.

Q5 Prove that $\dfrac{\cot x}{1 + \operatorname{cosec} x} + \dfrac{1 + \operatorname{cosec} x}{\cot x} \equiv 2 \sec x$.

Q6 Prove the identity $\dfrac{\operatorname{cosec} x + 1}{\operatorname{cosec} x - 1} \equiv 2 \sec^2 x + 2 \tan x \sec x - 1$.

Review Exercise — Chapter 2

Q1 Using trig values for common angles, evaluate the following in radians, between 0 and $\frac{\pi}{2}$:

a) $\sin^{-1}\dfrac{1}{\sqrt{2}}$

b) $\cos^{-1} 0$

c) $\tan^{-1}\sqrt{3}$

Q2 Sketch the graphs of $\sin^{-1} x$, $\cos^{-1} x$ and $\tan^{-1} x$, showing their domains and ranges.

Q3 The following diagram shows the curve $y = \dfrac{1}{1 + \cos x}$ for $0 \le x \le \frac{\pi}{2}$:

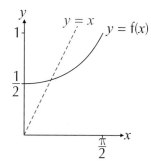

a) If $y = f(x)$, show that $f^{-1}(x) = \cos^{-1}\left(\dfrac{1}{x} - 1\right)$.

b) State the domain and range of this inverse function.

c) Sketch $y = f^{-1}(x)$ on the same axes as $y = f(x)$.

Q3 a) Hint: To find the inverse of a function, rearrange to make x the subject then replace x with $f^{-1}(x)$, and $f(x)$ with x (see page 13).

Q4 Given that $f(x) = \sin^{-1} x + \cos^{-1} x + \tan^{-1} x$, find the value, in radians, of:

a) $f(1)$

b) $f(-1)$

Q5 For $\theta = 30°$, find the exact values of:

a) $\operatorname{cosec} \theta$

b) $\sec \theta$

c) $\cot \theta$

Q6 Sketch the graphs of cosecant, secant and cotangent for $-2\pi \le x \le 2\pi$.

Q7 a) Describe the transformation that maps $y = \sec x$ onto $y = \sec 4x$.

b) What is the period, in radians, of the graph $y = \sec 4x$?

c) Sketch the graph of $y = \sec 4x$ for $0 \le x \le \pi$.

d) For what values of x in this interval is $\sec 4x$ undefined?

Q7 d) Hint: Look at the positions of the asymptotes on the transformed graph.

Q8   Use the identity $\cos^2 \theta + \sin^2 \theta \equiv 1$ to produce the identity $\sec^2 \theta \equiv 1 + \tan^2 \theta$.

Q9   Use the trig identities to show that $\cot^2 \theta + \sin^2 \theta \equiv \text{cosec}^2 \theta - \cos^2 \theta$.

Q10 Given that $x = \text{cosec } \theta$ and $y = \cot^2 \theta$, show that $y = x^2 - 1$.

Q11 If $x = \sec \theta$ and $y = 2 \tan \theta$, express y in terms of x only.

Q12 a) Show that the equation $\text{cosec}^2 x = \dfrac{3 \cot x + 4}{2}$ can be written as:
            $2 \cot^2 x - 3 \cot x - 2 = 0$.

   b) Hence solve the equation $\text{cosec}^2 x = \dfrac{3 \cot x + 4}{2}$.
       Give all the values of x in the interval $0 \leq x \leq 2\pi$ in
       radians to 2 decimal places.

Q13 Given that θ is acute and $\cos \theta = \dfrac{1}{2}$:

   a) Give the exact value of $\sec \theta$.

   b) Use Pythagoras' Theorem to find the value of $\tan \theta$.

   c) Use the identity $\sec^2 \theta \equiv 1 + \tan^2 \theta$ to find the value of $\tan \theta$
       and confirm that it is the same as in part b).

   d) Give the exact value of $\cot \theta$.

   e) Using the identity $\text{cosec}^2 \theta \equiv 1 + \cot^2 \theta$,
       give the exact value of $\sin \theta$.

> **Q13 b) Hint:** Draw a right-angled triangle and label the lengths of any sides that you can deduce from $\cos \theta$.

Exam-Style Questions — Chapter 2

1   a)   Sketch the graph of $y = \operatorname{cosec} x$ for $-\pi \le x \le \pi$.

(3 marks)

   b)   Solve the equation $\operatorname{cosec} x = \dfrac{5}{4}$ for $-\pi \le x \le \pi$.

   Give your answers correct to 3 significant figures.

(3 marks)

   c)   Solve the equation $\operatorname{cosec} x = 3 \sec x$ for $-\pi \le x \le \pi$.
   Give your answers correct to 3 significant figures.

(3 marks)

2   **Figure 1** shows the graph of $y = \cos^{-1} x$, where y is in radians.
   A and B are the end points of the graph.

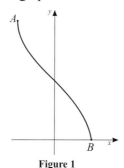

Figure 1

   a)   Write down the coordinates of A and B.

(2 marks)

   b)   Express x in terms of y.

(1 mark)

   c)   Solve, to 3 significant figures, the equation $\cos^{-1} x = 2$
   for the interval shown on the graph.

(2 marks)

3   a)   Show that $\dfrac{2 \sin x}{1 - \cos x} - \dfrac{2 \cos x}{\sin x} \equiv 2 \operatorname{cosec} x$.

(4 marks)

   b)   Use this result to find all the solutions for which

   $$\dfrac{2 \sin x}{1 - \cos x} - \dfrac{2 \cos x}{\sin x} = 4 \qquad 0 < x < 2\pi.$$

(3 marks)

4   a)   (i)   Using an appropriate identity, show that $3 \tan^2 \theta - 2 \sec \theta = 5$
      can be written as $3 \sec^2 \theta - 2 \sec \theta - 8 = 0$.

(2 marks)

      (ii)   Hence or otherwise show that $\cos \theta = -\frac{3}{4}$ or $\cos \theta = \frac{1}{2}$.

(3 marks)

   b)   Use your results from part a) above to solve the equation $3 \tan^2 2x - 2 \sec 2x = 5$
   for $0 \le x \le 180°$. Give your answers to 2 decimal places.

(3 marks)

1. Exponential and Logarithmic Graphs

Exponentials and logarithms are just types of functions. You've already seen them in C2, but for C3 you'll need to know about a special case of each — the exponential function and the natural logarithm.

Exponential functions

You should be familiar with these from C2 — but we'll begin with a short recap. The main feature of **exponential growth / decay** is that the **rate of increase / decrease** of the function is **proportional** to the function itself.

So if you plotted the **gradient** of an exponential function $y = a^x$, it would have the **same shape** as $y = a^x$.

The main points to remember for $y = a^x$ functions (a > 1) are:

Tip: For $0 < a < 1$, the graph does the opposite — so as $x \to \infty, y \to 0$ and as $x \to -\infty, y \to \infty$.

- As $x \to \infty, y \to \infty$ (and the gradient also $\to \infty$).

- As $x \to -\infty, y \to 0$ (which means that a^x is **always positive**).

- When $x = 0, y = 1$ (so all exponential graphs go through **(0, 1)** on the y-axis).

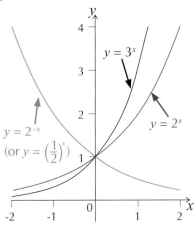

For C3, you need to know about a value of 'a' for which the **gradient** of $y = a^x$ is **exactly the same** as a^x. That value is known as **e**, an **irrational number** around 2.7183 (it's stored in your calculator just like π). This **special case** of an exponential function, $y = e^x$, is called **'the' exponential function**.

Tip: An **irrational number** is a real number which can't be written as a fraction $\frac{a}{b}$ (where a and b are both integers and $b \neq 0$).

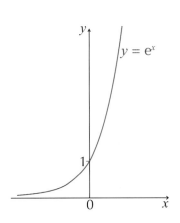

Because e is just a number, the graph of **$y = e^x$** has all the properties of $y = a^x$:

- $y = e^x$ cuts the y-axis at **(0, 1)**.

- As $x \to \infty, e^x \to \infty$ and as $x \to -\infty, e^x \to 0$.

- $y = e^x$ **does not exist** for $y \leq 0$ (i.e. $e^x > 0$ — it can't be zero or negative).

- The **domain** of $f(x) = e^x$ is $x \in \mathbb{R}$ (the set of all real numbers).

- The **range** is $f(x) > 0$ (see page 1).

Tip: e^x gets infinitely close to 0 but never reaches it. $y = 0$ is called an **asymptote** of the graph.

Logarithmic functions

ln x (also known as $\log_e x$, or 'natural log') is the **inverse function** of e^x.

- $y = \ln x$ is the **reflection** of $y = e^x$ in the line $y = x$.
- It cuts the x-axis at **(1, 0)** (so **ln 1 = 0**).
- As $x \to \infty$, $\ln x \to \infty$, but it happens very slowly.
- As $x \to 0$, $\ln x \to -\infty$.
- **ln** x **does not exist** for $x \le 0$ (i.e. x can't be zero or negative).
- The **domain** of $f(x) = \ln x$ is $x > 0$.
- The **range** is $f(x) \in \mathbb{R}$.

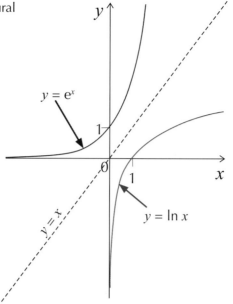

Tip: For more on functions and their inverses see p.12-14.

Just like any other set of inverse functions, doing one function to the other gets you **back to** x on its own.
You get the following very useful formulas which will help you to solve equations later in the chapter:

$$e^{\ln x} = x$$
$$\ln(e^x) = x$$

Transformations

You can **transform** the graphs of **exponential** and **logarithmic** functions using the methods from Chapter 1. Just let $f(x) = e^x$ or $\ln x$ and apply transformations to $f(x)$ in the same way as any other function (see pages 27-30).

The graph of e^{-x} comes up quite often. It's just the graph of e^x **reflected** in the **y-axis**. You can see this by letting $f(x) = e^x$ and $g(x) = e^{-x}$.
Then $g(x) = e^{-x} = e^{(-x)} = f(-x)$. So $g(x)$ is a reflection of $f(x)$ in the y-axis.

Tip: Remember, $f(-x)$ is just a reflection of $f(x)$ in the y-axis.

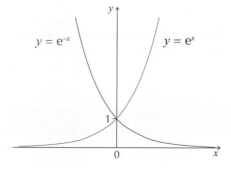

Just like **the exponential function**, the graph of $y = \ln(-x)$ is the graph of $y = \ln x$ reflected in the y-axis. It passes through **(-1, 0)** and still has an asymptote at $x = 0$.

Example 1

a) **Draw the graph of $y = \ln(-x)$ on the same axes as $y = \ln x$.**

- Let $f(x) = \ln x$.
- Then $\ln(-x) = f(-x)$.
- So $y = \ln(-x)$ is the graph of $y = \ln x$ reflected in the y-axis.
- The intersection with the x-axis is also reflected in the y-axis to become $(-1, 0)$.

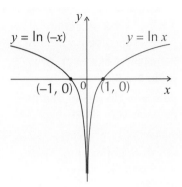

b) **Sketch $y = 3e^{0.5x}$ on the same axes as $y = e^x$.**

- Let $f(x) = e^x$.
- Then $3e^{0.5x} = 3(e^{(0.5x)}) = 3f(0.5x) = 3f\left(\frac{x}{2}\right)$.
- So we 'stretch' the graph of $y = e^x$ by a factor of 2 along the x-axis and a factor of 3 along the y-axis to get $y = 3e^{0.5x}$.
- The graph goes through $(0, 3)$ instead of $(0, 1)$ due to the y-axis stretch.

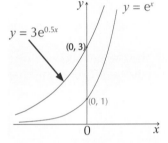

Tip: Remember that the function $f(\frac{1}{a}x)$ is $f(x)$ stretched along the x-axis by a factor of a.

Example 2

Draw the graph of $y = 5 + \ln(x + 2)$

- Let $f(x) = \ln x$.
- Then $\ln(x + 2) = f(x + 2)$
- So first draw the graph of $y = \ln(x + 2)$ by translating the graph of $y = \ln x$ left along the x-axis by 2 units.
- Then draw the graph of $y = 5 + \ln(x + 2)$ by translating the graph of $y = \ln(x + 2)$ up the y-axis by 5 units.
- The graph has an asymptote at $x = -2$ and intersects the y-axis at $5 + \ln 2$. (Put $x = 0$ into the function to get this value.)

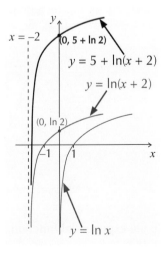

Q1 On the same axes, sketch the graphs of:

a) $y = 2^x$
b) $y = 3^{-x}$
c) $y = e^x$

Q2 Sketch each of the following functions on the same axes as $y = \ln x$ labelling any asymptotes:

a) $y = 2\ln x$
b) $y = \ln (x - 2)$
c) $y = 0.5\ln (-x)$
d) $y = 1 + \ln (x + 1)$

Q3 Sketch each graph on the same axes as $y = e^x$ labelling any asymptotes:

a) $y = 2e^x - 4$
b) $y = 0.5e^{-x}$
c) $y = e^{(0.5x + 2)}$
d) $y = 1 + e^{(x + 1)}$

Q4 Find the missing coordinates A, B and C on the following graphs:

a) $y = 3\ln\left(\frac{x}{2}\right)$
b) $y = \ln(-3x) + 2$
c) $y = 3 - \ln(-x)$

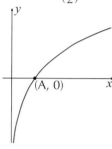
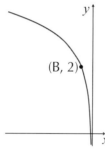
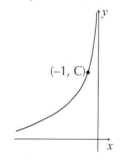

Q4 Hint: If you can't work it out by looking at the graph, try putting the x or y coordinate into the equation to work out what the missing coordinate is.

Q5 Write down the coordinates of the marked points A, B and C and the equations of the asymptotes D, E and F on these graphs:

a) $y = 3e^{\frac{x}{2}}$
b) $y = 2 + e^{-3x}$
c) $y = 3 - e^{-x}$

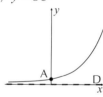
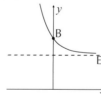
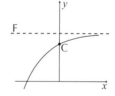

Q6 What functions are shown in the following graphs?

a) $y = f(x)$
b) $y = g(x)$
c) $y = h(x)$

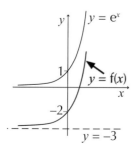
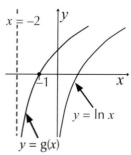
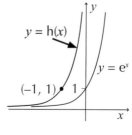

Q6 Hint: Look where intercept and asymptotes have moved to, and whether the gradient has changed to work out how the graph of $y = \ln x$ or $y = e^x$ has been transformed.

2. Using Exponentials and Logarithms

Learning Objective:

- Be able to solve equations containing functions of $\ln x$ and e^x.

In this section you'll see how to solve equations containing ln x and e^x. You'll need to use the fact that ln x is the inverse of e^x (and vice versa), and use the log laws you came across in C2.

Solving equations

You can use the **log laws** from C2 as well as the **formulas** from the previous topic to **solve equations**.

Formulas
$e^{\ln x} = x$
$\ln (e^x) = x$

Log Laws
$\ln x + \ln y = \ln (xy)$
$\ln x - \ln y = \ln \left(\frac{x}{y}\right)$
$\ln x^k = k\ln x$

Example 1

Solve the following equations, giving your answers as exact solutions.

a) $e^x = 10$

Apply ln to both sides to remove the e function.

$$e^x = 10$$

$\ln e^x = x$.

$$\ln e^x = \ln 10$$
$$x = \ln 10$$

b) $e^{(0.5x + 1)} = 20$

Apply ln to both sides to remove the e function.

$$e^{(0.5x + 1)} = 20$$
$$\ln e^{(0.5x + 1)} = \ln 20$$
$$0.5x + 1 = \ln 20$$
$$0.5x = \ln 20 - 1$$
$$x = \frac{\ln 20 - 1}{0.5}$$
$$x = 2\ln 20 - 2$$

c) $\ln (2x - 1) = 2$

Apply e to both sides to remove the ln function.

$$\ln (2x - 1) = 2$$
$$e^{\ln(2x - 1)} = e^2$$
$$2x - 1 = e^2$$

$e^{\ln x} = x$

$$2x = e^2 + 1$$
$$x = \frac{e^2 + 1}{2}$$

Tip: If the question asks you to give an exact solution, leave the answer as a logarithm or exponential.

d) ln $(x^4) = 1$

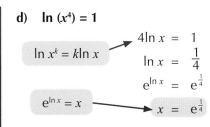

$$4\ln x = 1$$
$$\ln x = \frac{1}{4}$$
$$e^{\ln x} = e^{\frac{1}{4}}$$

ln $x^k = k$ln x

$e^{\ln x} = x$

$$x = e^{\frac{1}{4}}$$

Example 2

a) Solve the equation 2ln x – ln $2x = 6$, giving your answer as an exact value of x.

Use log laws to simplify the left hand side.

$$2\ln x - \ln 2x = 6$$

$$\ln x^2 - \ln 2x = 6$$

ln $x^k = k$ln x

$$\ln\left(\frac{x^2}{2x}\right) = 6$$ ln $x - $ ln $y = $ ln $\left(\frac{x}{y}\right)$

$$\ln\left(\frac{x}{2}\right) = 6$$

Apply the inverse function e^x to both sides to find x.

$$e^{\ln\left(\frac{x}{2}\right)} = e^6$$

$e^{\ln x} = x$

$$\frac{x}{2} = e^6$$

$$x = 2e^6$$

Since you need an exact value, leave it in exponential form.

b) Find the two exact solutions of the equation $e^x + 5e^{-x} = 6$.

A big clue here is that you're asked for more than one solution. Think quadratics...

Multiply each part of the equation by e^x to get rid of e^{-x}.

$$e^x + 5e^{-x} = 6$$

$$e^{2x} + 5 = 6e^x$$

$$e^{2x} - 6e^x + 5 = 0$$

> **Tip:** Remember basic powers laws:
> $$(e^x)^2 = e^{2x}$$
> $$e^{-x} \times e^x = e^0 = 1.$$

Substitute y for e^x to get a quadratic in y. Since you're asked for exact solutions, it will probably factorise.

$$y^2 - 6y + 5 = 0$$

$$(y - 1)(y - 5) = 0$$

$$y = 1 \quad \text{and} \quad y = 5.$$

Put e^x back in and apply the inverse function ln x to both sides.

$$e^x = 1 \quad \text{and} \quad e^x = 5.$$

$$\ln e^x = \ln 1 \quad \text{and} \quad \ln e^x = \ln 5$$

ln $e^x = x$.

$$x = \ln 1 = 0 \quad \text{and} \quad x = \ln 5$$

Again, you're asked for an exact answer so leave it in this form.

Q1   a)   Find x in terms of y if $y = e^x$.

       b)   Find b in terms of a if $a = \ln b$.

Q2   Solve these equations, giving your answers as exact solutions.

       a) $e^x = 7$

       b) $5e^{3t} = 11$

       c) $2e^{(-2x)} = 6$

       d) $e^{(0.5x + 3)} = 9$

       e) $10 - 3e^{(1 - 2x)} = 8$

Q3   Solve these equations, giving

       (i)   an exact solution

       (ii) a solution correct to 3 s.f.

       a) $\ln x = -2$

       b) $3\ln (2x) = 7$

       c) $\ln (5t - 3) = 4$

       d) $6\ln (8 - 2t) = 10$

       e) $6 - \ln (0.5x) = 3$

Q4 Hint: Remember the log law $\ln x^k = k \ln x$.

Q4   Solve these equations, giving your answers in terms of $\ln 3$.

       a) $e^{3x} = 27$

       b) $e^{-4x} = 9$

       c) $e^{(6x - 1)} = \dfrac{1}{3}$

       d) $3e^{(2x + 3)} = \dfrac{1}{27}$

       e) $\dfrac{1}{3}e^{(1 - x)} - 3 = 0$

Q5 Hint: Try making a substitution. Also, 'where possible' gives you a hint that there might not be any solutions.

Q5   Solve, where possible, giving

       (i)   an exact answer

       (ii) a solution correct to 3 s.f.

       a) $e^{2x} - 7e^x + 12 = 0$

       b) $e^{7x} - 3e^{5x} = 0$

       c) $3e^{2x} + 10e^x + 3 = 0$

       d) $e^{4x} + 4e^{2x} + 5 = 0$

       e) $e^x + e^{-x} = 6$

Q6   Solve these equations, giving exact answers.

       a) $\ln 5 + \ln x = 7$

       b) $\ln (2x) + \ln (3x) = 15$

       c) $\ln (x^2 - 4) - \ln (2x) = 0$

       d) $3\ln (x^2) + 5\ln x = 2$

Review Exercise — Chapter 3

Q1   Write down the exponential functions with base e shown in the following graphs.

a)

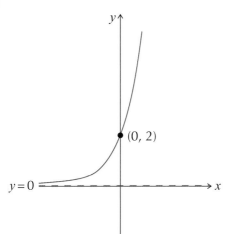

b)

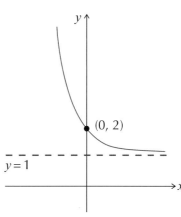

Q1 Hint: Where the question says base e, it just means that the function you are looking for has an e in it — instead of an exponential of the form a^x where a can be anything.

Q2   Find the missing coordinates A and B, and lines C and D for the following functions.

a) $y = \ln(x + 2)$

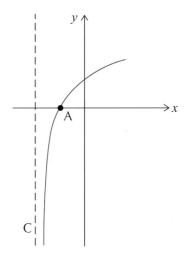

b) $y = 3 + \ln x$

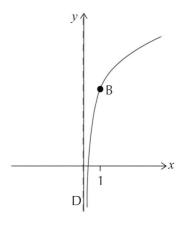

Q3   Plot the following graphs on the same axes, for $-2 \le x \le 2$:

a) $y = 4e^x$

b) $y = 4e^{-x}$

c) $y = 4\ln x$

d) $y = \ln 4x.$

Q4 a) Plot the following graphs on separate axes.
    In each case, draw the graph of $y = e^x$ on the same axes.
    (i) $y = 2 + e^x$
    (ii) $y = e^{\frac{x}{2}} - 1$
    (iii) $y = e^{3x} - 0.5$
    (iv) $y = 5 - 3e^x$

    b) Describe the series of transformations from $y = e^x$ to each of the functions (i) - (iv) above.

Q5 a) Plot the following graphs on separate axes.
    In each case, draw the graph of $y = \ln x$ on the same axes.
    (i) $y = 1 + \ln x$
    (ii) $y = \ln (2x)$
    (iii) $y = 3\ln x - 1$
    (iv) $y = 5\ln (-x)$

    b) Describe the series of transformations from $y = \ln x$ to each of the functions (i) - (iv) above.

Q6 Find the value of x, to 4 decimal places, when:
    a) $e^{2x} = 6$
    b) $\ln (x + 3) = 0.75$
    c) $3e^{-4x+1} = 5$
    d) $\ln x + \ln 5 = \ln 4$.

Q7 Solve the following equations, giving your solutions as exact values:
    a) $2\ln x - \ln (2x) = 2$
    b) $\ln (2x - 7) + \ln 4 = -3$

Q8 Sketch graphs of the following, labelling key points and asymptotes:
    a) $y = 2 - e^{x+1}$
    b) $y = 5e^{0.5x} + 5$
    c) $y = \ln (2x) + 1$
    d) $y = \ln (x + 5)$

Q9 Solve the following equations giving your solutions as exact values:
    a) $2e^{2x} + e^x = 3$.
    b) $e^{8x} - e^{4x} - 6 = 0$

1   a)   Given that $6e^x = 3$, find the exact value of x.

(2 marks)

b)   Find the exact solutions to the equation:
$$e^{2x} - 8e^x + 7 = 0.$$

(4 marks)

c)   Given that $4 \ln x = 3$, find the exact value of x.

(2 marks)

d)   Solve the equation:
$$\ln x + \frac{24}{\ln x} = 10$$

giving your answers as exact values of x.

(4 marks)

2   The sketch below shows the function $y = e^{ax} + b$, where a and b are constants.

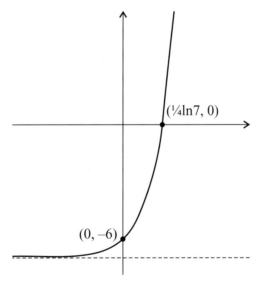

($\frac{1}{4}\ln 7$, 0)

(0, −6)

Find the values of a and b, and the equation of the asymptote shown on the sketch.

(5 marks)

3   Solve the following equations, giving your answers as exact values of x.

a) $2e^x + 18e^{-x} = 20$

(4 marks)

b) $2\ln x - \ln 3 = \ln 12$

(3 marks)

4   A curve has the equation $y = \ln(4x - 3)$.

    a)   The point A with coordinates $(a, 1)$ lies on the curve.
Find a to 2 decimal places.

                  (2 marks)

    b)   The curve only exists for $x > b$. State the value of b.

                  (2 marks)

    c)   Sketch the curve, labelling the asymptote and x-intercept.

                  (2 marks)

5   A point P lies on a curve C with equation:

$$y = 3e^{2 - 2x}$$

The y-coordinate of P is 27.

    a)   Find the x-coordinate of P in terms of $\ln 3$.

                  (3 marks)

    b)   Sketch the curve C, labelling the asymptote and the y-intercept.

                  (3 marks)

    c)   Rearrange the equation for C to make x the subject.

                  (2 marks)

6   The sketch below shows the function $y = 4\ln(x - A)$, where A is a constant.

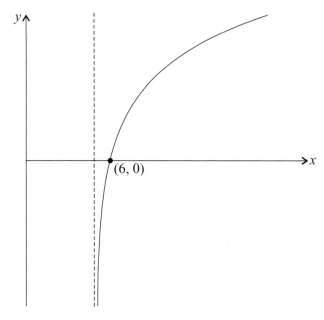

    a)   Find the value of A, and hence give the equation of the asymptote shown.

                  (3 marks)

The graph of the function passes through the point $(B, 8)$.

    b)   Find the exact value of B.

                  (2 marks)

1. Chain Rule

You covered differentiation in AS Maths, and now you'll see it again — but with new rules for more complicated functions. The first of the new rules is the chain rule, which you use for differentiating functions of functions, like sin x².

The chain rule

The **chain rule** helps you **differentiate** complicated functions by **splitting them up** into functions that are easier to differentiate. The trick is spotting **how** to split them up, and choosing the right bit to **substitute**. Once you've worked out how to split up the function, you can differentiate it using this **formula**:

$$\text{If } y = f(u) \text{ and } u = g(x)$$
$$\text{then:}$$
$$\frac{dy}{dx} = \frac{dy}{du} \times \frac{du}{dx}$$

To differentiate a function using the chain rule, just follow these steps:

- Pick a suitable function of x for 'u' and rewrite y in terms of u.

- Differentiate u (with respect to x) to get $\frac{du}{dx}$ and differentiate y (with respect to u) to get $\frac{dy}{du}$.

- Stick it all in the formula and write everything in terms of x.

The important part is **choosing** which bit to make into u. The aim is to split it into **two separate functions** that you can **differentiate easily**.

- If you have a function inside **brackets**, then the part **inside** the brackets is normally u:

  $y = (x + 1)^2$ can be written as $y = u^2$ where $u = x + 1$.

  Now both u^2 and $x + 1$ are **easy to differentiate**, and the chain rule formula does the hard work for you.

- If there's a **trig function** or **log** involved, it's usually the part **inside** the trig function or log:

  $y = \sin x^2$ can be written as $y = \sin u$ where $u = x^2$.

  Again, you end up with 2 functions that are **easy to differentiate**, so you just differentiate each one **separately** then put it all in the **formula**.

Learning Objectives:

- Be able to identify which part of a function to use as u in the chain rule.
- Be able to use the chain rule to differentiate functions of functions.
- Be able to use the chain rule to convert dx/dy into dy/dx.

Tip: It may help you to think of the derivatives as fractions (they're not, but it's a good way to think of it).

Then the du's cancel:

$$\frac{dy}{du} \times \frac{du}{dx} = \frac{dy}{dx}$$

If you remember this you'll never get the order wrong.

Tip: Don't worry if you don't know how to differentiate trig functions yet — it's covered later in this chapter.

Example 1

Find $\dfrac{dy}{dx}$ if $y = (6x - 3)^5$.

- First of all, decide which part of the function to replace with u. In this case, the bit inside the brackets is easy to differentiate, so that's u.

$$y = (6x - 3)^5, \text{ so let } y = u^5 \text{ where } u = 6x - 3$$

- Next, differentiate the two parts separately:

$$\frac{dy}{du} = 5u^4 \quad \text{and} \quad \frac{du}{dx} = 6$$

- Finally, put everything back into the chain rule formula.

$$\frac{dy}{dx} = \frac{dy}{du} \times \frac{du}{dx} = 5u^4 \times 6 = 30u^4 = \boxed{30(6x - 3)^4}$$

Tip: Make sure you always substitute the function back in for u. It'll cost you marks if you don't.

Now that you can differentiate **functions of functions** using the chain rule, you can find the equation of a **tangent** or **normal** to a curve that has an equation given by a function of a function.

Example 2

Find the equation of the tangent to the curve $y = \dfrac{1}{\sqrt{x^2 + 3x}}$ at $(1, \tfrac{1}{2})$.

- This function's a little more complicated than the previous one, so it will help to first rewrite it in terms of powers:

$$y = \frac{1}{\sqrt{x^2 + 3x}} = (x^2 + 3x)^{-\frac{1}{2}}$$

- Then identify which part to turn into u.

$$y = (x^2 + 3x)^{-\frac{1}{2}}, \text{ so let } y = u^{-\frac{1}{2}} \text{ where } u = (x^2 + 3x)$$

Tip: When you get a question with a root or fraction, always rewrite it in terms of powers. Remember, $1/x$ is the same as x^{-1} and $\sqrt{x}$ is the same as $x^{\frac{1}{2}}$.

- Once again you now have two functions you can differentiate:

$$y = u^{-\frac{1}{2}} \Rightarrow \frac{dy}{du} = (-\frac{1}{2})u^{-\frac{3}{2}} = -\frac{1}{2(\sqrt{x^2 + 3x})^3}$$

$$u = x^2 + 3x \Rightarrow \frac{du}{dx} = 2x + 3$$

- Now put it all back into the chain rule formula:

$$\frac{dy}{dx} = \frac{dy}{du} \times \frac{du}{dx} = (-\frac{1}{2(\sqrt{x^2 + 3x})^3}) \times (2x + 3) = -\frac{2x + 3}{2(\sqrt{x^2 + 3x})^3}$$

- To find the equation of the tangent, you first need to know the gradient at the point $(1, \tfrac{1}{2})$, so put the x-value into your equation for $\dfrac{dy}{dx}$:

$$\frac{dy}{dx} = -\frac{(2 \times 1) + 3}{2(\sqrt{1^2 + (3 \times 1)})^3} = -\frac{5}{16}$$

- Then use your gradient and the values you're given to find c:

$$y = mx + c \Rightarrow \frac{1}{2} = (-\frac{5}{16} \times 1) + c \Rightarrow c = \frac{13}{16}$$

Tip: You could also use $y - y_1 = m(x - x_1)$ to find the equation of the line.

- So the equation of the tangent at $(1, \tfrac{1}{2})$ is $\boxed{y = -\dfrac{5}{16}x + \dfrac{13}{16}}$

Exercise 1.1

Q1 Differentiate with respect to x:

a) $y = (x + 7)^2$

b) $y = (2x - 1)^5$

c) $y = 3(4 - x)^8$

d) $y = (3 - 2x)^7$

e) $y = (x^2 + 3)^5$

f) $y = (5x^2 + 3)^2$

Q2 Find $f'(x)$ for the following:

a) $f(x) = (4x^3 - 9)^8$

b) $f(x) = (6 - 7x^2)^4$

c) $f(x) = (x^2 + 5x + 7)^6$

d) $f(x) = (x + 4)^{-3}$

e) $f(x) = (5 - 3x)^{-2}$

f) $f(x) = \dfrac{1}{(5 - 3x)^4}$

g) $f(x) = (3x^2 + 4)^{\frac{3}{2}}$

h) $f(x) = \dfrac{1}{\sqrt{5 - 3x}}$

Q2 Hint: Remember $f'(x)$ is just another way of writing dy/dx.

Q3 Find the exact value of $\dfrac{dy}{dx}$ when $x = 1$ for:

a) $y = \dfrac{1}{\sqrt{5x - 3x^2}}$

b) $y = \dfrac{12}{\sqrt[3]{x + 6}}$

Q4 Differentiate $(\sqrt{x} + \dfrac{1}{\sqrt{x}})^2$ with respect to x by:

a) Multiplying the brackets out and differentiating term by term.

b) Using the chain rule.

Q5 Find the equation of the tangent to the curve $y = (x - 3)^5$ at $(1, -32)$

Q6 Find the equation of the tangent to the curve $y = (2x - 3)^7$ at the point $(2, 1)$.

Q7 Find the equation of the normal to the curve $y = \frac{1}{4}(x - 7)^4$ when $x = 6$.

Q7 Hint: Remember, the gradient of the normal to a curve is just $-1 \div$ gradient of the tangent (this was in C1 if you need a refresher).

Q8 Find the equation of the normal to the curve $y = \left(\dfrac{x}{4} - 2\right)^3$ at the point $(4, -1)$, in the form $ax + by + c = 0$ where a, b and c are integers.

Q9 Find the value of $\dfrac{dy}{dx}$ when $x = 1$ for $y = (7x^2 - 3)^{-4}$.

Q10 Find $f'(x)$ if $f(x) = \dfrac{7}{\sqrt[3]{3 - 2x}}$.

Q11 Find the equation of the tangent to the curve $y = \sqrt{5x - 1}$ when $x = 2$, in the form $ax + by + c = 0$, $a, b, c \in \mathbb{Z}$.

Q11 Hint: Remember that a, b, c $\in \mathbb{Z}$ means that a, b and c are integers.

Q12 Find the equation of the normal to the curve $y = \sqrt[3]{3x - 7}$ when $x = 5$.

Q13 Find the equation of the tangent to the curve $y = (x^4 + x^3 + x^2)^2$ when $x = -1$.

Finding $\dfrac{dy}{dx}$ when $x = f(y)$

The principle of the chain rule can also be used where **x is given in terms of y** (i.e. $x = f(y)$). This comes from a little mathematical rearranging, and you'll find it's often quite useful:

Tip: As with the chain rule, treat the derivatives as fractions to make this result easier to follow (they're not actually fractions though).

$$\frac{dy}{dx} \times \frac{dx}{dy} = \frac{dy}{dy} = 1, \text{ so rearranging gives } \frac{dy}{dx} = \frac{1}{\left(\frac{dx}{dy}\right)}.$$

So to differentiate $x = f(y)$, use:

$$\boxed{\frac{dy}{dx} = \frac{1}{\left(\frac{dx}{dy}\right)}}$$

Example

A curve has the equation $x = y^3 + 2y - 7$. Find $\dfrac{dy}{dx}$ at the point $(-4, 1)$.

- Forget that the x's and y's are in the 'wrong' place and differentiate as usual:

$$x = y^3 + 2y - 7 \Rightarrow \frac{dx}{dy} = 3y^2 + 2.$$

- Use $\dfrac{dy}{dx} = \dfrac{1}{\left(\frac{dx}{dy}\right)}$ to find $\dfrac{dy}{dx}$: $\quad \dfrac{dy}{dx} = \dfrac{1}{3y^2 + 2}$

- $y = 1$ at the point $(-4, 1)$, so put this in the equation:

$$\frac{dy}{dx} = \frac{1}{3(1)^2 + 2} = \frac{1}{5} = 0.2, \text{ so } \frac{dy}{dx} = 0.2 \text{ at the point } (-4, 1).$$

Exercise 1.2

Q1 Find $\dfrac{dy}{dx}$ for each of the following functions at the given point. In each case, express $\dfrac{dy}{dx}$ in terms of y.

a) $x = 3y^2 + 5y + 7$ at $(5, -1)$ b) $x = y^3 - 2y$ at $(-4, -2)$

c) $x = (2y + 1)(y - 2)$ at $(3, -1)$ d) $x = \dfrac{4 + y^2}{y}$ at $(5, 4)$

Q2 Find $\dfrac{dy}{dx}$ if $x = (2y^3 - 5)^3$.

Q3 Find $\dfrac{dy}{dx}$ if $x = \sqrt{4 + y}$ by:

a) Finding $\dfrac{dx}{dy}$ first.

b) Rearranging into the form $y = f(x)$.

2. Differentiation of e^x and $\ln x$

Differentiating exponentials and logarithms is actually a lot easier than you might think because each one follows certain rules.

Differentiating e^x

In the last chapter (see p.58) you saw that 'e' was just a number for which the **gradient of e^x was e^x**, which makes it pretty simple to **differentiate**:

$$y = e^x$$
$$\frac{dy}{dx} = e^x$$

(see p.58)

You can use the chain rule to show another useful relation involving exponentials. If you replace x with f(x), you have a **function of a function**:

$y = e^{f(x)}$, so let $y = e^u$ where $u = f(x)$

So $\dfrac{dy}{du} = e^u = e^{f(x)}$ (see above) and $\dfrac{du}{dx} = f'(x)$

Putting it into the chain rule formula you get:

$$\frac{dy}{dx} = \frac{dy}{du} \times \frac{du}{dx} = e^{f(x)} \times f'(x) = f'(x)e^{f(x)}$$

- This works because $e^{f(x)}$ is a special case — the 'e' part stays the same when you differentiate, so you only have to worry about the f(x) part. You can just learn the formula:

$$y = e^{f(x)}$$
$$\frac{dy}{dx} = f'(x)e^{f(x)}$$

- You can use this formula to differentiate difficult exponentials.

Example 1

Find $\dfrac{dy}{dx}$ if $y = e^{(3x-2)}$

- Using the formula above, you can see that y is in the form $e^{f(x)}$ where $f(x) = 3x - 2$.

- Differentiating f(x) is very easy: $f'(x) = 3$

- Now just put the right parts back into the formula for $\dfrac{dy}{dx}$.

$$y = e^{(3x-2)} \quad \Rightarrow \quad \frac{dy}{dx} = f'(x)e^{f(x)} = 3e^{(3x-2)}$$

Learning Objectives:

- Be able to differentiate e^x and $\ln x$.
- Be able to use the rules of differentiation for e^x and $\ln x$ to differentiate more complex functions using the chain rule.
- Be able to use these methods to answer questions on tangents, normals and turning points.

Example 2

If $f(x) = e^{x^2} + 2e^x$, find $f'(x)$ for $x = 0$.

- The function is in 2 parts, so let's break it down into its two bits and differentiate them separately:

- The second bit's easy: If $f(x) = 2e^x$ then $f'(x) = 2e^x$ too.

- For the first bit, you could just use the formula you used on the previous examples, but let's use the chain rule here just to show how it works.

$$y = e^{x^2}, \text{ so let } y = e^u \text{ where } u = x^2$$

- Both u and y are now easy to differentiate:

$$\frac{dy}{du} = e^u \text{ and } \frac{du}{dx} = 2x$$

$$\frac{dy}{dx} = \frac{dy}{du} \times \frac{du}{dx} = e^u \times 2x = 2xe^{x^2}$$

- Now put the bits back together:

$$f'(x) = 2xe^{x^2} + 2e^x$$

- And finally, work out the value of $f'(x)$ at $x = 0$:

$$f'(0) = (2 \times 0 \times e^{0^2}) + 2e^0$$

$$f'(0) = 0 + 2$$

$$f'(0) = 2$$

Tip: Remember that $e^0 = 1$.

Example 3

Differentiate $y = e^{2x} - 6x$. Find the exact coordinates of the turning point of the curve $y = e^{2x} - 6x$ and determine the nature of this point.

- To find the coordinates of turning points, you need to find where $\frac{dy}{dx}$ is equal to zero.

- Like in example 2, split the function up into two parts and differentiate the parts separately.

- The second bit's easy: $y = -6x \Rightarrow \frac{dy}{dx} = -6$

- For the first bit, use the formula given at the start of this section.

$$y = e^{2x} = e^{f(x)}$$

$$f(x) = 2x \text{ so } f'(x) = 2$$

$$\frac{dy}{dx} = f'(x)e^{f(x)} = 2e^{2x}$$

- Now just put the two parts back together:

$$\frac{dy}{dx} = 2e^{2x} - 6$$

- Now to find any turning points, set $\frac{dy}{dx} = 0$ and rearrange to find x and y.

$$0 = 2e^{2x} - 6 \quad \Rightarrow \quad e^{2x} = 3 \quad \Rightarrow \quad 2x = \ln 3 \quad \Rightarrow \quad x = 0.5\ln 3$$

$$y = e^{2x} - 6x \quad \Rightarrow \quad y = e^{\ln 3} - 3\ln 3 \quad \Rightarrow \quad y = 3 - 3\ln 3$$

Tip: Remember that $e^{\ln x} = x$.

So the turning point is at $(0.5\ln 3, 3 - 3\ln 3)$

- To determine the nature of the turning point, differentiate again and put the coordinates of the turning point in $\frac{d^2y}{dx^2}$.

$$\frac{dy}{dx} = 2e^{2x} - 6 = 2e^{f(x)} - 6$$

$$\frac{d^2y}{dx^2} = 2f'(x)e^{f(x)} = 2(2 \times e^{2x}) = 4e^{2x}$$

So when $x = 0.5\ln 3$, $\frac{d^2y}{dx^2} = 4e^{\ln 3} = 12$

Tip: Remember that d^2y/dx^2 is positive for minimums and negative for maximums.

- $\frac{d^2y}{dx^2}$ is positive so the turning point is a minimum.

Exercise 2.1

Q1 Differentiate with respect to x:

a) $y = e^{3x}$ b) $y = e^{2x-5}$ c) $y = e^{x+7}$

d) $y = e^{3x+9}$ e) $y = e^{7-2x}$ f) $y = e^{x^3}$

Q2 Find $f'(x)$ if $f(x) = e^{x^3 + 3x}$

Q3 Find $f'(x)$ if $f(x) = e^{x^3 - 3x - 5}$

Q4 Find $f'(x)$ if $f(x) = e^{x(2x+1)}$

Q5 Find $f'(x)$ if $f(x) = \frac{1}{2}(e^x - e^{-x})$

Q6   Find $f'(x)$ if $f(x) = e^{(x+3)(x+4)}$

Q7 Hint: Differentiating each term separately will make this easier.

Q7   Find $f'(x)$ if $f(x) = e^{x^4 + 3x^2} + 2e^{2x}$

Q8   Find the equation of the tangent to the curve $y = e^{2x}$ at the point $(0, 1)$.

Q9   Find the equation of the tangent to the curve $y = e^{3(x-2)}$ at the point $(2, 1)$.

Q10 Hint: 'Leave the numbers in exact form' means leave them in the form e^a (where a is a number) rather than working out the actual numbers.

Q10 Find the equation of the tangent to the curve $y = e^{2x^2}$ when $x = 1$. Leave the numbers in your answer in exact form.

Q11 Find the equation of the normal to the curve $y = e^{2x-4}$ at the point $(2, 1)$.

Q12 Find the equation of the normal to the curve $y = e^{3x} + 3$ where it cuts the y-axis.

Q13 Find the equation of the normal to the curve $y = e^{3(x-1)}$ when $x = 2$. Leave the numbers in your answer in exact form.

Q14 Show that the curve $y = e^{x^3 - 3x - 5}$ has stationary points at $x = \pm 1$.

Q15 Hint: To determine the nature of the turning point you need to look at the sign of $\frac{d^2y}{dx^2}$ at the turning point.

Q15 Find the x-coordinate of the turning point for the curve $y = e^{3x} - 6x$ and determine the nature of this point. Leave the numbers in your answer in exact form.

Differentiating ln x

The natural logarithm of a function is the logarithm with base e, written as ln x. Differentiating natural logarithms also uses the chain rule:

- If $y = \ln x$, then $x = e^y$ (see page 59).

Tip: Have a look back at page 72 for more on dx/dy.

- Differentiating gives $\frac{dx}{dy} = e^y$, and $\frac{dy}{dx} = \frac{1}{\left(\frac{dx}{dy}\right)} = \frac{1}{e^y} = \frac{1}{x}$ (since $x = e^y$).

- This gives the result:

$$y = \ln x$$
$$\frac{dy}{dx} = \frac{1}{x}$$

Find $\dfrac{dy}{dx}$ if $y = \ln (2x + 3)$.

- It's a function of a function, so use the **chain rule**:

  $$y = \ln (2x + 3), \text{ so let } y = \ln u \text{ where } u = 2x + 3$$

  $$\Rightarrow \frac{dy}{du} = \frac{1}{u} \text{ (p.76)} = \frac{1}{2x + 3} \text{ and } \frac{du}{dx} = 2$$

- Now put all the parts into the chain rule formula:

  $$\frac{dy}{dx} = \frac{dy}{du} \times \frac{du}{dx} = \frac{1}{2x + 3} \times 2 = \frac{2}{2x + 3}$$

Find $\dfrac{dy}{dx}$ if $y = \ln (x^2 + 3)$.

- Use the **chain rule** again for this one: $y = \ln u$ and $u = x^2 + 3$.

  $$\frac{dy}{du} = \frac{1}{u} = \frac{1}{x^2 + 3} \text{ and } \frac{du}{dx} = 2x.$$

  $$\Rightarrow \frac{dy}{dx} = \frac{dy}{du} \times \frac{du}{dx} = \frac{1}{x^2 + 3} \times 2x = \frac{2x}{x^2 + 3}$$

- Look at the final answer from those examples. It comes out to $\dfrac{f'(x)}{f(x)}$.

- This isn't a coincidence — it will always be the case for $y = \ln (f(x))$, so you can just learn the result:

$$\boxed{\begin{array}{c} y = \ln (f(x)) \\[4pt] \dfrac{dy}{dx} = \dfrac{f'(x)}{f(x)} \end{array}}$$

Example

Find f′(x) if f(x) = ln (x³ – 4x).

- f(x) is in the form ln (g(x)), so use the formula above:

  $$f'(x) = \frac{g'(x)}{g(x)}$$

  $$g(x) = x^3 - 4x \quad \Rightarrow \quad g'(x) = 3x^2 - 4$$

- Put this into the formula:

  $$f(x) = \ln (x^3 - 4x) \quad \Rightarrow \quad f'(x) = \frac{g'(x)}{g(x)} = \frac{3x^2 - 4}{x^3 - 4x}$$

Tip: You can check this answer using the chain rule, like in the previous example.

Q1 Differentiate with respect to x:

    a) $y = \ln(3x)$ b) $y = 3\ln x$ c) $y = \ln(1 + x)$

    d) $y = \ln(5 + x)$ e) $y = \ln(1 + 5x)$ f) $y = 4\ln(4x - 2)$

Q2 Hint: It might help to simplify the logs before differentiating them.

Q2 Differentiate with respect to x:

    a) $y = \ln(1 + x^2)$ b) $y = \ln(4 - 2x^2)$ c) $y = \ln(2 + x)^2$

    d) $y = 3\ln x^3$ e) $y = 2\ln(3x^2 + 3x)$ f) $y = \ln(x^3 + x^2)$

Q3 Find $f'(x)$ if $f(x) = \ln \dfrac{1}{x}$.

Q4 Find $f'(x)$ if $f(x) = \ln \sqrt{x}$.

Q5-9 Hint: You'll need to rewrite some of these questions as the sum or difference of two logarithms before differentiating them. Log rules were covered in Chapter 3 if you need a reminder.

Q5 Find $f'(x)$ if $f(x) = \ln\left(\sqrt{\dfrac{1-x}{1+x}}\right)$.

Q6 Find $f'(x)$ if $f(x) = \ln\left((2x + 1)^2 \sqrt{x - 4}\right)$.

Q7 Find $f'(x)$ if $f(x) = \ln(x - \sqrt{x - 4})$.

Q8 Find $f'(x)$ if $f(x) = \ln\left(\dfrac{(3x + 1)^2}{\sqrt{2x + 1}}\right)$.

Q9 Differentiate $y = \ln(x\sqrt{x + 4})$.

Q10 Find the equation of the tangent to the curve $y = \ln(3x)$ at the point $(\frac{1}{3}, 0)$.

Q11 Find the equation of the tangent to the curve $y = \ln(3x)^2$:

    a) when $x = -2$ b) when $x = 2$

Q11, 12 Hint: Rewrite $\ln(f(x))^k$ as $k\ln(f(x))$ to make differentiation simpler.

Q12 Find the equation of the normal to the curve $y = \ln(x + 6)^2$:

    a) when $x = -3$ b) when $x = 0$

Q13 Find any stationary points for the curve $y = \ln(x^3 - 3x^2 + 3x)$.

3. Differentiation of Trig Functions

Trig functions are also pretty easy to differentiate once you learn the rules for sin, cos and tan. In this section you'll see how to differentiate trig functions and then use the chain rule to differentiate the more tricky ones.

Learning Objectives:

- Be able to differentiate sin, cos and tan.
- Be able to use the rules for differentiating trig functions in more complicated functions that require the chain rule.

Differentiating sin, cos and tan

- For **trigonometric functions** where the angle is measured in **radians** the following rules apply:

If $y =$	$\dfrac{dy}{dx} =$
$\sin x$	$\cos x$
$\cos x$	$-\sin x$
$\tan x$	$\sec^2 x$

- These equations can be combined with the **chain rule** to differentiate **more complicated** functions.

Tip: Remember that $\sec x = 1/\cos x$ — there's more about this on p.41.

Examples

Differentiate the following with respect to x:

a) $y = \cos (2x)$.

- Rewrite the function in 'chain rule notation':

$$y = \cos (2x), \quad \text{so let} \quad y = \cos u \ \text{where} \ u = 2x$$

$$\text{So } \frac{dy}{du} = -\sin u = -\sin (2x) \quad \text{and} \quad \frac{du}{dx} = 2$$

$$\frac{dy}{dx} = \frac{dy}{du} \times \frac{du}{dx} = \boxed{-2 \sin (2x)}$$

b) $y = 4 \sin (x^2 + 1)$.

- As before, work out which part needs to be u for the chain rule:

$$y = 4 \sin (x^2 + 1), \quad \text{so let} \quad y = 4 \sin u \ \text{where} \ u = x^2 + 1$$

$$\text{So } \frac{dy}{du} = 4 \cos u = 4 \cos (x^2 + 1) \quad \text{and} \quad \frac{du}{dx} = 2x$$

$$\frac{dy}{dx} = \frac{dy}{du} \times \frac{du}{dx} = 4 \cos (x^2 + 1) \times 2x = \boxed{8x \cos (x^2 + 1)}$$

c) Find $\dfrac{dy}{dx}$ when $x = \tan (3y)$.

- First find $\dfrac{dx}{dy}$ with, you guessed it, the chain rule:

$$x = \tan u, \, u = 3y \quad \Rightarrow \quad \frac{dx}{du} = \sec^2 u = \sec^2 (3y) \text{ and } \frac{du}{dy} = 3$$

$$\frac{dx}{dy} = \frac{dx}{du} \times \frac{du}{dy} = 3 \sec^2 (3y)$$

Tip: Have a look back at page 72 for more on 1 / dx/dy.

- Then use $\dfrac{dy}{dx} = \dfrac{1}{\left(\dfrac{dx}{dy}\right)}$ to get the final answer:

$$\frac{dy}{dx} = \frac{1}{3\sec^2(3y)} = \frac{1}{3}\cos^2(3y)$$

Once you get the hang of it, you don't need to use the chain rule every time. If it's a **simple function** inside, e.g. sin (kx), it just differentiates to $k\cos(kx)$. If it's more **complicated** though, like sin (x^3), it's worth using the **chain rule**.

When differentiating trig functions it's important to know **which part of the function** to turn into u.

- It's **not** always the part **inside the brackets.**

Tip: Remember $\cos^2 x$ is another way of writing $(\cos x)^2$.

- When you have a trig function multiplied by itself, like $\cos^2 x$, it's often easiest to turn the **trig function itself** into u.

Example

Find $\dfrac{dy}{dx}$ if $y = \sin^3 x$.

- Start off by rewriting the function as $y = (\sin x)^3$

- Now you have a function of a function and can carry out the chain rule in exactly the same way as before:

$$y = (\sin x)^3, \quad \text{so let} \quad y = u^3 \text{ where } u = \sin x$$

Tip: Don't get $(\sin x)^3$ confused with $\sin x^3$ — for this, you'd take $u = x^3$, so end up with $3x^2 \cos x^3$ when you differentiate.

- Differentiate y and u:

$$y = u^3 \ \Rightarrow \ \frac{dy}{du} = 3u^2 = 3\sin^2 x \quad \text{and} \quad \frac{du}{dx} = \cos x$$

- Then put it all into the chain rule formula:

$$\frac{dy}{dx} = \frac{dy}{du} \times \frac{du}{dx} = 3\sin^2 x \cos x$$

When you're differentiating trig functions, you'll sometimes be asked to **rearrange** your answer to show it's equal to a **different** trig function. It's worth making sure you're familiar with **trig identities** (there are some on page 50, and in C2) so you can spot which ones to use and when to use them.

Example

For $y = \dfrac{1}{2}\tan^2 x$, show that $\dfrac{dy}{dx} = \tan x + \tan^3 x$.

- First rewrite the equation to make the chain rule easier to use:

$$y = \frac{1}{2}\tan^2 x \ \Rightarrow \ y = \frac{1}{2}(\tan x)^2$$

- Turn the tan x into u and differentiate y and u:

$$y = \frac{1}{2}u^2 \text{ where } u = \tan x \quad \Rightarrow \quad \frac{dy}{du} = u = \tan x, \frac{du}{dx} = \sec^2 x$$

- Putting it into the chain rule formula gives:

$$\frac{dy}{dx} = \tan x \sec^2 x$$

> **Tip:** Once you've got the derivative you need to play around with it and use the trig identities to get it in the form you're asked for in the question.

- From the target answer in the question it looks like you need to get rid of the $\sec^2 x$, so use the identity $\sec^2 x \equiv 1 + \tan^2 x$ (see page 50):

$$\tan x \sec^2 x \equiv \tan x (1 + \tan^2 x)$$

$$\Rightarrow \frac{dy}{dx} = \tan x (1 + \tan^2 x)$$

$$= \boxed{\tan x + \tan^3 x} \text{ as required.}$$

Exercise 3.1

Q1 Differentiate with respect to x:

a) $y = \sin (3x)$

b) $y = \cos (-2x)$

c) $y = \cos \frac{x}{2}$

d) $y = \sin \left(x + \frac{\pi}{4}\right)$

e) $y = 6 \tan \frac{x}{2}$

f) $y = 3 \tan (5x)$

Q2 Find $f'(x)$ if $f(x) = 3 \tan (2x - 1)$.

Q3 Find $f'(x)$ if $f(x) = 3 \tan x + \tan (3x)$.

Q4 Find $f'(x)$ if $f(x) = \sin (x^2 + \frac{\pi}{3})$.

Q5 Find $f'(x)$ if $f(x) = \sin^2 x$.

Q6 Find $f'(x)$ if $f(x) = 2 \sin^3 x$.

Q7 a) Find $f'(x)$ if $f(x) = 3 \sin x + 2 \cos x$.

b) Find the value of x for which $f'(x) = 0$ and $0 \leq x \leq \frac{\pi}{2}$.

Q8 Find $\frac{dy}{dx}$ if $y = \frac{1}{\cos x}$.

Q9 Differentiate $y = \cos^2 x$ using the chain rule.

Q10 Find the gradient of the curve $y = \sin x$ when $x = \frac{\pi}{4}$.

Q12 For the curve $x = \sin(2y)$:

    a) Find the equation of the tangent at the point $\left(\frac{\sqrt{3}}{2}, \frac{\pi}{6}\right)$.

    b) Find the equation of the normal at the point $\left(\frac{\sqrt{3}}{2}, \frac{\pi}{6}\right)$.

Differentiating by using the chain rule twice

Sometimes you'll have to use the chain rule **twice** when you have a function of a function of a function, like $\sin^3(x^2)$.

Example

Find $\frac{dy}{dx}$ if $y = \sin^2(2x + 1)$

- Start by setting up the first stage of differentiation with the **chain rule**, remembering to rewrite the $\sin^2$ part to make differentiating easier:
$$y = \sin^2(2x + 1) = [\sin(2x + 1)]^2 \quad \Rightarrow \quad y = u^2, \, u = \sin(2x + 1)$$

- Finding $\frac{dy}{du}$ is easy, so start with that:
$$\frac{dy}{du} = 2u = 2\sin(2x + 1)$$

- To find $\frac{du}{dx}$ you're going to need the **chain rule again**, so just set it up with u in terms of v instead of y in terms of u.
$$u = \sin(2x + 1) \quad \text{so let} \quad u = \sin v \quad \text{where} \quad v = 2x + 1$$

Tip: Calling it v just means you don't end up with a load of u's floating around.

- Then go through the usual stages:
$$u = \sin v \Rightarrow \frac{du}{dv} = \cos v = \cos(2x + 1)$$
$$v = 2x + 1 \Rightarrow \frac{dv}{dx} = 2$$
$$\frac{du}{dx} = \frac{du}{dv} \times \frac{dv}{dx} = 2\cos(2x + 1)$$

- Now you have the value of $\frac{du}{dx}$ needed to complete the question:
$$\frac{dy}{dx} = \frac{dy}{du} \times \frac{du}{dx} = [2\sin(2x + 1)] \times [2\cos(2x + 1)]$$
$$= 4\sin(2x + 1)\cos(2x + 1)$$

Exercise 3.2

Q1   Find $\frac{dy}{dx}$ if:

Q1 Hint: Differentiating e was covered on page 73 and differentiating ln was covered on page 76.

    a) $y = \sin(\cos(2x))$ b) $y = 2\ln(\cos(3x))$

    c) $y = \ln(\tan^2(x))$ d) $y = e^{\tan(2x)}$

    e) $y = \sin^4(x^2)$ f) $y = e^{\sin^2 x}$

    g) $y = \tan^2(3x) + \sin x$ h) $y = e^{2\cos(2x)} + \cos^2(2x)$

4. Product Rule

The product rule is a way of differentiating two functions multiplied together. It's fairly simple to use, but can get tricky when put together with other rules.

Differentiating functions multiplied together

To differentiate two functions multiplied together, use the **product rule**:

$$\text{If } y = uv$$
$$\frac{dy}{dx} = u\frac{dv}{dx} + v\frac{du}{dx}$$

Where u and v are functions of x, i.e. $u(x)$ and $v(x)$.

Proving this rule is a lot trickier than anything covered in this section (and you won't need to know how to do it in the exam), but it goes like this:

When you first met differentiation, it might have been shown in terms of limits:

$$f'(x) = \lim_{h \to 0} \frac{f(x + h) - f(x)}{h}$$

So when you have a product to differentiate, this can be written as:

$$(fg)'(x) = \lim_{h \to 0} \frac{fg(x + h) - fg(x)}{h} = \lim_{h \to 0} \frac{f(x + h)g(x + h) - f(x)g(x)}{h}$$

The numerator of this fraction can be seen as the area of a **rectangle** $f(x + h)$ by $g(x + h)$ minus the area of a **rectangle** $f(x)$ by $g(x)$. It can therefore be rewritten as a sum of the areas of the "extra bits" on the diagram:

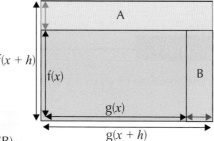

$$f(x + h)g(x + h) - f(x)g(x)$$
$$= \text{Area(A)} + \text{Area(B)}$$

$$\text{Area(A)} = g(x + h)[f(x + h) - f(x)] \qquad \text{Area(B)} = f(x)[g(x + h) - g(x)]$$

$$(fg)'(x) = \lim_{h \to 0} \left(\frac{g(x + h)[f(x + h) - f(x)] + f(x)[g(x + h) - g(x)]}{h} \right)$$

$$= \lim_{h \to 0} \left(\frac{g(x + h)[f(x + h) - f(x)]}{h} \right) + \lim_{h \to 0} \left(\frac{f(x)[g(x + h) - g(x)]}{h} \right)$$

As $h \to 0$, $x + h \to x$ so this bit is just $g(x)$.

This bit has no h's in it, so the limit as $h \to 0$ is just $f(x)$.

$$= \lim_{h \to 0}(g(x + h))\lim_{h \to 0}\left(\frac{f(x + h) - f(x)}{h}\right) + \lim_{h \to 0}(f(x))\lim_{h \to 0}\left(\frac{g(x + h) - g(x)}{h}\right)$$

$$= g(x)f'(x) + f(x)g'(x)$$

These are the definitions of $f'(x)$ and $g'(x)$.

Learning Objectives:

- Be able to use the product rule for differentiation and recognise when it's needed.

- Be able to use the product rule together with other rules for differentiation in order to differentiate more complicated functions.

Tip: The 'lim' notation means you take the value that the function approaches as h gets closer and closer to 0 — you might have seen it before in C1.

Tip: The length of the green arrow is $f(x + h) - f(x)$ and the length of the orange arrow is $g(x + h) - g(x)$.

Tip: $g(x)f'(x) + f(x)g'(x)$ is just another way of writing $u\frac{dv}{dx} + v\frac{du}{dx}$.

Differentiate $x^3 \tan x$ with respect to x.

- The crucial thing is to write down everything in **steps**. Start by identifying 'u' and 'v':

$$u = x^3 \text{ and } v = \tan x.$$

- Now differentiate these two **separately**, with respect to x:

$$\frac{du}{dx} = 3x^2 \text{ and } \frac{dv}{dx} = \sec^2 x.$$

- Very **carefully** put all the bits into the formula:

$$\frac{dy}{dx} = u\frac{dv}{dx} + v\frac{du}{dx} = (x^3 \times \sec^2 x) + (\tan x \times 3x^2)$$

- Finally, **rearrange** to make it look nicer:

$$\frac{dy}{dx} = x^3 \sec^2 x + 3x^2 \tan x$$

You might have to differentiate functions using a mixture of the **product rule** and the **chain rule** (as well as the rules for e, ln and trig functions).
In a question you might be told which rules to use, but it's not guaranteed, so make sure you get used to spotting when the different rules are needed.

Differentiate $e^{2x}\sqrt{2x - 3}$ with respect to x.

- It's a **product** of two functions, so start by identifying 'u' and 'v':

$$u = e^{2x} \text{ and } v = \sqrt{2x - 3}.$$

- Each of these needs the **chain rule** to differentiate:

$$\frac{du}{dx} = 2e^{2x} \text{ and } \frac{dv}{dx} = \frac{1}{\sqrt{2x - 3}}$$

- Put it all into the **product rule** formula:

$$\frac{dy}{dx} = u\frac{dv}{dx} + v\frac{du}{dx} = (e^{2x} \times \frac{1}{\sqrt{2x - 3}}) + (\sqrt{2x - 3} \times 2e^{2x})$$

- As before, **rearrange** it and then **simplify**:

$$\frac{dy}{dx} = e^{2x}\left(\frac{1}{\sqrt{2x - 3}} + 2(\sqrt{2x - 3})\right) = e^{2x}\left(\frac{1 + 2(2x - 3)}{\sqrt{2x - 3}}\right)$$

$$= \frac{e^{2x}(4x - 5)}{\sqrt{2x - 3}}$$

You'll also see questions that ask you to rearrange the final answer to 'show that' it's equal to something, or to solve an equation by differentiating.

Example 3

Show that the derivative of $x^2(2x - 1)^3$ is $2x(2x - 1)^2(5x - 1)$.

- As usual, **identify** u and v then differentiate them **separately**:

$$u = x^2 \text{ and } v = (2x - 1)^3$$

$$\Rightarrow \frac{du}{dx} = 2x \text{ and } \frac{dv}{dx} = 2 \times 3(2x - 1)^2 \text{ (using the chain rule for } \frac{dv}{dx})$$

- Then put it all into the **product rule formula**:

$$\frac{dy}{dx} = u\frac{dv}{dx} + v\frac{du}{dx} = [x^2 \times 6(2x - 1)^2] + [(2x - 1)^3 \times 2x] = 6x^2(2x - 1)^2 + 2x(2x - 1)^3$$

- This isn't exactly how the question wants the answer, so it needs a little more **rearranging**:

$$6x^2(2x - 1)^2 + 2x(2x - 1)^3 = 2x(2x - 1)^2(3x + (2x - 1))$$

$$= 2x(2x - 1)^2(5x - 1)$$

> **Tip:** In a 'show that' question it's good to look at the final answer so that you know you're on the right track. Here you can see you need to take out $2x(2x - 1)^2$ at some point, so it's worth starting with that.

Example 4

Solve the equation $\frac{d}{dx}[(x^3 + 3x^2)\ln x] = 2x^2 + 5x$, leaving your answer as an exact value of x.

- The $\frac{d}{dx}$ just tells you to differentiate the bit in brackets first. Since $(x^3 + 3x^2)\ln x$ is a **product** of two functions, use the **product rule**:

$$u = x^3 + 3x^2 \Rightarrow \frac{du}{dx} = 3x^2 + 6x \quad \text{and} \quad v = \ln x \Rightarrow \frac{dv}{dx} = \frac{1}{x} \text{ (see p.76)}$$

$$\text{So } \frac{d}{dx}((x^3 + 3x^2)\ln x) = [(x^3 + 3x^2) \times \frac{1}{x}] + [\ln x \times (3x^2 + 6x)]$$

$$= x^2 + 3x + (3x^2 + 6x)\ln x.$$

- Now put this into the equation from the question in place of $\frac{d}{dx}((x^3 + 3x^2)\ln x)$:

$$x^2 + 3x + (3x^2 + 6x)\ln x = 2x^2 + 5x$$

- Finally, rearrange and **solve** as follows:

$$(3x^2 + 6x)\ln x = 2x^2 + 5x - x^2 - 3x \Rightarrow (3x^2 + 6x)\ln x = x^2 + 2x$$

$$\Rightarrow \ln x = \frac{x^2 + 2x}{3(x^2 + 2x)} = \frac{1}{3}$$

$$\Rightarrow x = e^{\frac{1}{3}}$$

> **Tip:** The question asks for an exact value of x, so leave it in terms of e rather than a rounded decimal from your calculator.

Q1 Differentiate $y = x(x + 2)$ with respect to x by:

   a) Multiplying the brackets out and differentiating directly.

   b) Using the product rule.

Q2 Differentiate with respect to x:

   a) $y = x^2(x + 6)^3$

   b) $y = x^3(5x + 2)^4$

   c) $y = x^3e^x$

   d) $y = xe^{4x}$

   e) $y = xe^{x^2}$

   f) $y = e^{2x}\sin x$

Q3 b) Hint: Remember that $\dfrac{1}{\sqrt{x}} = x^{-\frac{1}{2}}$.

Q3 Find $f'(x)$ if:

   a) $f(x) = x^3(x + 3)^{\frac{1}{2}}$

   b) $f(x) = \dfrac{x^2}{\sqrt{x - 7}}$

   c) $f(x) = x^4\ln x$.

   d) $f(x) = 4x \ln x^2$.

   e) $f(x) = 2x^3 \cos x$

   f) $f(x) = x^2\cos(2x)$.

Q4 For parts a) and b), multiply out the brackets in your answer and simplify.

   a) Differentiate $y = (x + 1)^2(x^2 - 1)$.

   b) Differentiate $y = (x + 1)^3(x - 1)$.

   c) Your answers to part a) and part b) should be the same. Show by rearranging that the expressions for y in parts a) and b) are the same.

Q5 For the curve $y = xe^x$:

   a) Find the equation of the tangent to the curve at the point $(0, 0)$.

   b) Find the equation of the normal to the curve at the point $(0, 0)$.

Q6 Hint: Rewriting roots as powers can often help.

Q6 Find the equation of the tangent to the curve $y = (\sqrt{x + 2})(\sqrt{x + 7})$ at the point $(2, 6)$. Write your answer in the form $ax + by + c = 0$, where a, b and c are integers.

Q7 For the curve $y = \dfrac{\sqrt{x - 1}}{\sqrt{x + 4}}$

   a) Find the equation of the tangent to the curve when $x = 5$ in the form $ax + by + c = 0$ where a, b and c are integers.

   b) Find the equation of the normal to the curve when $x = 5$ in the form $ax + by + c = 0$ where a, b and c are integers.

Q8 Find any stationary points of the curve $y = (x - 2)^2(x + 4)^3$.

Q9 Hint: You'll need to use the chain rule before using the product rule.

Q9 Differentiate $y = e^{x^2\sqrt{x + 3}}$.

Q10 Find any stationary points for the curve $y = xe^{x - x^2}$.

5. Quotient Rule

You've seen how to differentiate products with the product rule, and now you'll see how to differentiate quotients (divisions) with the quotient rule.

Differentiating a function divided by a function

In maths a **quotient** is one thing **divided** by another. As with the product rule, there's a rule that lets you differentiate quotients easily — the **quotient rule**:

If $y = \dfrac{u}{v}$

$$\frac{dy}{dx} = \frac{v\dfrac{du}{dx} - u\dfrac{dv}{dx}}{v^2}$$

Where u and v are functions of x, i.e. $u(x)$ and $v(x)$.

There's also a proof for the quotient rule — again you won't need to know it for the exam, but you might find it helpful in understanding how it works.

- As before, start with the definition of differentiation.

$$\frac{d}{dx}f(x) = \lim_{h \to 0} \frac{f(x+h) - f(x)}{h}$$

- And so for the quotient $\dfrac{f(x)}{g(x)}$, this becomes

$$\frac{d}{dx}\left(\frac{f(x)}{g(x)}\right) = \lim_{h \to 0} \frac{\dfrac{f(x+h)}{g(x+h)} - \dfrac{f(x)}{g(x)}}{h}$$

- To neaten this up, put the top of the fraction over a common denominator $(g(x+h)g(x))$ and multiply this common denominator by the h.

$$\frac{d}{dx}\left(\frac{f(x)}{g(x)}\right) = \lim_{h \to 0} \frac{f(x+h)g(x) - f(x)g(x+h)}{g(x+h)g(x)h}$$

- The next stage is to add and subtract $f(x)g(x)$ and then factorise.

$$\frac{d}{dx}\left(\frac{f(x)}{g(x)}\right) = \lim_{h \to 0} \frac{f(x+h)g(x) - f(x)g(x) + f(x)g(x) - f(x)g(x+h)}{g(x+h)g(x)h}$$

$$\frac{d}{dx}\left(\frac{f(x)}{g(x)}\right) = \lim_{h \to 0} \frac{g(x)[f(x+h) - f(x)] - f(x)[g(x+h) - g(x)]}{g(x+h)g(x)h}$$

- You might start to recognise the top row here. Just to make it a little clearer, divide both the top and bottom by h, keeping $f(x)$ and $g(x)$ aside.

$$\frac{d}{dx}\left(\frac{f(x)}{g(x)}\right) = \lim_{h \to 0} \frac{g(x)\dfrac{f(x+h) - f(x)}{h} - f(x)\dfrac{g(x+h) - g(x)}{h}}{g(x+h)g(x)}$$

- The green bits on top are the definition of $f'(x)$ and $g'(x)$ from the start of this proof. As h tends to zero, the blue bit at the bottom becomes $g(x)g(x)$, or $(g(x))^2$:

$$\frac{d}{dx}\left(\frac{f(x)}{g(x)}\right) = \frac{g(x)f'(x) - f(x)g'(x)}{(g(x))^2}$$

Learning Objectives:

- Be able to use the quotient rule for differentiation and understand when it's needed.

- Be able to use the quotient rule alongside other methods for differentiating complex functions.

Tip: The quotient rule is basically just the product rule on $y = uv^{-1}$ — try it on two simple functions and see for yourself. The quotient rule is quicker to use though, and it's provided on the formula sheet.

Tip: Adding and subtracting the same thing is a classic trick in algebra. It's just like adding zero, and it can get you from algebraic mess to perfectly formed expressions.

Tip: The expression
$$\frac{g(x)f'(x) - f(x)g'(x)}{(g(x))^2}$$
is just another way of writing the quotient rule
$$\frac{v\dfrac{du}{dx} - u\dfrac{dv}{dx}}{v^2}.$$

Example 1

Find $\dfrac{dy}{dx}$ if $y = \dfrac{\sin x}{2x + 1}$.

- You can see that y is a **quotient** in the form of $\dfrac{u}{v}$.
  First identify u and v and differentiate them **separately**:

$$u = \sin x \;\Rightarrow\; \frac{du}{dx} = \cos x \quad \text{and} \quad v = 2x + 1 \;\Rightarrow\; \frac{dv}{dx} = 2$$

- Then just put the correct bits into the quotient rule. It's important that you get things in the right order, so concentrate on what's going where:

$$\frac{dy}{dx} = \frac{v\dfrac{du}{dx} - u\dfrac{dv}{dx}}{v^2} = \frac{(2x + 1)(\cos x) - (\sin x)(2)}{(2x + 1)^2}$$

- Now just neaten it up:

$$\frac{dy}{dx} = \frac{(2x + 1)\cos x - 2\sin x}{(2x + 1)^2}$$

Example 2

Find the gradient of the tangent to the curve with equation $y = \dfrac{2x^2 - 1}{3x^2 + 1}$ at the point $(1, 0.25)$.

- 'Find the gradient of the tangent' means you have to **differentiate**.

- First identify u and v for the **quotient** rule, and differentiate **separately**:

$$u = 2x^2 - 1 \;\Rightarrow\; \frac{du}{dx} = 4x \quad \text{and} \quad v = 3x^2 + 1 \;\Rightarrow\; \frac{dv}{dx} = 6x$$

- Then put everything into the quotient rule:

$$\frac{dy}{dx} = \frac{v\dfrac{du}{dx} - u\dfrac{dv}{dx}}{v^2} = \frac{(3x^2 + 1)(4x) - (2x^2 - 1)(6x)}{(3x^2 + 1)^2}$$

- To make the expression **easier** to work with, **simplify** it where possible:

$$\frac{dy}{dx} = \frac{2x[2(3x^2 + 1) - 3(2x^2 - 1)]}{(3x^2 + 1)^2} = \frac{2x[6x^2 + 2 - 6x^2 + 3]}{(3x^2 + 1)^2}$$

$$= \frac{10x}{(3x^2 + 1)^2}$$

- Finally, put in $x = 1$ to find the gradient at $(1, 0.25)$:

$$\frac{dy}{dx} = \frac{10}{(3 + 1)^2} = 0.625$$

Example 3

Determine the nature of the stationary point of the curve $y = \dfrac{\ln x}{x^2}$ $(x > 0)$.

Tip: To determine the nature of the stationary points you're going to have to differentiate twice.

- First use the quotient rule to find $\dfrac{dy}{dx}$:

$$u = \ln x \Rightarrow \frac{du}{dx} = \frac{1}{x} \quad \text{and} \quad v = x^2 \Rightarrow \frac{dv}{dx} = 2x.$$

So $\dfrac{dy}{dx} = \dfrac{(x^2)(\frac{1}{x}) - (\ln x)(2x)}{x^4} = \dfrac{x - 2x\ln x}{x^4} = \dfrac{1 - 2\ln x}{x^3}$.

- The stationary points occur where $\dfrac{dy}{dx} = 0$ (i.e. zero gradient), so this is when:

$$\frac{1 - 2\ln x}{x^3} = 0 \Rightarrow \ln x = \frac{1}{2} \Rightarrow x = e^{\frac{1}{2}}.$$

- To find out whether it's a maximum or minimum, differentiate $\dfrac{1 - 2\ln x}{x^3}$ using the quotient rule to get $\dfrac{d^2y}{dx^2}$.

$$u = 1 - 2\ln x \Rightarrow \frac{du}{dx} = -\frac{2}{x} \quad \text{and} \quad v = x^3 \Rightarrow \frac{dv}{dx} = 3x^2.$$

So $\dfrac{d^2y}{dx^2} = \dfrac{(x^3)(-\frac{2}{x}) - (1 - 2\ln x)(3x^2)}{x^6} = \dfrac{6x^2\ln x - 5x^2}{x^6} = \dfrac{6\ln x - 5}{x^4}$

- Now put in the x-value of your stationary point:

$$\frac{d^2y}{dx^2} = \frac{6\ln e^{\frac{1}{2}} - 5}{(e^{\frac{1}{2}})^4} = \frac{3 - 5}{e^2} = -0.27...$$

Tip: Negative second derivative means maximum and positive means minimum — it's covered in C1 if you can't quite remember.

- $\dfrac{d^2y}{dx^2}$ is negative, so it's a maximum turning point.

As you saw on page 79, the derivative of $\tan x$ is $\sec^2 x$.
Because $\tan x = \dfrac{\sin x}{\cos x}$, you can prove this using the quotient rule.

Example 4

Differentiate $y = \tan x$ with respect to x.

- First write it out as a quotient and set up u and v for the quotient rule:

$$y = \frac{\sin x}{\cos x} = \frac{u}{v}, \text{ so } u = \sin x, \frac{du}{dx} = \cos x \text{ and } v = \cos x, \frac{dv}{dx} = -\sin x$$

- Then just put all the right bits into the quotient rule:

$$\frac{dy}{dx} = \frac{v\frac{du}{dx} - u\frac{dv}{dx}}{v^2} = \frac{\cos x \cos x - \sin x(-\sin x)}{\cos^2 x} = \frac{\cos^2 x + \sin^2 x}{\cos^2 x}$$

$$= \frac{1}{\cos^2 x} = \sec^2 x$$

Tip: The identity $\cos^2 x + \sin^2 x \equiv 1$ was used here to simplify.

Q1 Differentiate with respect to x:

  a) $y = \dfrac{(x + 5)}{(x - 3)}$

  b) $y = \dfrac{(x - 7)^4}{(5 - x)^3}$

  c) $y = \dfrac{e^x}{x^2}$

  d) $y = \dfrac{3x}{(x - 1)^2}$

Q2 Find $f'(x)$ if $f(x) = \dfrac{x^3}{(x + 3)^3}$

Q3 Find $f'(x)$ if $f(x) = \dfrac{x^2}{\sqrt{x - 7}}$

Q4 Find $f'(x)$ if $f(x) = \dfrac{e^{2x}}{e^{2x} + e^{-2x}}$

Q5 Find $f'(x)$ if $f(x) = \dfrac{x}{\sin x}$

Q6 Find $f'(x)$ if $f(x) = \dfrac{\sin x}{x}$

Q7 Find $f'(x)$ if $f(x) = \dfrac{x^2}{\tan x}$,
    giving your answer in terms of $\cot x$ and $\csc x$.

Q8 a) Differentiate $y = \dfrac{x}{\cos (2x)}$

   b) Show that $\dfrac{dy}{dx} = 0$ when $x = -\dfrac{1}{2}\cot (2x)$
      (don't try to solve this equation).

Q9 For the curve $y = \dfrac{1}{1 + 4\cos x}$:

   a) Find the equation of the tangent to the curve when $x = \dfrac{\pi}{2}$.

   b) Find the equation of the normal to the curve when $x = \dfrac{\pi}{2}$.

Q10 For the curve $y = \dfrac{2x}{\cos x}$, find the exact value of $\dfrac{dy}{dx}$ when $x = \dfrac{\pi}{3}$.

Q11 Show that if $y = \dfrac{x - \sin x}{1 + \cos x}$ then $\dfrac{dy}{dx} = \dfrac{x\sin x}{(1 + \cos x)^2}$.

Q12 Find any stationary points on the curve $y = \dfrac{\cos x}{4 - 3\cos x}$
     in the range $0 \le x \le 2\pi$.

Q13 Differentiate $y = e^{\frac{1+x}{1-x}}$

6. More Differentiation

In this section you'll see how to differentiate reciprocals of trig functions —
sec x, cosec x and cot x. All of these can be derived from the quotient rule.

Learning Objectives:

- Be able to differentiate cosec, sec and cot.
- Be able to use these results to differentiate more complicated functions.

Differentiating cosec, sec and cot

Remember from page 41 the definitions of these trig functions:

$$\operatorname{cosec} x \equiv \frac{1}{\sin x} \qquad \sec x \equiv \frac{1}{\cos x} \qquad \cot x \equiv \frac{1}{\tan x} \equiv \frac{\cos x}{\sin x}$$

- Since **cosec**, **sec** and **cot** are just **reciprocals** of **sin**, **cos** and **tan**, the quotient rule can be used to differentiate them.

- These results are on the **formula sheet**, but it will help a lot if you can show where they come from.

If y =	$\dfrac{dy}{dx} =$
cosec x	$-\operatorname{cosec} x \cot x$
sec x	$\sec x \tan x$
cot x	$-\operatorname{cosec}^2 x$

Tip: If you can't remember which trig functions give a negative result when you differentiate them, just remember it's all the ones that begin with c — cos, cosec and cot.

Examples

Use the quotient rule to differentiate $y = \dfrac{\cos x}{\sin x}$, and hence show that for $y = \cot x$, $\dfrac{dy}{dx} = -\operatorname{cosec}^2 x$.

- Start off by identifying $u = \cos x$ and $v = \sin x$.

- Differentiating separately gives:

$$\frac{du}{dx} = -\sin x \ \text{ and } \ \frac{dv}{dx} = \cos x \ (\text{see page 79})$$

$$\frac{dy}{dx} = \frac{(\sin x \times -\sin x) - (\cos x \times \cos x)}{(\sin x)^2} = \frac{-\sin^2 x - \cos^2 x}{\sin^2 x}$$

- Simplify using a trig identity: $\sin^2 x + \cos^2 x \equiv 1$ seems fitting.

$$\frac{dy}{dx} = \frac{-(\sin^2 x + \cos^2 x)}{\sin^2 x} = \frac{-1}{\sin^2 x}.$$

Tip: 'Show that' questions on trig functions often involve using a common identity, so make sure you know them — see page 50, and look back at C2.

- Linking this back to the question, since $\tan x \equiv \dfrac{\sin x}{\cos x}$, and $\cot x \equiv \dfrac{1}{\tan x}$, then $y = \dfrac{\cos x}{\sin x} = \cot x$.

- And as $\operatorname{cosec} x \equiv \dfrac{1}{\sin x}$, then:

$$\frac{dy}{dx} = \frac{-1}{\sin^2 x} = -\operatorname{cosec}^2 x.$$

Tip: You could also use the chain rule on $\dfrac{1}{\sin x} = (\sin x)^{-1}$.

Show that $\dfrac{d}{dx}\operatorname{cosec} x = -\operatorname{cosec} x \cot x$.

- $\operatorname{cosec} x \equiv \dfrac{1}{\sin x}$, so use the **quotient rule**:

$$u = 1 \ \Rightarrow \ \frac{du}{dx} = 0 \ \text{ and } \ v = \sin x \ \Rightarrow \ \frac{dv}{dx} = \cos x$$

$$\frac{dy}{dx} = \frac{v\frac{du}{dx} - u\frac{dv}{dx}}{v^2} = \frac{(\sin x \times 0) - (1 \times \cos x)}{\sin^2 x} = -\frac{\cos x}{\sin^2 x}$$

- Since $\cot x \equiv \dfrac{\cos x}{\sin x}$, and $\operatorname{cosec} x \equiv \dfrac{1}{\sin x}$:

$$\frac{dy}{dx} = \frac{1}{\sin x} \times \left(-\frac{\cos x}{\sin x}\right) = -\operatorname{cosec} x \cot x.$$

Show that $\dfrac{d}{dx}\sec x = \sec x \tan x$.

- Using the quotient rule for $\sec x \equiv \dfrac{1}{\cos x}$:

$$u = 1 \ \Rightarrow \ \frac{du}{dx} = 0 \ \text{ and } \ v = \cos x \ \Rightarrow \ \frac{dv}{dx} = -\sin x$$

$$\frac{dy}{dx} = \frac{v\frac{du}{dx} - u\frac{dv}{dx}}{v^2} = \frac{(\cos x \times 0) - (1 \times -\sin x)}{\cos^2 x} = \frac{\sin x}{\cos^2 x}$$

- Since $\tan x \equiv \dfrac{\sin x}{\cos x}$, and $\sec x \equiv \dfrac{1}{\cos x}$,

$$\frac{dy}{dx} = \frac{1}{\cos x} \times \frac{\sin x}{\cos x} = \sec x \tan x.$$

As with other rules covered in this chapter, the rules for $\sec x$, $\operatorname{cosec} x$ and $\cot x$ can be used with the **chain**, **product** and **quotient rules** and in combination with all the other functions you've seen so far.

Examples

Find $\dfrac{dy}{dx}$ **if** $y = \cot \dfrac{x}{2}$.

- This is a function (cot) of a function ($\frac{x}{2}$), so you're going to need the chain rule.

- Although $\cot x \equiv \dfrac{\cos x}{\sin x}$, you don't need the quotient rule as you know that $\cot x$ differentiates to give $-\operatorname{cosec}^2 x$.

- You can go straight to identifying u to use in the chain rule:

$$y = \cot u \ \Rightarrow \ \frac{dy}{du} = -\operatorname{cosec}^2 u = -\operatorname{cosec}^2 \frac{x}{2}$$

$$u = \frac{x}{2} \ \Rightarrow \ \frac{du}{dx} = \frac{1}{2}$$

$$\Rightarrow \frac{dy}{dx} = \frac{dy}{du} \times \frac{du}{dx} = -\frac{1}{2}\operatorname{cosec}^2\frac{x}{2}$$

Find $\dfrac{\mathrm{d}y}{\mathrm{d}x}$ if $y = \sec(2x^2)$.

This is another **function of a function**, so more chain rule:

$$y = \sec u \ \text{ and } \ u = 2x^2$$

$$\dfrac{\mathrm{d}y}{\mathrm{d}u} = \sec u \tan u \ (\text{from page 91}) = \sec(2x^2)\tan(2x^2)$$

$$\dfrac{\mathrm{d}u}{\mathrm{d}x} = 4x$$

$$\text{So } \dfrac{\mathrm{d}y}{\mathrm{d}x} = \dfrac{\mathrm{d}y}{\mathrm{d}u} \times \dfrac{\mathrm{d}u}{\mathrm{d}x} = 4x\sec(2x^2)\tan(2x^2)$$

Find $\dfrac{\mathrm{d}y}{\mathrm{d}x}$ if $y = \mathrm{e}^x \cot x.$

This is a **product** of two functions, so think 'product rule':

$$u = \mathrm{e}^x \ \text{ and } \ v = \cot x$$

$$\Rightarrow \ \dfrac{\mathrm{d}u}{\mathrm{d}x} = \mathrm{e}^x \text{ and } \dfrac{\mathrm{d}v}{\mathrm{d}x} = -\mathrm{cosec}^2\, x \ (\text{see page 91})$$

$$\Rightarrow \ \dfrac{\mathrm{d}y}{\mathrm{d}x} = u\dfrac{\mathrm{d}v}{\mathrm{d}x} + v\dfrac{\mathrm{d}u}{\mathrm{d}x} = (\mathrm{e}^x \times -\mathrm{cosec}^2\, x) + (\cot x \times \mathrm{e}^x)$$

$$= \mathrm{e}^x(\cot x - \mathrm{cosec}^2\, x).$$

Tip: If it was a more difficult function than x inside the 'cot', you'd do this in exactly the same way but use the chain rule for working out $\dfrac{\mathrm{d}v}{\mathrm{d}x}$.

Exercise 6.1

Q1 Differentiate with respect to x:

a) $y = \mathrm{cosec}\,(2x)$ b) $y = \mathrm{cosec}^2\, x$ c) $y = \cot(7x)$

d) $y = \cot^7 x$ e) $y = x^4 \cot x$ f) $y = (x + \sec x)^2$

g) $y = \mathrm{cosec}\,(x^2 + 5)$ h) $y = \mathrm{e}^{3x}\sec x$ i) $y = (2x + \cot x)^3$

Q2 Find $\mathrm{f}'(x)$ if $\mathrm{f}(x) = \dfrac{\sec x}{x + 3}.$

Q3 Find $\mathrm{f}'(x)$ if $\mathrm{f}(x) = \sec \dfrac{1}{x}.$

Q4 Find $\mathrm{f}'(x)$ if $\mathrm{f}(x) = \sec \sqrt{x}\,.$

Q5 Find $\mathrm{f}'(x)$ if $\mathrm{f}(x) = (\sec x + \mathrm{cosec}\, x)^2.$

Q6 Find $\mathrm{f}'(x)$ if $\mathrm{f}(x) = \dfrac{1}{x \cot x}.$

Q7 Find $f'(x)$ if $f(x) = e^x \operatorname{cosec} x$.

Q8 Find $f'(x)$ if $f(x) = e^{3x} \sec x$.

Q9 Find $f'(x)$ if $f(x) = e^{3x} \cot (4x)$.

Q10 Find $f'(x)$ if $f(x) = e^{-2x} \operatorname{cosec} (4x)$.

Q11 Find $f'(x)$ if $f(x) = \ln (x) \operatorname{cosec} x$.

Q12 Find $f'(x)$ if $f(x) = \sqrt{\sec x}$.

Q13 Find $f'(x)$ if $f(x) = e^{\sec x}$.

Q14 a) Find $f'(x)$ if $f(x) = \ln (\operatorname{cosec} x)$.

b) Show that the function in part a) can be written as $-\ln (\sin x)$ and differentiate it — you should get the same answer as in part a).

Q14 Hint: Remember the log laws from p.62.

Q15 Find $f'(x)$ if $f(x) = \ln (x + \sec x)$.

Q16 Differentiate $y = \sec (\sqrt{x^2 + 5})$.

Review Exercise — Chapter 4

Q1 State which (if any) of the chain, product and quotient rules could be used to differentiate the following functions (don't actually differentiate them):

a) $f(x) = e^{2x}$

b) $f(x) = \sin x \cos x$

c) $f(x) = \sin x \cos x^2$

d) $f(x) = \dfrac{\ln (8x)}{(x + 1)^2}$

e) $f(x) = \dfrac{e^x}{x^2 \cos^2 x}$

f) $f(x) = \dfrac{\sin x^2}{\cos (2x) \ln x^3}$

Q1 Hint: Some of these functions could be differentiated in more than one way — write down all the rules that could be used.

Q2 Differentiate with respect to x:

a) $y = \sqrt{x^3 + 2x^2}$

b) $y = \dfrac{1}{\sqrt{x^3 + 2x^2}}$

c) $y = e^{5x^2}$

d) $y = \ln (6 - x^2)$

Q3 Find $\dfrac{dy}{dx}$ as a function of x when:

a) $x = 2e^{2y}$

b) $x = \ln (2y + 3)$

Q3 b) Hint: Remember, if $x = \ln a$ then $a = e^x$.

Q4 Find $f'(x)$ for the following functions:

a) $f(x) = \sin^2 (x + 2)$

b) $f(x) = 2\cos (3x)$

c) $f(x) = \sqrt{\tan x}$

Q5 Find the value of the gradient for:

a) $y = e^{2x}(x^2 - 3)$ when $x = 0$

b) $y = (\ln x)(\sin x)$ when $x = 1$

Q6 Find the equation of the tangent to the curve $y = \dfrac{6x^2 + 3}{4x^2 - 1}$ at the point $(1, 3)$.

Q7 Differentiate with respect to x:

a) $y = \sqrt{\operatorname{cosec} x}$

b) $y = \cot (x^2 + 5)$

c) $y = \dfrac{\sec x}{x^2}$

d) $y = e^{2x} \operatorname{cosec} (5x)$

Q8 Find $\dfrac{dy}{dx}$ when $x = 0$ for $y = \operatorname{cosec} (3x - 2)$.

Q9 Find the coordinates of the stationary point on the curve $y = \dfrac{e^x}{\sqrt{x}}$.

Q10 Find the equation of the normal to the curve

$y = 3 \operatorname{cosec} \frac{x}{4}$ when $x = \pi$ (x is in radians)

Q11 Find $f'(x)$ if $f(x) = e^{\cos (3x)}$.

Q12 Find $f'(x)$ if $f(x) = \dfrac{\cos x^2}{\ln (2x)}$.

Q13 Find $f'(x)$ if $f(x) = \sin (4x) \tan x^3$.

Q14 Find $\dfrac{dy}{dx}$ when $x = 1$ if $y = e^{x^2} \sqrt{x + 1}$.

Q15 Differentiate the following with respect to x.

a) $\sqrt{(e^x + e^{2x})}$.

b) $3e^{2x+1} - \ln (1 - x^2) + 2x^3$.

Q16 A curve C has the equation $y = (x^2 - 1)^3$

a) Differentiate y with respect to x.

b) Hence find the equation of the normal to the curve C when $x = 2$ in the form $ax + by + c = 0$, where a, b, and c are integers.

Q17 Differentiate with respect to x:

a) $y = \cos x \ln x^2$

b) $y = \dfrac{e^{x^2 - x}}{(x + 2)^4}$

Q18 Find $\dfrac{dy}{dx}$ if $y = \dfrac{\sqrt{x^2 + 3}}{\cos 3x}$.

Exam-Style Questions — Chapter 4

1   Find $\dfrac{dy}{dx}$ for each of the following functions. Simplify your answer where possible.

     a) $y = \ln(3x + 1)\sin(3x + 1)$.

                                                     (4 marks)

     b) $y = \sin^3(2x^2)$

                                                     (3 marks)

     c) $y = 2\operatorname{cosec}(3x)$

                                                     (2 marks)

2   Use the quotient rule to show that, for the function $f(x) = \sec x$:

$$f'(x) = \sec x \tan x.$$

                                                     (4 marks)

3   A sketch of the function $f(x) = 4\ln(3x)$ is shown in the diagram.

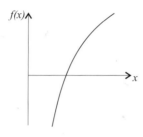

     a)   Find $f'(x)$ at the point where $x = 1$.

                                                     (3 marks)

     b)   Find the equation of the tangent to the curve at the point $x = 1$.

                                                     (3 marks)

4   A curve with equation $y = e^x \sin x$ has two turning points in the interval $-\pi \le x \le \pi$.

     a)   Find the value of x at each of these turning points.

                                                     (6 marks)

     b)   Determine the nature of each of the turning points.

                                                     (5 marks)

5   The curve shown below has the equation $x = \sqrt{y^2 + 3y}$.

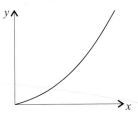

a)   Find $\dfrac{dy}{dx}$ at the point (2, 1).   *(5 marks)*

b)   Hence find the equation of the tangent to the curve at (2, 1), in the form
     $y = ax + b$, where a and b are constants.   *(2 marks)*

6   Differentiate the following with respect to x.

a) $\sqrt{(e^x + e^{2x})}$.   *(3 marks)*

b) $3e^{2x+1} - \ln(1 - x^2) + 2x^3$.   *(3 marks)*

7   Find the gradient of the tangent to the curve:
$$y = \sin^2 x - 2\cos(2x)$$
at the point where $x = \dfrac{\pi}{6}$ radians.   *(4 marks)*

8   Given that $y = \dfrac{e^x + x}{e^x - x}$, find $\dfrac{dy}{dx}$ when $x = 0$.   *(3 marks)*

9   Find the equation of the normal to the curve $x = \sin(4y)$ that passes through the point $\left(0, \dfrac{\pi}{4}\right)$.
     Give your answer in the form $y = mx + c$, where m and c are constants to be found.
                                                                            (6 marks)

1. Integration of $(ax + b)^n$

You've already seen how to integrate functions of the form x^n in C1 and C2. In this section you'll see how to integrate functions which are linear transformations of x^n — functions of the form $(ax + b)^n$.

Integrating $(ax + b)^n$, $n \neq -1$

In C1, you learnt to think of **integration** as the **opposite of differentiation**. This means that if you differentiate a function, then **integrating** the result will get you back to the function you started with. Here are a few examples to show how you can use this technique to integrate functions of the form $(ax + b)^n$.

Example 1

a) **Differentiate $(3x + 4)^5$ with respect to x.**

Using the **chain rule**, $\frac{d}{dx}(3x + 4)^5 = 5(3x + 4)^4 \times 3 = \boxed{15(3x + 4)^4}$.

b) **Use your answer to a) to find $\int (3x + 4)^4 \, dx$.**

- From part a) you know that:

$$(3x + 4)^5 \xrightarrow{\text{Differentiation}} 15(3x + 4)^4$$

- Integration is the **opposite of differentiation** so:

$$(3x + 4)^5 + C \xleftarrow{\text{Integration}} 15(3x + 4)^4$$

This means:

$$\int 15(3x + 4)^4 \, dx = (3x + 4)^5 + c$$

$$\Rightarrow 15 \int (3x + 4)^4 \, dx = (3x + 4)^5 + c$$

$$\Rightarrow \int (3x + 4)^4 \, dx = \frac{1}{15}(3x + 4)^5 + \frac{C}{15}$$

$$= \frac{1}{15}(3x + 4)^5 + C$$

Divide by the constant term to get the integral you're after.

$\frac{C}{15}$ is just another constant term — you can call it C.

Tip: The **chain rule** (see p.69) is used to differentiate a function of a function $f(g(x))$: If $y = f(u)$ and $u = g(x)$ then:

$$\frac{dy}{dx} = \frac{dy}{du} \times \frac{du}{dx}$$

Tip: Don't forget that for indefinite integrals (integrals without limits) you need to add a constant of integration, C.

Tip: You can take constant factors outside of integrations and put them at the front to make things easier (see C1).

Example 2

Given that $\frac{d}{dx}((2x - 3)^{-3}) = -6(2x - 3)^{-4}$, find $\int (2x - 3)^{-4} \, dx$.

Use the same method as above:

- $(2x - 3)^{-3}$ differentiates to give $-6(2x - 3)^{-4}$.
- So $\int -6(2x - 3)^{-4} \, dx = (2x - 3)^{-3} + c$

$$-6 \int (2x - 3)^{-4} \, dx = (2x - 3)^{-3} + c$$

$$\int (2x - 3)^{-4} \, dx = -\frac{1}{6}(2x - 3)^{-3} + C$$

Taking the constant out.

Dividing by –6.

This method gives us a **general result** for integrating all functions of the form $(ax + b)^n$.

Tip: This doesn't work for $n = -1$ because you'd end up having to divide by $n + 1 = 0$. See page 104 for a method of integrating x^{-1} and $(ax + b)^{-1}$.

Differentiating $(ax + b)^{n+1}$ using the chain rule gives $a(n + 1)(ax + b)^n$.

So
$$\int a(n + 1)(ax + b)^n \, dx = (ax + b)^{n+1} + c$$
$$a(n + 1) \int (ax + b)^n \, dx = (ax + b)^{n+1} + c$$

Dividing by $a(n + 1)$ gives the general expression:

$$\int (ax + b)^n \, dx = \frac{1}{a(n + 1)}(ax + b)^{n+1} + C$$

Examples

Find the following integrals using the general expression for $\int (ax + b)^n \, dx$:

a) $\int (3 - 4x)^2 \, dx$

Write down the values of a, b and n and then substitute them into the formula. Here $a = -4$, $b = 3$ and $n = 2$.

$$\int (3 - 4x)^2 \, dx = \frac{1}{-4 \times 3}(3 - 4x)^3 + C = -\frac{1}{12}(3 - 4x)^3 + C$$

$a = -4$ $n + 1 = 3$

Tip: You can always differentiate your answer to check it — you should get back to what you started with.

b) $\int (3x - 2)^{-2} \, dx$

Here $a = 3$, $b = -2$ and $n = -2$, so substitute these values into the formula.

$$\int (3x - 2)^{-2} \, dx = \frac{1}{3 \times -1}(3x - 2)^{-1} + C = -\frac{1}{3}(3x - 2)^{-1} + C$$

$a = 3$ $n + 1 = -1$

$$= -\frac{1}{3(3x - 2)} + C$$

c) $\int_4^{12} (2x + 1)^{\frac{1}{2}} \, dx$

This is a **definite integral** — it has limits, so your answer will be a **number** and you don't need to bother with the **constant of integration**.

Here $a = 2$, $b = 1$ and $n = \frac{1}{2}$, so substitute these values into the formula.

$$\int_4^{12} (2x + 1)^{\frac{1}{2}} \, dx = \left[\frac{1}{2 \times \frac{3}{2}}(2x + 1)^{\frac{3}{2}} \right]_4^{12} = \left[\frac{1}{3}(2x + 1)^{\frac{3}{2}} \right]_4^{12} = \frac{1}{3}\left[(2x + 1)^{\frac{3}{2}} \right]_4^{12}$$

$a = 2$ $n + 1 = \frac{3}{2}$

Be careful adding 1 to fractional powers.

Tip: Remember from C1 and C2 that when you integrate a definite integral, you put the function in square brackets and write the limits on the right.

Now evaluate the integral at the limits:

$$\int_4^{12} (2x + 1)^{\frac{1}{2}} \, dx = \frac{1}{3}\left[(2x + 1)^{\frac{3}{2}} \right]_4^{12} = \frac{1}{3}\left[((2 \times 12) + 1)^{\frac{3}{2}} \right] - \frac{1}{3}\left[((2 \times 4) + 1)^{\frac{3}{2}} \right]$$

$$= \frac{1}{3}\left[\left(25^{\frac{3}{2}}\right) \right] - \frac{1}{3}\left[\left(9^{\frac{3}{2}}\right) \right] = \frac{125}{3} - \frac{27}{3} = \frac{98}{3}$$

In C1, you learnt that definite integrals work out the **area** between a curve and the x-axis. To find the area between a curve $y = f(x)$ and the x-axis over an interval, just integrate $f(x)$ with respect to x over that interval.

Example

Work out the area enclosed by the curve $y = (x - 2)^3$, the x-axis and the lines $x = 2$ and $x = 3$.

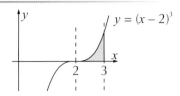

- You just need to integrate the curve $y = (x - 2)^3$ between $x = 2$ and $x = 3$, i.e. evaluate $\int_2^3 (x - 2)^3 \, dx$

- Use the formula with $a = 1$, $b = -2$ and $n = 3$ to work out the integral.

$$\int_2^3 (x - 2)^3 \, dx = \tfrac{1}{4}[(x - 2)^4]_2^3$$

- Substitute in the limits of integration to find the area.

$$x = 3 \qquad x = 2$$

$$\int_2^3 (x - 2)^3 \, dx = \tfrac{1}{4}[(3 - 2)^4] - \tfrac{1}{4}[(2 - 2)^4] = \tfrac{1}{4}[1^4] - \tfrac{1}{4}[0^4]$$

$$= \tfrac{1}{4} - 0 = \boxed{\tfrac{1}{4}}$$

Exercise 1.1

Q1 Integrate with respect to x:
a) $(2x + 9)^4$
b) $(x + 10)^{10}$
c) $(4x + 3)^5$
d) $(5x)^7$
e) $(7x - 2)^{-8}$
f) $(3 - 5x)^{-2}$
g) $(10x - 3)^{\frac{11}{8}}$
h) $(3x - 4)^{-\frac{4}{3}}$

Q2 a) Show that $\int 8(2x - 4)^4 \, dx = \dfrac{4(2x - 4)^5}{5} + C$.

b) Evaluate the definite integral $\int_{\frac{3}{2}}^{\frac{5}{2}} 8(2x - 4)^4 \, dx$.

Q3 Evaluate $\int_0^1 (6x + 1)^{-3} \, dx$.

Q4 The curve $y = f(x)$ goes through the point $\left(1, \dfrac{3}{35}\right)$ and $f'(x) = (8 - 7x)^4$. Find $f(x)$.

Q5 Find the area between the curve $y = (-x - 1)^{12}$ and the x-axis for $-1 \leq x \leq 0$.

Q6 Integrate the function $(9 - y)^{\frac{1}{6}} + (9 - y)^{-6}$ with respect to y.

Q6 Hint: You'll only need one constant of integration (each term produces a constant but you can just combine them into one term).

Q7 Show that $\int \dfrac{-6}{(12x + 5)^2} \, dx = \dfrac{1}{24x + 10} + C$.

2. Integration of e^x and $\frac{1}{x}$

The functions e^x and $1/x$ are pretty easy to integrate — it's just the opposite of differentiating e^x and $\ln x$. Simple.

Integrating e^x and e^{ax+b}

e^x differentiates to give e^x, so it makes sense that e^x **integrates** to give $e^x + C$.

$$\int e^x dx = e^x + C$$

Example

Integrate the function $6x^2 - 4x + 3e^x$ with respect to x.

- When integrating a function like this, you integrate each term separately so:
$$\int 6x^2 - 4x + 3e^x\, dx = \int 6x^2\, dx - \int 4x\, dx + \int 3e^x\, dx$$

- The first two terms are of the form x^n so they integrate to $2x^3$ and $2x^2$ respectively.

- Using the rule above, the third term is:
$$\int 3e^x\, dx = 3\int e^x\, dx = 3e^x + c$$

- Putting this all together gives:
$$\int 6x^2 - 4x + 3e^x\, dx = \boxed{2x^3 - 2x^2 + 3e^x + C}$$

On p.99-100 you saw how to integrate **linear transformations** of x^n by differentiating with the **chain rule** and working backwards. You can do the same with functions of the form e^{ax+b} where a and b are constants. Start by considering what you get when you **differentiate** functions of the form e^{ax+b} using the chain rule and work backwards.

Tip: This method of differentiating f($ax + b$) using the chain rule and working backwards to find an integral can be used with any of the functions that you know the derivative of — you'll see it used a lot in the next few sections.

Example

a) **Differentiate the function e^{4x-1} with respect to x.**

Using the chain rule, $\dfrac{d}{dx}(e^{4x-1}) = \boxed{4e^{4x-1}}$

b) **Using your answer to a), find the integral $\displaystyle\int e^{4x-1} dx$.**

Reversing the process of differentiation to get integration we have:
$$\frac{d}{dx}(e^{4x-1}) = 4e^{4x-1} \Rightarrow \int 4e^{4x-1} dx = e^{4x-1} + c$$
$$\Rightarrow 4\int e^{4x-1} dx = e^{4x-1} + c$$

Take out the factor of 4 and divide by it.
$$\Rightarrow \boxed{\int e^{4x-1} dx = \frac{1}{4}e^{4x-1} + C}$$

This method gives you a **general rule** for integrating functions of the form e^{ax+b}:

$$\int e^{ax+b}\,dx = \frac{1}{a}e^{ax+b} + C$$

This means you just need to **divide** by the **coefficient of** x and add a constant of integration — the e^{ax+b} bit **doesn't change**.

Examples

Integrate the following:

a) e^{7x}

If you differentiated e^{7x} you'd get $7e^{7x}$, so you need to divide by 7 (the coefficient of x) when integrating.

$$\int e^{7x}\,dx = \frac{1}{7}e^{7x} + C$$

b) $2e^{4-3x}$

Multiplying by 2 doesn't change the integration — the coefficient of x is -3, so divide by -3 and you're done.

$$\int 2e^{4-3x}\,dx = -\frac{2}{3}e^{4-3x} + C$$

Tip: Notice that if you differentiated $2e^{4-3x}$, you'd get $-6e^{4-3x}$, so you need to divide by -3 when you integrate — it's simple really.

c) $e^{\frac{x}{2}}$

If you differentiated this one using the **chain rule**, you'd get $\frac{1}{2}e^{\frac{x}{2}}$, so you need to multiply by 2 (divide by $\frac{1}{2}$) to integrate.

$$\int e^{\frac{x}{2}}\,dx = \int e^{\frac{1}{2}x}\,dx = 2e^{\frac{x}{2}} + C$$

Exercise 2.1

Q1 Evaluate the following, giving exact answers:

a) $\int 2e^x\,dx$ b) $\int 4x + 7e^x\,dx$ c) $\int e^{10x}\,dx$

d) $\int e^{-3x} + x\,dx$ e) $\int e^{\frac{7}{2}x}\,dx$ f) $\int e^{4x-2}\,dx$

g) $\int \frac{1}{2}e^{2-\frac{3}{2}x}\,dx$ h) $\int e^{4(\frac{x}{3}+1)}\,dx$

Q2 Find the equation of the curve that has the derivative $\frac{dy}{dx} = 10e^{-5x-1}$ and passes through the origin.

Q3 Integrate the function e^{8y+5} with respect to y.

Q4 Evaluate the following definite integrals, giving exact answers:

a) $\int_2^3 e^{2x}\,dx$ b) $\int_{-1}^0 12e^{12x+12}\,dx$

c) $\int_{-\frac{\pi}{2}}^{\frac{\pi}{2}} e^{\pi-2x}\,dx$ d) $\int_3^6 \sqrt[6]{e^x} + \frac{1}{\sqrt[3]{e^x}}\,dx$

Q4 d) Hint: Remember:

$$\sqrt[n]{e^x} = e^{\frac{x}{n}}$$

$$\frac{1}{\sqrt[n]{e^x}} = e^{-\frac{x}{n}}$$

Integrating $\frac{1}{x}$ and $\frac{1}{ax+b}$

The method for integrating x^n and $(ax + b)^n$ on p.100 doesn't work for $n = -1$. For these functions you need to consider the fact that $\frac{d}{dx}(\ln x) = \frac{1}{x}$, which you should remember from Chapter 4 (p.76).

Example

Let $f(x) = \frac{1}{x}, x > 0$.

Integrate $f(x)$ with respect to x, given that $\frac{d}{dx}(\ln x) = \frac{1}{x}$.

Given the derivative of $\ln x$, integration is the opposite of differentiation, so:

$$\ln x \xrightarrow{\text{Differentiation}} \frac{1}{x}$$

$$\ln x + C \xleftarrow{\text{Integration}} \frac{1}{x}$$

So $\int \frac{1}{x}\,dx = $ $\boxed{\ln x + C.}$

Tip: You'll be working with logs all the time when integrating functions of the form $\frac{1}{x}$ — it'll help to remember the log laws from p.62:

$\log(ab) = \log a + \log b$

$\log\left(\frac{a}{b}\right) = \log a - \log b$

$\log(a^b) = b\log a$

So now we have a general result for integrating $\frac{1}{x}$:

$$\boxed{\int \frac{1}{x}\,dx = \ln|x| + C}$$

Notice that this result uses $|x|$ instead of just x. This is because the function $\ln x$ is **not defined** for **negative values** of x. Using the modulus means you'll never end up taking $\ln$ of a negative value.

Examples

Find the following integrals:

a) $\int \frac{5}{x}\,dx$

    5 is a **constant coefficient** — you can take it outside the integral so that you're just integrating $\frac{1}{x}$.

$$\int \frac{5}{x}\,dx = 5\int \frac{1}{x}\,dx = \boxed{5\ln|x| + C}$$

b) $\int_3^9 \frac{1}{3x}\,dx$

- Here $\frac{1}{3}$ is the coefficient, so it goes outside the integral.

$$\int_3^9 \frac{1}{3x}\,dx = \frac{1}{3}\int_3^9 \frac{1}{x}\,dx = \frac{1}{3}[\ln|x|]_3^9$$

- Now put in the limits and use log laws to simplify:

$$= \frac{1}{3}(\ln|9| - \ln|3|) = \frac{1}{3}\left(\ln\left(\frac{9}{3}\right)\right) \longleftarrow \ln a - \ln b = \ln \frac{a}{b}$$

$$= \boxed{\frac{1}{3}\ln 3}$$

You can integrate **linear transformations** of $\frac{1}{x}$ (i.e. functions of the form $\frac{1}{ax+b}$) by considering the result of differentiating $\ln|ax+b|$.

Example

Given that $\frac{d}{dx}(\ln|4x+2|) = \frac{4}{4x+2}$, **evaluate** $\int \frac{1}{4x+2}\,dx$.

$$\frac{d}{dx}(\ln|4x+2|) = \frac{4}{4x+2} \Rightarrow \int \frac{4}{4x+2}\,dx = \ln|4x+2| + c$$

$$\Rightarrow 4\int \frac{1}{4x+2}\,dx = \ln|4x+2| + c$$

$$\Rightarrow \int \frac{1}{4x+2}\,dx = \tfrac{1}{4}\ln|4x+2| + C$$

The **general result** for integrating functions of the form $\frac{1}{ax+b}$ is:

$$\int \frac{1}{ax+b}\,dx = \tfrac{1}{a}\ln|ax+b| + C$$

Tip: Evaluating $\int \frac{1}{3x}\,dx$ (from the example on page 104) in this way would give a 'different' answer, $\tfrac{1}{3}\ln|3x| + C$. But this expands to $\tfrac{1}{3}\ln|x| + \tfrac{1}{3}\ln 3 + C$ and the $\tfrac{1}{3}\ln 3$ becomes part of the constant of integration, so both answers are equivalent.

Example

Evaluate $\int \frac{1}{2x+5}\,dx$.

Using the general rule, $a = 2$ and $b = 5$ so the integral is:

$$\int \frac{1}{2x+5}\,dx = \tfrac{1}{2}\ln|2x+5| + C$$

Exercise 2.2

Q1 Evaluate the following:

a) $\int \frac{19}{x}\,dx$ b) $\int \frac{1}{7x}\,dx$ c) $\int \frac{1}{7x+2}\,dx$ d) $\int \frac{1}{1-3x}\,dx$

Q2 Integrate $y = \frac{1}{8x} - \frac{20}{x}$ with respect to x.

Q3 a) Show that $\int \frac{6}{x} - \frac{3}{x}\,dx = \ln|x^3| + C$.

b) Evaluate $\int_4^5 \frac{6}{x} - \frac{3}{x}\,dx$, giving an exact answer.

Q3 b) Hint: An exact answer means you'll leave it in terms of ln.

Q4 Show that $\int_b^a 15(5+3x)^{-1}\,dx = \ln\left|\frac{5+3a}{5+3b}\right|^5$.

Q4 Hint: Use the log laws on p.62 to simplify your answer.

Q5 The graph of the curve $y = f(x)$ passes through the point $(1, 2)$. The derivative of $f(x)$ is given by $f'(x) = \frac{4}{10-9x}$. Find $f(x)$.

Q6 a) Express the area bounded by the curve $y = \frac{-7}{16-2x}$, the x-axis, the y-axis, and the line $x = -3$ as an integral with respect to x.

b) Show that the area is equal to $\ln\left[\left(\frac{8}{11}\right)^{\frac{7}{2}}\right]$.

Q7 Given that $\int_1^A \frac{4}{6x-5}\,dx = 10$, find A, in terms of e.

3. Integration of Trigonometric Functions

There are a few trig functions which are really easy to integrate — once you've learnt them, you'll be able to integrate loads of complicated-looking trig functions quickly.

Integration of sin x and cos x

You learnt how to differentiate sin x and cos x in Chapter 4 — you should remember that sin x differentiates to cos x, and cos x differentiates to –sin x.

Working backwards from this, we get:

$$\int \sin x \, dx = -\cos x + C$$
$$\int \cos x \, dx = \sin x + C$$

Examples

Find the following integrals:

$$\int \cos x \, dx = \sin x + C$$

a) $\int 4 \cos x \, dx$

$$\int 4 \cos x \, dx = 4 \int \cos x \, dx = \boxed{4 \sin x + C}$$

b) $\int_0^\pi \frac{\sin x}{2} + \frac{1}{\pi} \, dx$

- Integrate each term separately:

Don't forget the minus sign.

$$\int_0^\pi \frac{\sin x}{2} + \frac{1}{\pi} \, dx = \int_0^\pi \frac{1}{2}\sin x + \frac{1}{\pi} \, dx = \left[\frac{1}{2}(-\cos x) + \frac{1}{\pi}x\right]_0^\pi$$

$$= \left[-\frac{1}{2}\cos x + \frac{1}{\pi}x\right]_0^\pi$$

- Put in the limits:

$$\left[-\frac{1}{2}\cos x + \frac{1}{\pi}x\right]_0^\pi = \left[-\frac{1}{2}\cos \pi + \left(\frac{1}{\pi} \times \pi\right)\right] - \left[-\frac{1}{2}\cos 0 + \left(\frac{1}{\pi} \times 0\right)\right]$$

$$= \left[-\frac{1}{2}(-1) + 1\right] - \left[-\frac{1}{2}(1) + 0\right]$$

$$= \left[\frac{1}{2} + 1\right] - \left[-\frac{1}{2} + 0\right] = \boxed{2}$$

c) $\int \frac{1}{2}(\cos x + 2\sin x) \, dx$

Multiply out and integrate each term separately:

$$\int \frac{1}{2}(\cos x + 2\sin x) \, dx = \int \frac{1}{2}\cos x + \sin x \, dx$$

$$= \frac{1}{2}\sin x + (-\cos x) + C$$

$$= \boxed{\frac{1}{2}\sin x - \cos x + C}$$

You can integrate **linear transformations** of $\sin x$ and $\cos x$ of the form $\sin(ax + b)$ and $\cos(ax + b)$.

- Differentiating $\sin(ax + b)$ using the **chain rule** gives:
$$a\cos(ax + b)$$

- So when **integrating** $\cos(ax + b)$, you need to divide by a, giving:
$$\frac{1}{a}\sin(ax + b).$$

The same can be done when integrating $\sin(ax + b)$, so we get:

$$\int \sin(ax + b)\,dx = -\frac{1}{a}\cos(ax + b) + C$$
$$\int \cos(ax + b)\,dx = \frac{1}{a}\sin(ax + b) + C$$

Example

Find $\int \sin(1 - 6x)\,dx$.

Using the general formula with $a = -6$ and $b = 1$ gives:

$$\int \sin(1 - 6x)\,dx = \frac{1}{-6} \times -\cos(1 - 6x) + C$$
$$= \frac{1}{6}\cos(1 - 6x) + C$$

Tip: You could also do this by noticing that differentiating $\cos(1 - 6x)$ with the chain rule gives $6\sin(1 - 6x)$, so
$$\int \sin(1 - 6x)\,dx$$
$$= \frac{1}{6}\cos(1 - 6x) + C$$

Exercise 3.1

Q1 Integrate the following functions with respect to x.

a) $\frac{1}{7}\cos x$ b) $-3\sin x$ c) $-3\cos x - 3\sin x$

d) $\sin 5x$ e) $\cos\left(\frac{x}{7}\right)$ f) $2\sin(-3x)$

g) $5\cos\left(3x + \frac{\pi}{5}\right)$ h) $-4\sin\left(4x - \frac{\pi}{3}\right)$ i) $\cos(4x + 3) + \sin(3 - 4x)$

Q2 Integrate $\frac{1}{2}\cos 3\theta - \sin\theta$ with respect to θ.

Q3 Evaluate the following definite integrals:
a) $\int_{0}^{\frac{\pi}{2}} \sin x\,dx$ b) $\int_{\frac{\pi}{6}}^{\frac{\pi}{3}} \sin 3x\,dx$ c) $\int_{-1}^{2} 3\sin(\pi x + \pi)\,dx$

Q4 Find an expression for the area between the curve $y = 2\pi\cos\left(\frac{\pi x}{2}\right)$ and the x-axis for $1 \le x \le 2$. State whether or not this area lies above the x-axis, justifying your answer.

Q5 Show that $\int_{\frac{\pi}{3}}^{\frac{\pi}{2}} \sin(-x) + \cos(-x)\,dx = \frac{1 - \sqrt{3}}{2}$.

Q6 Show that the area of the region bounded by the x-axis and the curve with equation $y = 5\cos\frac{x}{6}$, where $-2\pi \le x \le \pi$, is $15(1 + \sqrt{3})$.

Integration of sec² x

Another trigonometric function which is easy to integrate is the derivative of tan x, **sec² x**. Since tan x differentiates to sec² x, you get:

> **Tip:** This integral is given in the formula book — it's given as
>
> $\int \sec^2 kx\,\mathrm{d}x = \frac{1}{k}\tan kx + C.$

$$\int \sec^2 x\,\mathrm{d}x = \tan x + C$$

Example 1

Find $\int 2\sec^2 x + 4x\,\mathrm{d}x$.

Integrate each term separately.

$$\int 2\sec^2 x + 4x\,\mathrm{d}x = 2\int \sec^2 x\,\mathrm{d}x + \int 4x\,\mathrm{d}x = \boxed{2\tan x + 2x^2 + C}$$

Unsurprisingly, you can use the chain rule in reverse again to integrate functions of the form sec²$(ax + b)$:

$$\int \sec^2(ax + b)\,\mathrm{d}x = \frac{1}{a}\tan(ax + b) + C$$

Example 2

Find $\int \cos 4x - 2\sin 2x + \sec^2\left(\frac{1}{2}x\right)\mathrm{d}x$.

Integrate each term separately using the results from above and p.106-107:

$$\int \sec^2\left(\tfrac{1}{2}x\right)\mathrm{d}x = \frac{1}{\left(\frac{1}{2}\right)}\tan\left(\tfrac{1}{2}x\right) = 2\tan\left(\tfrac{1}{2}x\right)$$

$$\int \cos 4x\,\mathrm{d}x = \frac{1}{4}\sin 4x$$

$$\int \cos 4x - 2\sin 2x + \sec^2\left(\tfrac{1}{2}x\right)\mathrm{d}x = \frac{1}{4}\sin 4x + \cos 2x + 2\tan\left(\tfrac{1}{2}x\right) + C$$

$$\int -2\sin 2x\,\mathrm{d}x = -2\left(-\tfrac{1}{2}\cos 2x\right) = \cos 2x$$

Exercise 3.2

Q1 Find the following integrals:

a) $\int 2\sec^2 x + 1\,\mathrm{d}x$ b) $\int \sec^2 9x\,\mathrm{d}x$ c) $\int 20\sec^2 3y\,\mathrm{d}y$

d) $\int \sec^2 \frac{x}{7}\,\mathrm{d}x$ e) $\int_0^{\frac{\pi}{3}} \frac{1}{\cos^2\theta}\,\mathrm{d}\theta$ f) $\int_0^{\frac{\pi}{4}} 3\sec^2(-3x)\,\mathrm{d}x$

Q2 Find the area of the region bounded by the x-axis, the curve with equation $y = \sec^2 x$, and the lines $x = \frac{2}{3}\pi$ and $x = \pi$.

Q3 Integrate $\sec^2(x + \alpha) + \sec^2(3x + \beta)$ with respect to x, where α and β are constants.

Q4 Let A be a constant. Integrate $5A\sec^2\left(\frac{\pi}{3} - 2\theta\right)$ with respect to θ between the limits of $\theta = \frac{\pi}{12}$ and $\theta = \frac{\pi}{6}$.

Integration of other trigonometric functions

There are some other more complicated trig functions which are really easy to integrate. They are the **derivatives** of the functions **cosec x**, **sec x** and **cot x**.

You may remember these derivatives from Chapter 4, but here's a recap:

$$\frac{d}{dx}(\cosec x) = -\cosec x \cot x$$

$$\frac{d}{dx}(\sec x) = \sec x \tan x \qquad \frac{d}{dx}(\cot x) = -\cosec^2 x$$

Reversing the differentiation gives the following three integrals. They'll be really useful when integrating complicated trig functions.

$$\int \cosec x \cot x \, dx = -\cosec x + C$$
$$\int \sec x \tan x \, dx = \sec x + C$$
$$\int \cosec^2 x \, dx = -\cot x + C$$

As always, you can integrate **linear transformations** of these functions (functions of the form **cosec(ax + b)cot(ax + b)**, **sec(ax + b)tan(ax + b)** and **cosec²(ax + b)**) by **dividing** by the coefficient of x.

$$\int \cosec(ax + b)\cot(ax + b) \, dx = -\frac{1}{a}\cosec(ax + b) + C$$
$$\int \sec(ax + b)\tan(ax + b) \, dx = \frac{1}{a}\sec(ax + b) + C$$
$$\int \cosec^2(ax + b) \, dx = -\frac{1}{a}\cot(ax + b) + C$$

Tip: The $ax + b$ bit has to be the same in each trig function — e.g. you couldn't integrate sec x tan 3x using these formulas.

Examples

Find the following:

a) $\int 2\sec x \tan x \, dx$

Take the constant outside the integral.

$$\int 2\sec x \tan x \, dx = 2\int \sec x \tan x \, dx = 2(\sec x + c) = \boxed{2\sec x + C}$$

b) $\int_0^\pi \cosec^2\left(\frac{x}{2} - \frac{\pi}{4}\right) dx$

This is a definite integral, so you need to evaluate between the limits.

$$\int_0^\pi \cosec^2\left(\frac{x}{2} - \frac{\pi}{4}\right) dx = \left[-\frac{1}{\left(\frac{1}{2}\right)}\cot\left(\frac{x}{2} - \frac{\pi}{4}\right)\right]_0^\pi$$

$$\cot x = \frac{1}{\tan x}$$

Divide by the coefficient of x.

$$= -2\left[\cot\left(\frac{x}{2} - \frac{\pi}{4}\right)\right]_0^\pi = -2\left[\frac{1}{\tan\left(\frac{x}{2} - \frac{\pi}{4}\right)}\right]_0^\pi$$

Put in the limits.

$$= -2\left(\frac{1}{\tan\left(\frac{\pi}{2} - \frac{\pi}{4}\right)} - \frac{1}{\tan\left(0 - \frac{\pi}{4}\right)}\right)$$

$$= -2\left(\frac{1}{\tan\left(\frac{\pi}{4}\right)} - \frac{1}{\tan\left(-\frac{\pi}{4}\right)}\right) = -2\left(\frac{1}{1} - \frac{1}{(-1)}\right) = \boxed{-4}$$

c) $\int 8\cosec(2x+1)\cot(2x+1)\,dx$ — Take the constant outside the integral.

$$\int 8\cosec(2x+1)\cot(2x+1)\,dx = 8\int \cosec(2x+1)\cot(2x+1)\,dx$$
$$= 8\left(-\tfrac{1}{2}\cosec(2x+1)+c\right)$$

Don't forget to **divide** by the x coefficient.

$$= -4\cosec(2x+1)+C$$

Example

Find $\int 10\sec 5x\tan 5x + \tfrac{1}{2}\cosec 3x\cot 3x - \cosec^2(6x+1)\,dx$.

- Integrate each bit in turn:

$$\int 10\sec 5x\tan 5x\,dx = 10\left(\tfrac{1}{5}\sec 5x\right)$$
$$= 2\sec 5x$$

$$\int \tfrac{1}{2}\cosec 3x\cot 3x\,dx = \tfrac{1}{2}\left(-\tfrac{1}{3}\cosec 3x\right)$$
$$= -\tfrac{1}{6}\cosec 3x$$

Tip: These three integrals should really all have a constant of integration on the end, but we'll just add a combined constant of integration when we do the final integration.

Don't forget the minus that comes from the integration.

$$\int -\cosec^2(6x+1)\,dx = -\left(-\tfrac{1}{6}\cot(6x+1)\right)$$
$$= \tfrac{1}{6}\cot(6x+1)$$

- Putting these terms together and adding the constant gives:

$$\int 10\sec 5x\tan 5x + \tfrac{1}{2}\cosec 3x\cot 3x - \cosec^2(6x+1)\,dx$$
$$= 2\sec 5x - \tfrac{1}{6}\cosec 3x + \tfrac{1}{6}\cot(6x+1) + C$$

Exercise 3.3

Q1 Find the following integrals:

a) $\int \cosec^2 11x\,dx$

b) $\int 5\sec 10\theta\tan 10\theta\,d\theta$

c) $\int -\cosec(x+17)\cot(x+17)\,dx$

d) $\int -3\cosec 3x\cot 3x\,dx$

e) $\int 13\sec\left(\tfrac{\pi}{4}-x\right)\tan\left(\tfrac{\pi}{4}-x\right)dx$

Q2 Find $\int 10\cosec^2\left(\alpha-\tfrac{x}{2}\right) - 60\sec(\alpha-6x)\tan(\alpha-6x)\,dx$

Q3 Integrate the function $6\sec 2x\tan 2x + 6\cosec 2x\cot 2x$ with respect to x between the limits of $x = \tfrac{\pi}{12}$ and $x = \tfrac{\pi}{8}$.

Q4 Find the area of the region bounded by $y = \cosec^2(3x)$, the x-axis and the lines $x = \tfrac{\pi}{12}$ and $x = \tfrac{\pi}{6}$.

4. Integration of $\frac{f'(x)}{f(x)}$

Fractions in which the numerator is the derivative of the denominator are pretty easy to integrate too — there is a general formula which comes from the chain rule.

Integrating $\frac{f'(x)}{f(x)}$

- If you have a fraction that has a function of x as the numerator and a different function of x as the denominator, e.g. $\frac{x-2}{x^3+1}$, you'll probably struggle to integrate it.

- However, if you have a fraction where the **numerator** is the **derivative** of the **denominator**, e.g. $\frac{3x^2}{x^3+1}$, it integrates to give ln of the denominator.

- In general terms, this is written as:

$$\int \frac{f'(x)}{f(x)}\, dx = \ln|f(x)| + C$$

- This rule won't surprise you if you remember differentiating $\ln|f(x)|$ using the chain rule in Chapter 4 — the derivative with respect to x of $\ln|f(x)|$ is $\frac{f'(x)}{f(x)}$.

The hardest bit about integrations like this is recognising that the denominator differentiates to give the numerator — once you've spotted that you can just use the formula.

Examples

Integrate the following functions with respect to x.

a) $\frac{2x}{x^2+1}$

- Differentiate the denominator to see what it gives:

$$\frac{d}{dx}(x^2+1) = 2x \quad \longleftarrow \text{This is the **numerator**.}$$

- The numerator is the derivative of the denominator so use the formula:

$$\int \frac{2x}{x^2+1}\, dx = \boxed{\ln|x^2+1| + C}$$

b) $\frac{x(3x-4)}{x^3-2x^2-1}$

- Differentiate the denominator:

$$\frac{d}{dx}(x^3-2x^2-1) = 3x^2-4x = x(3x-4) \quad \longleftarrow \text{This is the **numerator**.}$$

- Use the formula:

$$\int \frac{x(3x-4)}{x^3-2x^2-1}\, dx = \boxed{\ln|x^3-2x^2-1| + C}$$

Tip: You should get used to spotting when the numerator is the derivative of the denominator — you won't have to differentiate the denominator every time. Sometimes you might need to expand out some brackets before you notice it.

The numerator might be a **multiple** of the derivative of the denominator just to confuse things. When this happens, just put the multiple **in front** of the ln.

Examples

Find:

a) $\int \dfrac{8x^3 - 4}{x^4 - 2x}\, dx$

- Differentiating: $\dfrac{d}{dx}(x^4 - 2x) = 4x^3 - 2$

  and $8x^3 - 4 = 2(4x^3 - 2)$

- The numerator is $2 \times$ the derivative of the denominator, so

  $\int \dfrac{8x^3 - 4}{x^4 - 2x}\, dx = 2\int \dfrac{4x^3 - 2}{x^4 - 2x}\, dx = \boxed{2\ln|x^4 - 2x| + C}$

b) $\int \dfrac{3\sin 3x}{\cos 3x + 2}\, dx$

- Differentiating:

  $\dfrac{d}{dx}(\cos 3x + 2) = -3\sin 3x$

- The numerator is **minus** the derivative of the denominator, so

  $\int \dfrac{3\sin 3x}{\cos 3x + 2}\, dx = -\int \dfrac{-3\sin 3x}{\cos 3x + 2}\, dx = -\ln|\cos 3x + 2| + C$

- You can make the answer a lot neater by combining it all into **one logarithm** — a question might ask you to do this.

  $= -\ln|\cos 3x + 2| - \ln k = \boxed{-\ln|k(\cos 3x + 2)|}$

  The minus sign is just to avoid fractions in the logarithm.

  C is just a constant. We can express C as a logarithm — call it $-\ln k$, where k is a constant.

Tip: Any constant can be expressed as a logarithm because the range of the ln function is $f(x) \in \mathbb{R}$.

You can use this method to integrate **trig functions** by writing them as fractions:

- You might have noticed from part b) above that you can work out the integral of **tan x** using this method:

  $\tan x = \dfrac{\sin x}{\cos x}$, and $\dfrac{d}{dx}(\cos x) = -\sin x$

Tip: The integral of tan is given in the formula book as $\ln|\sec x|$. This is the same as $-\ln|\cos x|$ by the laws of logs.

- The numerator is **minus** the **derivative** of the **denominator**, so

  $\int \tan x\, dx = \int \dfrac{\sin x}{\cos x}\, dx = -\ln|\cos x| + C$

There are some other **trig functions** that you can integrate in the same way. These integrals are given in the **formula booklet**, so you won't need to learn them — just how to use them.

$$\int \operatorname{cosec} x \, dx = -\ln|\operatorname{cosec} x + \cot x| + C$$
$$\int \sec x \, dx = \ln|\sec x + \tan x| + C$$
$$\int \cot x \, dx = \ln|\sin x| + C$$

Tip: As always, if you're integrating a linear transformation of any of these functions, of the form $f(ax + b)$, then divide by a when you integrate.

You can check these results easily by using **differentiation** — differentiate the right-hand side of the results to get the left-hand sides.

Remember that differentiating $\ln|f(x)|$ gives $\frac{f'(x)}{f(x)}$.

Examples

Find the following integrals:

a) $\int 2 \sec x \, dx$

Use the result for sec x above.
There is a constant of 2 so put that at the front.

$$\int 2 \sec x \, dx = \boxed{2\ln|\sec x + \tan x| + C}$$

b) $\int \frac{\cot x}{5} \, dx$

Use the result for cot x above.
$\frac{\cot x}{5} = \frac{1}{5}\cot x$ so there is a constant of $\frac{1}{5}$ — put that at the front.

$$\int \frac{\cot x}{5} \, dx = \boxed{\frac{1}{5}\ln|\sin x| + C}$$

c) $\int 2(\operatorname{cosec} x + \sec x) \, dx$

$$\int 2(\operatorname{cosec} x + \sec x) \, dx = \int 2\operatorname{cosec} x + 2\sec x \, dx$$
$$= -2\ln|\operatorname{cosec} x + \cot x| + 2\ln|\sec x + \tan x| + C$$
$$= \boxed{2\ln\left|\frac{\sec x + \tan x}{\operatorname{cosec} x + \cot x}\right| + C}$$

Use log laws to simplify.

d) $\int \frac{1}{2} \operatorname{cosec} 2x \, dx$.

You can just use the result on the previous page — so all you have to do is work out what happens to the coefficient of x. The coefficient of x is 2, so divide by 2 when you integrate:

$$\int \frac{1}{2} \operatorname{cosec} 2x \, dx = -\frac{1}{4} \ln |\operatorname{cosec} 2x + \cot 2x| + C$$

Divide $\frac{1}{2}$ by 2.

Tip: Check this by differentiating (using the chain rule with $u = \operatorname{cosec} 2x + \cot 2x$).

Exercise 4.1

Q1 Find the following integrals:

a) $\int \frac{4x^3}{x^4 - 1} \, dx$

b) $\int \frac{2x - 1}{x^2 - x} \, dx$

c) $\int \frac{x^4}{3x^5 + 6} \, dx$

d) $\int \frac{12x^3 + 18x^2 - 3}{x^4 + 2x^3 - x} \, dx$

e) $\int \frac{2 \cos 2x}{1 + \sin 2x} \, dx$

f) $\int \frac{2(e^{2x} + 3e^x)}{e^{2x} + 6e^x} \, dx$

g) $\int \frac{e^x}{3(e^x + 3)} \, dx$

h) $\int \frac{2 \cos 2x}{1 + \sin 2x} \, dx$

i) $\int \frac{\sin 3x}{\cos 3x - 1} \, dx$

j) $\int \frac{3 \operatorname{cosec} x \cot x + 6x}{\operatorname{cosec} x - x^2 + 4} \, dx$

k) $\int \frac{\sec^2 x}{\tan x} \, dx$

l) $\int \frac{\sec x \tan x}{\sec x + 5} \, dx$

Q2 Show that $\int \frac{4 \cos(2x + 7)}{\sin(2x + 7)} \, dx = 2 \ln |k \sin(2x + 7)|$

Q3 Prove that:

a) $\int \sec x \, dx = \ln |\sec x + \tan x| + C$

b) $\int \operatorname{cosec} x \, dx = - \ln |\operatorname{cosec} x + \cot x| + C$

Q3 Hint: Try multiplying the bit inside the integral by $\frac{\sec x + \tan x}{\sec x + \tan x}$ in part a) — there's a similar trick for part b) as well.

Q4 Find the following integrals:

a) $\int 2 \tan x \, dx$

b) $\int \tan 2x \, dx$

c) $\int 4 \operatorname{cosec} x \, dx$

d) $\int \cot 3x \, dx$

e) $\int \frac{1}{2} \sec 2x \, dx$

f) $\int 3 \operatorname{cosec} 6x \, dx$

Q5 Find $\int \frac{\sec^2 x}{2 \tan x} - 4 \sec 2x \tan 2x + \frac{\operatorname{cosec} 2x \cot 2x - 1}{\operatorname{cosec} 2x + 2x} \, dx$

114 Chapter 5 Integration

5. Integrating $\dfrac{du}{dx}$ f'(u)

This section will show you how to integrate certain products of functions. You can use the chain rule in reverse to integrate special products of functions and their derivatives.

Learning Objectives:

- Be able to integrate products of the form $\dfrac{du}{dx}$ f'(u) using the chain rule in reverse.

- Know and be able to use a result for integrating products of the form f'(x)[f(x)]^n.

Integrating using the reverse of the chain rule

On p.69, you saw the chain rule for differentiating a **function of a function**.

- Here it is in the form it was given on p.69:

  If $y = $ f(u) and $u = $ g(x)
  then:

  $$\frac{dy}{dx} = \frac{dy}{du} \times \frac{du}{dx}$$

- Since integration is the opposite of differentiation, you have:

  $$y \xrightarrow{\text{Differentiation}} \frac{dy}{du} \times \frac{du}{dx}$$

  $$y + C \xleftarrow[\text{Integration}]{} \frac{dy}{du} \times \frac{du}{dx}$$

- So $\int \dfrac{dy}{du} \times \dfrac{du}{dx}\, dx = y + C$.

- Writing f(u) instead of y and f'(u) instead of $\dfrac{dy}{du}$ gives:

  $$\int \frac{du}{dx} \text{f}'(u)\, dx = \text{f}(u) + C$$

If you're integrating an expression which contains a **function of a function**, f(u), try differentiating the function u. If the **derivative** of u is also part of the expression, you might be able to use the formula above.

This result's a bit more difficult to grasp — but after a few examples it should make complete sense.

Tip: To evaluate integrals like this you have to integrate with respect to u (because f'(u) is $\dfrac{dy}{du}$).

Example

a) **Differentiate** $y = e^{2x^2}$ **using the chain rule.**

  Let $u = 2x^2$, then $y = e^u$. By the chain rule,

  $$\frac{dy}{dx} = \frac{dy}{du} \times \frac{du}{dx} = e^u \times 4x = e^{2x^2} \times 4x = 4xe^{2x^2}$$

b) Find $\int 4xe^{2x^2}\,dx$ **using your answer to part a).**

Look for the bit that would have been u in the chain rule — here it's $2x^2$.

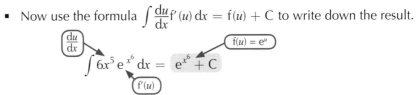

$$\int 4x\,e^{2x^2}\,dx = e^{2x^2} + C$$

with labels $\dfrac{du}{dx}$, $f'(u)$, $f(u)$

Examples

Find the following integrals:

a) $\int 6x^5 e^{x^6}\,dx$

- Here, $u = x^6$ — it appears once differentiated ($\mathbf{6x^5}$) and once within a function (e^{x^6}).

- Split the integral into $\dfrac{du}{dx}$ and $f'(u)$: $\int 6x^5 e^{x^6}\,dx$ with $\dfrac{du}{dx}$ and $f'(u)$ labelled.

Tip: You might need to take a constant outside of the integral to get it in the form $\int \dfrac{du}{dx} f'(u)\,dx$. There's an example of this is part c).

- Now use the formula $\int \dfrac{du}{dx} f'(u)\,dx = f(u) + C$ to write down the result.

$$\int 6x^5 e^{x^6}\,dx = e^{x^6} + C$$

with labels $\dfrac{du}{dx}$, $f'(u)$, $f(u) = e^u$

b) $\int e^{\sin x}\cos x\,dx$

- Here, $u = \sin x$.

- Write $\dfrac{du}{dx}$ and $f'(u)$: $\dfrac{du}{dx} = \cos x$ and $f'(u) = e^{\sin x}$

- Use the formula to write down the result.

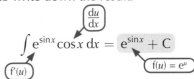

$$\int e^{\sin x}\cos x\,dx = e^{\sin x} + C$$

with labels $\dfrac{du}{dx}$, $f'(u)$, $f(u) = e^u$

c) $\int x^4 \sin(x^5)\,dx$

- Here, $u = x^5$.

- You'll need to take out a constant to get the integral you want.

$$\int x^4 \sin(x^5)\,dx = \frac{1}{5}\int 5x^4 \sin(x^5)\,dx$$

Tip: In this one, $u = x^5$, so $\dfrac{du}{dx} = 5x^4$.

The derivative is almost the term in the product, but it's multiplied by 5, so we just need to divide by 5.

- Now split up the integral: $\dfrac{du}{dx} = 5x^4$ and $f'(u) = \sin(x^5)$

- Use the formula.

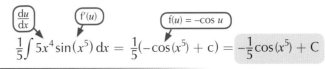

$$\frac{1}{5}\int 5x^4 \sin(x^5)\,dx = \frac{1}{5}(-\cos(x^5) + c) = -\frac{1}{5}\cos(x^5) + C$$

with labels $\dfrac{du}{dx}$, $f'(u)$, $f(u) = -\cos u$

Find the following integrals:

Q1 $\int 2xe^{x^2}\,dx$

Q2 $\int 6x^2 e^{2x^3}\,dx$

Q3 $\int \frac{1}{2\sqrt{x}}e^{\sqrt{x}}\,dx$

Q4 $\int x^3 e^{x^4}\,dx$

Q5 $\int (4x-1)e^{\left(x^2-\frac{1}{2}x\right)}\,dx$

Q6 $\int 2x\sin(x^2+1)\,dx$

Q7 $\int x^3 \cos(x^4)\,dx$

Q8 $\int x\sec^2(x^2)\,dx$

Q9 $\int e^{\cos x}\sin x\,dx$

Q10 $\int \cos 2x\, e^{\sin 2x}\,dx$

Q11 $\int \sec^2 x\, e^{\tan x}\,dx$

Q12 $\int \sec x \tan x\, e^{\sec x}\,dx$

Integrating $f'(x) \times [f(x)]^n$

Some products are made up of a **function** and its **derivative**:

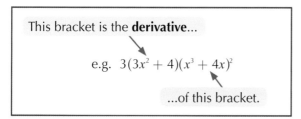

This bracket is the **derivative**...

e.g. $3(3x^2+4)(x^3+4x)^2$

...of this bracket.

If you spot that part of a product is the **derivative** of the other part of it (which is raised to a **power**), you can integrate it using this rule (which is just a special case of the 'reverse chain rule' on p.115):

$$\int (n+1)f'(x)[f(x)]^n\,dx = [f(x)]^{n+1}+C$$

This function is the **derivative**...

...of this function.

Tip: To get this formula, rewrite the 'reverse chain rule' on p.115, replacing the function 'u' with '$f(x)$' and the function '$f(u)$' with '$[f(x)]^{n+1}$'.

Then $\frac{du}{dx}$ will be replaced with $f'(x)$ and $f'(u)$ will be replaced with $(n+1)[f(x)]^n$.

Remember that this result needs you to have a multiple of $n+1$ (not n) — you can check this by **differentiating** the right-hand side using the **chain rule**.

Watch out for any other multiples too — you might have to **multiply** or **divide** by a **constant**.

This will probably make more sense if you have a look at some examples:

Examples

Evaluate the following integrals:

a) $\int 12x^3(2x^4 - 5)^2 \, dx$

- Here, $f(x) = 2x^4 - 5$, so $f'(x) = 8x^3$.
  $n = 2$, so $n + 1 = 3$.

  So $\int (n + 1)f'(x)[f(x)]^n \, dx = [f(x)]^{n+1} + C$
  $\Rightarrow \int 3(8x^3)(2x^4 - 5)^2 \, dx = \int 24x^3(2x^4 - 5)^2 \, dx = (2x^4 - 5)^3 + c$

- Divide everything by **2** to match the original integral:
  $$\int 12x^3(2x^4 - 5)^2 \, dx = \boxed{\frac{1}{2}(2x^4 - 5)^3 + C}$$

b) $\int 8 \cosec^2 x \cot^3 x \, dx$

Tip: This one looks pretty horrific, but it isn't too bad once you spot that $-\cosec^2 x$ is the derivative of $\cot x$.

- For this one, $f(x) = \cot x$, so $f'(x) = -\cosec^2 x$.
  $n = 3$, so $n + 1 = 4$.

  So $\int (n + 1)f'(x)[f(x)]^n \, dx = [f(x)]^{n+1} + c$
  $\Rightarrow \int -4\cosec^2 x \cot^3 x \, dx = \cot^4 x + c$

- Multiply everything by **–2** to match the original integral:
  $$\int 8 \cosec^2 x \cot^3 x \, dx = \boxed{-2\cot^4 x + C}$$

c) $\int (x - 2)\sqrt{x^2 - 4x + 5} \, dx$

- You can write the square root as a **fractional power**:
  $$\int (x - 2)\sqrt{x^2 - 4x + 5} \, dx = \int (x - 2)(x^2 - 4x + 5)^{\frac{1}{2}} \, dx$$

- Now, $f(x) = x^2 - 4x + 5$, so $f'(x) = 2x - 4$.
  $n = \frac{1}{2}$, so $n + 1 = \frac{3}{2}$.

  So $\int (n + 1)f'(x)[f(x)]^n \, dx = [f(x)]^{n+1} + c$
  $\Rightarrow \int \frac{3}{2}(2x - 4)(x^2 - 4x + 5)^{\frac{1}{2}} \, dx = (x^2 - 4x + 5)^{\frac{3}{2}} + c$

- $\frac{3}{2}(2x - 4) = 3(x - 2)$, so you need to divide everything by **3** to match the original integral:
  $$\int (x - 2)\sqrt{x^2 - 4x + 5} \, dx = \boxed{\frac{1}{3}(x^2 - 4x + 5)^{\frac{3}{2}} + C}$$

d) $\int \dfrac{\cos x}{\sin^4 x}\, dx$

- Write $\dfrac{1}{\sin^4 x}$ as a negative power.

$$\int \frac{\cos x}{\sin^4 x}\, dx = \int \frac{\cos x}{(\sin x)^4}\, dx = \int \cos x (\sin x)^{-4}\, dx$$

- Now, **f(x) = sin x**, so $f'(x) = \cos x$.
  $n = -4$, so $n + 1 = -3$.

$$\text{So } \int (n+1)f'(x)[f(x)]^n\, dx = [f(x)]^{n+1} + c$$
$$\Rightarrow \int -3\cos x(\sin x)^{-4}\, dx = (\sin x)^{-3} + c$$
$$\Rightarrow \int \frac{-3\cos x}{\sin^4 x}\, dx = \frac{1}{\sin^3 x} + c$$

- Divide everything by **−3** to match the original integral:

$$\int \frac{\cos x}{\sin^4 x}\, dx = \boxed{-\frac{1}{3\sin^3 x} + C}$$

Exercise 5.2

Q1 Find the following indefinite integrals:

a) $\displaystyle\int 6x(x^2 + 5)^2\, dx$

b) $\displaystyle\int (2x + 7)(x^2 + 7x)^4\, dx$

c) $\displaystyle\int (x^3 + 2x)(x^4 + 4x^2)^3\, dx$

d) $\displaystyle\int \frac{2x}{(x^2 - 1)^3}\, dx$

e) $\displaystyle\int \frac{6e^{3x}}{(e^{3x} - 5)^2}\, dx$

f) $\displaystyle\int \sin x \cos^5 x\, dx$

g) $\displaystyle\int 2\sec^2 x \tan^3 x\, dx$

h) $\displaystyle\int 3e^x (e^x + 4)^2\, dx$

i) $\displaystyle\int 32(2e^{4x} - 3x)(e^{4x} - 3x^2)^7\, dx$

j) $\displaystyle\int \frac{\cos x}{(2 + \sin x)^4}\, dx$

k) $\displaystyle\int 5\,\text{cosec}\,x \cot x\, \text{cosec}^4 x\, dx$

l) $\displaystyle\int 2\,\text{cosec}^2 x \cot^3 x\, dx$

Q2 Find the following integrals:

a) $\displaystyle\int 6\tan x \sec^6 x\, dx$

b) $\displaystyle\int \cot x\, \text{cosec}^3 x\, dx$

> **Q1-2 Hint:** You'll need the derivatives of cosec, sec and cot:
>
> $\dfrac{d}{dx}(\text{cosec}\,x) = -\text{cosec}\,x \cot x$
>
> $\dfrac{d}{dx}(\sec x) = \sec x \tan x$
>
> $\dfrac{d}{dx}(\cot x) = -\text{cosec}^2 x$

Q3 Integrate the following functions with respect to x:

a) $4\cos x\, e^{\sin x}(e^{\sin x} - 5)^3$

b) $(\sin x\, e^{\cos x} - 4)(e^{\cos x} + 4x)^6$

Q4 Integrate:

a) $\displaystyle\int \frac{\sec^2 x}{\tan^4 x}\, dx$

b) $\displaystyle\int \cot x\, \text{cosec}\,x \sqrt{\text{cosec}\,x}\, dx$

6. Integration by Substitution

Learning Objectives:

- Understand that integration by substitution is the reverse of differentiating using the chain rule.
- Use integration by substitution to integrate functions, including calculating definite integrals.
- Be able to integrate using substitutions that require trig identities.

Some of the integrals you'll come across in C3 look pretty nasty. Fortunately, there are a couple of really useful techniques which can make tricky-looking integrals easier to deal with. The first is integration by substitution.

Integration by substitution

You'll be familiar with using the **chain rule** to differentiate a **function of a function**. **Integration by substitution** is a way of **integrating** a function of a function by simplifying the integral. Like differentiating with the chain rule, to integrate by substitution you have to write part of the function in terms of u, where u is some **function** of x.

Here's the method:

> - You'll be given an integral that's made up of **two functions of x**.
> - **Substitute** u for one of the functions of x to give a function that's **easier to integrate**.
> - Next, find $\dfrac{du}{dx}$, and **rewrite** it so that dx is on its own.
> - **Rewrite** the original integral in terms of u and du.
> - You should now be left with something that's **easier** to integrate — just **integrate** as normal, then at the last step **replace** u with the **original substitution**.

Tip: You might have to do a bit of rearranging to get u in terms of x.

Tip: You'll normally be told what substitution to use (unless it's a really easy one).

Tip: This integral is of the form $f'(x) \times [f(x)]^n$ (p.117-119). You could use the rule you learnt back there for this kind of integral, but you've been asked to do it by substitution.

Example 1

Use the substitution $u = x^2 - 2$ to find $\displaystyle\int 4x(x^2 - 2)^4 \, dx$.

- Start by differentiating u with respect to x:

$$u = x^2 - 2 \implies \frac{du}{dx} = 2x$$

- Now rearrange the equation for $\dfrac{du}{dx}$ to get dx on its own:

$$\frac{du}{dx} = 2x \implies du = 2x \, dx$$
$$\implies dx = \frac{1}{2x} du$$

> $\dfrac{du}{dx}$ isn't really a fraction, but you can treat it like one for this bit.

- Substitute what you've got so far back into the original expression:

$$\int 4x(x^2 - 2)^4 \, dx = \int 4xu^4 \frac{1}{2x} du = \int 2u^4 du$$

> The remaining x's cancel.

- Now you've got a much simpler expression to integrate with respect to u:

$$\int 2u^4 du = \frac{2}{5}u^5 + C$$

- And finally, substitute $u = x^2 - 2$ back in:

$$= \frac{2}{5}(x^2 - 2)^5 + C$$

That first example worked out nicely, because the x's **cancelled out** when you substituted in the expressions for u and dx. It isn't always quite so straightforward — sometimes you need to get rid of some x's by **rearranging** the equation for u.

Example 2

Find $\int x(3x + 2)^3 \, dx$, using the substitution $u = 3x + 2$.

- Start by finding $\dfrac{du}{dx}$ and then rearrange to get dx on its own:

$$u = 3x + 2 \implies \frac{du}{dx} = 3 \implies dx = \frac{1}{3}du$$

Tip: The expression in brackets is often the thing you substitute.

- If you substitute for u and dx, you end up with an x still in the integral:

$$\int x(3x + 2)^3 \, dx = \int xu^3 \frac{1}{3}du$$

Tip: Note that this integral cannot be done using methods from pages 117-119.

- To get rid of that x, you have to rearrange the equation for u:

$$u = 3x + 2 \implies x = \frac{u - 2}{3}$$

- So $\int x(3x + 2)^3 \, dx \quad = \int \left(\frac{u - 2}{3}\right)u^3 \frac{1}{3}du$

$$= \int \frac{u^4 - 2u^3}{9} \, du$$

$$= \frac{1}{9}\left(\frac{u^5}{5} - \frac{u^4}{2}\right) + C$$

$$= \frac{u^5}{45} - \frac{u^4}{18} + C$$

$$= \frac{(3x + 2)^5}{45} - \frac{(3x + 2)^4}{18} + C$$

Tip: Don't forget to rewrite your answer in terms of x again at the end.

Some integrations look really tricky, but with a clever substitution they can be made a lot simpler.

Example 3

Find $\int 3x\sqrt{(2 - x^2)} \, dx$, using the substitution $u = \sqrt{2 - x^2}$.

- Start by differentiating both sides of the substitution with respect to x, then rearrange to get an expression for dx.

$$\text{So } u = \sqrt{2 - x^2} \implies \frac{du}{dx} = -\frac{x}{\sqrt{2 - x^2}} = -\frac{x}{u}$$

$$\implies u\frac{du}{dx} = -x$$

$$\implies -\frac{u}{x}du = dx$$

Tip: The chain rule is used here to differentiate.

- Now substitute what you've got into the original integral:

$$\int 3x\sqrt{(2 - x^2)} \, dx = \int 3x \times u \times -\frac{u}{x}du$$

$$= \int -3u^2 \, du$$

$$= -u^3 + C$$

$$= -\left(\sqrt{2 - x^2}\right)^3 + C$$

Q1 Find the following integrals using the given substitutions:

a) $\int 12(x+3)^5 \, dx, \quad u = x+3$

b) $\int (11-x)^4 \, dx, \quad u = 11-x$

c) $\int 24x(x^2+4)^3 \, dx, \quad u = x^2+4$

d) $\int \sin^5 x \cos x \, dx, \quad u = \sin x$

e) $\int x(x-1)^5 \, dx, \quad u = x-1$

f) $\int 6x\sqrt{(x^2+1)} \, dx, \quad u = \sqrt{x^2+1}$

g) $\int \frac{x}{\sqrt{(4-x^2)}} \, dx, \quad u = \sqrt{4-x^2}$

h) $\int \frac{15(\ln x)^4}{x} \, dx, \quad u = \ln x$

Q2 Use an appropriate substitution to find:

a) $\int 21(x+2)^6 \, dx$

b) $\int (5x+4)^3 \, dx$

c) $\int x(2x+3)^3 \, dx$

d) $\int 24x(x^2-5)^7 \, dx$

Q3 Use the substitution $u = \sqrt{2x-1}$ to find $\int \frac{4x}{\sqrt{(2x-1)}} \, dx$.

Q4 Use the substitution $u = 4 - \sqrt{x}$ to find $\int \frac{1}{4-\sqrt{x}} \, dx$.

Q5 Use the substitution $u = 1 + e^x$ to find $\int \frac{e^{2x}}{1+e^x} \, dx$.

Definite integrals

If you're given a **definite integral** to find using a substitution, it's important that you remember to **change** the *x*-limits to *u*-limits. To do this, put the *x*-limits into the equation for *u* to find the corresponding values of *u*.

Doing it this way means you **don't** have to **put x back in** at the last step — just put the values of *u* into the integration for *u*.

Examples

a) Use the substitution $u = \cos x$ to find $\int_{\frac{\pi}{2}}^{2\pi} -12\sin x \cos^3 x \, dx$.

- As with indefinite integrals, start by differentiating *u*, and rearranging to get d*x* on its own:

$$u = \cos x \implies \frac{du}{dx} = -\sin x \implies dx = -\frac{1}{\sin x} du$$

- Now use the substitution to change the limits of the integral from *x*-values to *u*-values:

$$x = \frac{\pi}{2} \implies u = \cos \frac{\pi}{2} = 0$$
$$x = 2\pi \implies u = \cos 2\pi = 1$$

- Substitute all that back into the original integral, and solve:

$$\int_{\frac{\pi}{2}}^{2\pi} -12\sin x \cos^3 x \, dx = \int_0^1 -12\sin x \, u^3 \frac{-1}{\sin x} du$$

$$= \int_0^1 12u^3 \, du = \left[3u^4\right]_0^1$$

$$= [3(1)^4] - [3(0)^4] = 3 - 0 = \boxed{3}$$

These are the *x*-limits.

These are the *u*-limits.

Tip: You could also solve this one using the method on p.117.

b) Find $\int_2^{\frac{7}{2}} x\sqrt{2x-3}\ dx$, **using the substitution** $u = \sqrt{2x-3}$.

- Differentiate the substitution, and rearrange to get dx on its own:

$$u = \sqrt{2x-3} \;\Rightarrow\; \frac{du}{dx} = \frac{1}{\sqrt{2x-3}} = \frac{1}{u} \;\Rightarrow\; dx = u\ du$$

- Rearrange the substitution to get an expression for x:

$$u = \sqrt{2x-3} \;\Rightarrow\; x = \frac{u^2+3}{2}$$

- Convert the limits from x-values to u-values:

$$x = 2 \quad\Rightarrow\quad u = \sqrt{2(2)-3} = \sqrt{1} = 1$$

$$x = \frac{7}{2} \quad\Rightarrow\quad u = \sqrt{2\left(\frac{7}{2}\right)-3} = \sqrt{4} = 2$$

- Substituting everything back into the original integral gives:

$$\begin{aligned}
\int_2^{\frac{7}{2}} x\sqrt{2x-3}\ dx &= \int_1^2 \frac{u^2+3}{2} \times u \times u\ du \\
&= \frac{1}{2}\int_1^2 u^4 + 3u^2\ du \\
&= \frac{1}{2}\left[\frac{u^5}{5} + u^3\right]_1^2 \\
&= \left[\frac{2^5}{10} + \frac{2^3}{2}\right] - \left[\frac{1^5}{10} + \frac{1^3}{2}\right] = \frac{36}{5} - \frac{3}{5} = \boxed{\frac{33}{5}}
\end{aligned}$$

Exercise 6.2

Q1 Find the exact values of the following using the given substitutions:

a) $\int_{\frac{2}{3}}^1 (3x-2)^4\ dx,\quad u = 3x-2$ b) $\int_0^1 x^2(2x^3-1)^2\ dx,\quad u = 2x^3-1$

c) $\int_0^{\frac{\pi}{6}} 8\sin^3 x\cos x\ dx,\quad u = \sin x$ d) $\int_0^{\sqrt{3}} x\sqrt{x^2+1}\ dx,\quad u = \sqrt{x^2+1}$

Q2 Use an appropriate substitution to find the exact value of each of the following:

a) $\int_2^{\sqrt{5}} x(x^2-3)^4\ dx$ b) $\int_1^2 x(3x-4)^3\ dx$ c) $\int_2^{10} \frac{x}{\sqrt{x-1}}\ dx$

Q3 Using the substitution $u = 3 - \sqrt{x}$, find the area bounded by the curve $y = \dfrac{1}{3 - \sqrt{x}}$, the x-axis and the lines $x = 1$ and $x = 4$.
Give your answer in the form $a + b\ln 2$, where a and b are integers.

Q3 Hint: It doesn't matter if the substitution makes the upper limit lower than the lower limit — but if you prefer them the 'right' way round, you can swap them and put a minus sign in front of the whole integral. You'll get the same answer both ways.

Q4 Find $\int_0^1 2e^x(1+e^x)^3\ dx$ (to 1 d.p.), using the substitution $u = 1 + e^x$.

Q5 Find the area bounded by the curve $y = \dfrac{x}{\sqrt{3x+1}}$, the x-axis and the lines $x = 1$ and $x = 5$. Use the substitution $u = \sqrt{3x+1}$.

Trig identities

Tip: If you need a reminder of the trig identities, they're given in Chapter 2 — see p.50.

Trig identities and **formulas** can make for some pretty tricky **integration questions** involving trig functions. Here are a couple of examples:

Examples

a) Use the substitution $u = \tan x$ to find $\int \dfrac{\sec^4 x}{\sqrt{\tan x}}\, dx$.

- First, work out what all the substitutions will be. Start by finding dx:

$$u = \tan x \;\Rightarrow\; \frac{du}{dx} = \sec^2 x \;\Rightarrow\; dx = \frac{1}{\sec^2 x}\, du$$

- This substitution for dx will leave $\sec^2 x$ on the numerator — so now you need to find $\sec^2 x$ in terms of u:

  From the identity $\sec^2 x \equiv 1 + \tan^2 x$, $\quad u = \tan x \Rightarrow \sec^2 x \equiv 1 + u^2$

- Then substitute all these bits into the integral:

$$\int \frac{\sec^4 x}{\sqrt{\tan x}}\, dx = \int \frac{(1 + u^2) \times \sec^2 x}{\sqrt{u}} \times \frac{1}{\sec^2 x}\, du$$

$$= \int \frac{1}{\sqrt{u}} + \frac{u^2}{\sqrt{u}}\, du = \int u^{-\frac{1}{2}} + u^{\frac{3}{2}}\, du$$

$$= 2u^{\frac{1}{2}} + \frac{2}{5}u^{\frac{5}{2}} + C = 2\sqrt{\tan x} + \frac{2}{5}\sqrt{\tan^5 x} + C$$

b) Calculate $\int_{\frac{1}{2}}^{\frac{\sqrt{3}}{2}} \dfrac{4}{\sqrt{1 - x^2}}\, dx$, using the substitution $x = \sin \theta$, where $-\dfrac{\pi}{2} \le \theta \le \dfrac{\pi}{2}$.

- Start by differentiating x with respect to θ, and use the result to find dx:

$$x = \sin \theta \;\Rightarrow\; \frac{dx}{d\theta} = \cos \theta \;\Rightarrow\; dx = \cos \theta\, d\theta$$

Tip: Notice that $\sin \theta$ has an inverse because θ is restricted to between $-\frac{\pi}{2}$ and $\frac{\pi}{2}$.

- Use the substitution to convert the limits from x to θ:

$$x = \sin \theta \Rightarrow \theta = \sin^{-1} x. \text{ So } x = \frac{\sqrt{3}}{2} \Rightarrow \theta = \frac{\pi}{3} \text{ and } x = \frac{1}{2} \Rightarrow \theta = \frac{\pi}{6}$$

Tip: The identity $\sin^2\theta + \cos^2\theta \equiv 1$ was used to simplify the integral here.

- Now solve the integral:

$$\int_{\frac{1}{2}}^{\frac{\sqrt{3}}{2}} \frac{4}{\sqrt{1 - x^2}}\, dx = \int_{\frac{\pi}{6}}^{\frac{\pi}{3}} \frac{4}{\sqrt{1 - \sin^2\theta}} \cos \theta\, d\theta = \int_{\frac{\pi}{6}}^{\frac{\pi}{3}} \frac{4\cos\theta}{\sqrt{\cos^2\theta}}\, d\theta$$

$$= \int_{\frac{\pi}{6}}^{\frac{\pi}{3}} 4\, d\theta = [4\theta]_{\frac{\pi}{6}}^{\frac{\pi}{3}} = \frac{4\pi}{3} - \frac{2\pi}{3} = \frac{2\pi}{3}$$

Exercise 6.3

Q1-2 Hint: Remember, the phrase 'exact value' is usually a clue that the answer will include a surd or π.

Q1 Find the exact value $\int_0^1 \dfrac{1}{1 + x^2}\, dx$ using the substitution $x = \tan \theta$ where $-\dfrac{\pi}{2} \le \theta \le \dfrac{\pi}{2}$.

Q2 Use the substitution $x = 2\sin \theta$, where $-\dfrac{\pi}{2} \le \theta \le \dfrac{\pi}{2}$, to find the exact value of $\int_1^{\sqrt{3}} \dfrac{1}{(4 - x^2)^{\frac{3}{2}}}\, dx$.

Q3 Find $\int 2\tan^3 x\, dx$ using the substitution $u = \sec^2 x$.

7. Integration by Parts

Sadly, not every integration problem can be solved with a nifty substitution or a clever trick. Integration by parts is another way to deal with integrating a product of two functions — it involves both differentiation and integration.

Learning Objectives:

- Understand that integration by parts comes from the product rule.
- Be able to use integration by parts to integrate functions.
- Be able to integrate functions where integration by parts has to be applied more than once.

Integration by parts

If you have a **product** to integrate but you can't use any of the methods you've learnt so far, you might be able to use **integration by parts**.

The **formula** for integrating by parts is:

$$\int u\frac{dv}{dx}\,dx = uv - \int v\frac{du}{dx}\,dx$$

where u and v are both functions of x.

Here's the **proof** of this formula. You're **not** expected to know it for the exam, but you might find it useful.

Start with the **product rule**:

- If u and v are both functions of x, then

$$\frac{d}{dx}uv = u\frac{dv}{dx} + v\frac{du}{dx}$$

- Integrate both sides of the product rule with respect to x:

$$\int \frac{d}{dx}uv\,dx = \int u\frac{dv}{dx}\,dx + \int v\frac{du}{dx}\,dx$$

- On the left-hand side, uv is differentiated, then integrated — so you end up back at uv:

$$uv = \int u\frac{dv}{dx}\,dx + \int v\frac{du}{dx}\,dx$$

- Now just rearrange to get:

$$\int u\frac{dv}{dx}\,dx = uv - \int v\frac{du}{dx}\,dx$$

Tip: You should be familiar with the product rule from Chapter 4.

Tip: The integration by parts formula is sometimes written
$$\int uv'\,dx = uv - \int vu'\,dx$$
— you might find this version easier to use.

- The hardest thing about integration by parts is **deciding** which bit of your product should be u and which bit should be $\frac{dv}{dx}$.
- There's no set rule for this — you just have to look at both parts, see which one **differentiates** to give something **nice**, then set that one as u.
- For example, if you have a product that has a **single x** as one part of it, choose this to be u. It differentiates to **1**, which makes **integrating** $v\frac{du}{dx}$ very easy.

Examples

a) Find $\int 2xe^x dx$.

- Start by working out what should be u and what should be $\frac{dv}{dx}$ — choose them so that $v\frac{du}{dx}$ is easier to integrate than $2xe^x$.

  The two factors are $2x$ and e^x, so try them both ways round:

  If $u = 2x$ and $\frac{dv}{dx} = e^x$, then $v\frac{du}{dx} = 2e^x$ ◄─── Easier to integrate than $2xe^x$.

  If $u = e^x$ and $\frac{dv}{dx} = 2x$, then $v\frac{du}{dx} = x^2e^x$

  So let $u = 2x$ and $\frac{dv}{dx} = e^x$.

Tip: You don't always need to work out both possible versions. Here, e^x won't change whether you integrate it or differentiate it, so you just need to think about whether the integration would be made easier by differentiating $2x$ or by integrating it.

- Put u, v, $\frac{du}{dx}$ and $\frac{dv}{dx}$ into the integration by parts formula:

  $u = 2x \Rightarrow \frac{du}{dx} = 2, \ \frac{dv}{dx} = e^x \Rightarrow v = e^x$

  $\int 2xe^x dx = \int u\frac{dv}{dx} dx = uv - \int v\frac{du}{dx} dx$

  $= 2xe^x - \int 2e^x dx$ ◄─── Don't forget the constant of integration.

  $= 2xe^x - 2e^x + C$

b) Find $\int x^3 \ln x \, dx$.

- Choose u and $\frac{dv}{dx}$:

  Let $u = \ln x$ and $\frac{dv}{dx} = x^3$.

  $u = \ln x \Rightarrow \frac{du}{dx} = \frac{1}{x}, \ \frac{dv}{dx} = x^3 \Rightarrow v = \frac{x^4}{4}$

Tip: If you have a product that has $\ln x$ as one of its factors, let $u = \ln x$, as $\ln x$ is easy to differentiate but quite tricky to integrate (see page 127).

- Put u, v, $\frac{du}{dx}$ and $\frac{dv}{dx}$ into the integration by parts formula:

  $\int x^3 \ln x \, dx = \frac{x^4 \ln x}{4} - \int \frac{x^4}{4} \times \frac{1}{x} dx$

  $= \frac{x^4 \ln x}{4} - \frac{1}{4}\int x^3 dx$

  $= \frac{x^4 \ln x}{4} - \frac{x^4}{16} + C$

Until now, you haven't been able to integrate **ln x**, but **integration by parts** gives you a way to get around this. The trick is to write ln x as $1 \cdot \ln x$.

- You can write ln x as $1 \cdot \ln x$. So let $u = \ln x$ and let $\frac{dv}{dx} = 1$.

  $u = \ln x \implies \frac{du}{dx} = \frac{1}{x}$

  $\frac{dv}{dx} = 1 \implies v = x$

- Putting these into the formula gives:

  $\int \ln x \, dx = x \ln x - \int x \frac{1}{x} \, dx$

  $\qquad\qquad = x \ln x - \int 1 \, dx$

  $\qquad\qquad = x \ln x - x + C$

You can use **integration by parts** on definite integrals too. The only change from the method for indefinite integrals is that you have to **apply the limits** of the integral to the **uv** bit.

The integration by parts formula for definite integrals can be written like this:

$$\int_a^b u \frac{dv}{dx} \, dx = \left[uv \right]_a^b - \int_a^b v \frac{du}{dx} \, dx$$

Example

Find the exact value of $\int_0^{\frac{\pi}{2}} 4x \sin\left(\frac{x}{2}\right) dx$.

- Choose u and $\frac{dv}{dx}$.

  $\sin\left(\frac{x}{2}\right)$ will give a cos function whether you integrate or differentiate it, so the only way to get a simpler $\int v \frac{du}{dx} \, dx$ is to make $u = 4x$.

  Let $u = 4x$ and $\frac{dv}{dx} = \sin\left(\frac{x}{2}\right)$

  $u = 4x \implies \frac{du}{dx} = 4$

  $\frac{dv}{dx} = \sin\left(\frac{x}{2}\right) \implies v = -2 \cos\left(\frac{x}{2}\right)$

- Substitute everything into the formula and complete the integration:

  $\int_0^{\frac{\pi}{2}} 4x \sin\left(\frac{x}{2}\right) dx = \left[-8x \cos\left(\frac{x}{2}\right) \right]_0^{\frac{\pi}{2}} - \int_0^{\frac{\pi}{2}} -8 \cos\left(\frac{x}{2}\right) dx$

  $\qquad\qquad = -8 \left[x \cos\left(\frac{x}{2}\right) \right]_0^{\frac{\pi}{2}} + 16 \left[\sin\left(\frac{x}{2}\right) \right]_0^{\frac{\pi}{2}}$

  $\qquad\qquad = -8 \left[\frac{\pi}{2} \cos\left(\frac{\pi}{4}\right) - 0 \cos(0) \right] + 16 \left[\sin\left(\frac{\pi}{4}\right) - \sin(0) \right]$

  $\qquad\qquad = -8 \left[\frac{\pi}{2} \frac{1}{\sqrt{2}} \right] + 16 \left[\frac{1}{\sqrt{2}} \right]$

  $\qquad\qquad = -\frac{4\pi}{\sqrt{2}} + \frac{16}{\sqrt{2}}$

  $\qquad\qquad = 8\sqrt{2} - 2\pi\sqrt{2}$

Tip: Go back to p.106 if you want a reminder about integrating trig functions.

Q1 Use integration by parts to find:

a) $\int xe^x \, dx$ b) $\int xe^{-x} \, dx$ c) $\int xe^{-\frac{x}{3}} \, dx$ d) $\int x(e^x + 1) \, dx$

Q2 Use integration by parts to find:

a) $\int x \sin x \, dx$ b) $\int 2x \cos x \, dx$

c) $\int 3x \cos\left(\frac{1}{2}x\right) dx$ d) $\int 2x(1 - \sin x) \, dx$

Q3 Use integration by parts to find:

a) $\int 2 \ln x \, dx$ b) $\int x^4 \ln x \, dx$ c) $\int \ln 4x \, dx$ d) $\int \ln x^3 \, dx$

Q4 Use integration by parts to find:

a) $\int 20x(x + 1)^3 \, dx$ b) $\int 30x\sqrt{(2x + 1)} \, dx$

Q5 Use integration by parts to find the exact values of the following:

a) $\int_0^1 12xe^{2x} \, dx$ b) $\int_0^{\frac{\pi}{3}} 18x \sin 3x \, dx$ c) $\int_1^2 \frac{1}{x^2} \ln x \, dx$

Q6 Find $\int \dfrac{x}{e^{2x}} \, dx$.

Q7 Find $\int (x + 1)\sqrt{(x + 2)} \, dx$.

Q8 Find $\int \ln(x + 1) \, dx$.

Repeated use of integration by parts

Sometimes **integration by parts** leaves you with a function for $v\frac{du}{dx}$ which is **simpler** than the function you started with, but still **tricky to integrate**.

You might have to carry out integration by parts **again** to find $\int v\frac{du}{dx} \, dx$.

Example 1

Find $\int x^2 \sin x \, dx$.

- Let $u = x^2$ and let $\frac{dv}{dx} = \sin x$. Then $\frac{du}{dx} = 2x$ and $v = -\cos x$.

- Putting these into the formula gives:
$$\int x^2 \sin x \, dx = -x^2 \cos x - \int -2x \cos x \, dx = -x^2 \cos x + \int 2x \cos x \, dx$$

- $2x \cos x$ isn't very easy to integrate, but you can integrate by parts again:
Let $u_1 = 2x$ and let $\frac{dv_1}{dx} = \cos x$. Then $\frac{du_1}{dx} = 2$ and $v_1 = \sin x$.

- Putting these into the formula gives:
$$\int 2x \cos x \, dx = 2x \sin x - \int 2 \sin x \, dx = 2x \sin x + 2\cos x + C$$

- So $\int x^2 \sin x \, dx = -x^2 \cos x + \int 2x \cos x \, dx$
$$= -x^2 \cos x + 2x \sin x + 2\cos x + C$$

Tip: Calling the different parts u_1 and v_1 just means you don't get confused with the u and v used in the first integration.

Example 2

Use integration by parts to find $\int_2^3 x^2(x-1)^{-4}\,dx$.

- Let $u = x^2$ and let $\dfrac{dv}{dx} = (x-1)^{-4}$. Then $\dfrac{du}{dx} = 2x$ and $v = -\dfrac{1}{3}(x-1)^{-3}$.

- Putting these into the formula gives:
$$\int_2^3 x^2(x-1)^{-4}\,dx = \left[-\frac{x^2}{3}(x-1)^{-3}\right]_2^3 - \int_2^3 -\frac{2x}{3}(x-1)^{-3}\,dx$$
$$= \left[-\frac{x^2}{3}(x-1)^{-3}\right]_2^3 + \frac{2}{3}\int_2^3 x(x-1)^{-3}\,dx$$

> **Tip:** The formula for integrating $(ax+b)^n$ is used a few times in this example — go back to p.100 if you've forgotten how it works.

- $\int_2^3 x(x-1)^{-3}\,dx$ is still tricky to integrate. Use integration by parts again:

  Let $u_1 = x$ and let $\dfrac{dv_1}{dx} = (x-1)^{-3}$. Then $\dfrac{du_1}{dx} = 1$ and $v_1 = -\dfrac{1}{2}(x-1)^{-2}$.

- Put these into the formula:
$$\int_2^3 x(x-1)^{-3}\,dx = \left[-\frac{x}{2}(x-1)^{-2}\right]_2^3 - \int_2^3 -\frac{1}{2}(x-1)^{-2}\,dx$$
$$= \left[-\frac{x}{2}(x-1)^{-2}\right]_2^3 - \frac{1}{2}\left[(x-1)^{-1}\right]_2^3$$
$$= \left[-\frac{3}{2}(2)^{-2} + \frac{2}{2}(1)^{-2}\right] - \frac{1}{2}\left[2^{-1} - 1^{-1}\right]$$
$$= \left[-\frac{3}{8} + 1\right] - \frac{1}{2}\left[\frac{1}{2} - 1\right]$$
$$= \frac{5}{8} + \frac{1}{4} = \frac{7}{8}$$

- Now you can evaluate the original integral:
$$\int_2^3 x^2(x-1)^{-4}\,dx = \left[-\frac{x^2}{3}(x-1)^{-3}\right]_2^3 + \frac{2}{3}\int_2^3 x(x-1)^{-3}\,dx$$
$$= \left[-\frac{x^2}{3}(x-1)^{-3}\right]_2^3 + \frac{2}{3}\left(\frac{7}{8}\right)$$
$$= \left[\left(-\frac{9}{3}(2)^{-3}\right) - \left(-\frac{4}{3}(1)^{-3}\right)\right] + \frac{7}{12}$$
$$= \left[-\frac{9}{24} + \frac{4}{3}\right] + \frac{7}{12}$$
$$= \frac{23}{24} + \frac{7}{12}$$
$$= \boxed{\frac{37}{24}}$$

Exercise 7.2

Q1 Use integration by parts twice to find:

a) $\int x^2 e^x\,dx$ b) $\int x^2\cos x\,dx$ c) $\int 4x^2\sin 2x\,dx$

Q2 Find $\int_{-1}^0 x^2(x+1)^4\,dx$ using integration by parts.

Q3 Use integration by parts to find the area enclosed by the curve $y = x^2 e^{-2x}$, the x-axis and the lines $x = 0$ and $x = 1$.

8. Volumes of Revolution

Learning Objectives:

- Understand what is meant by the term 'volume of revolution'.
- Be able to calculate the volume of revolution for the rotation of a curve about the *x*-axis.
- Be able to calculate the volume of revolution for the rotation of a curve about the *y*-axis.

So far, you've seen integration used to find the area under a curve. Now you'll see how it can also be used to calculate the volume of certain solid shapes.

Rotating about the *x*-axis

- If you're given a **definite integral**, the solution you come up with is the **area under the graph** between the two **limits** (you did this back in C1 and C2).
- If you now **rotate** that area through 2π radians **about the *x*-axis**, you'll come up with a **solid** — and this is what you want to find the **volume** of.
- For example, you can calculate a **definite integral** to find the **area** bounded by the curve $y = 4 - x^2$, the *x*-axis and the lines $x = 0$ and $x = 2$...

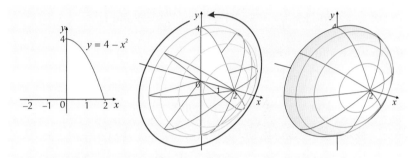

...and if you rotate that area in a full circle, centred at the *x*-axis, you get a sort of dome shape. The **volume** of the dome is a **volume of revolution**.

- The **formula** for finding the **volume of revolution** is:

$$V = \pi \int_{x_1}^{x_2} y^2 \, dx$$

where y is a function of x (i.e. $y = f(x)$) and x_1 and x_2 are the limits of x.

You need to **learn** this formula for your exam — it's **not** on the formula sheet.

Tip: V is the volume of the solid you get when you rotate R:

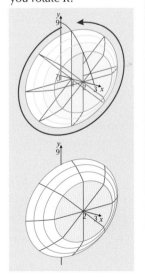

Example 1

The region R is enclosed by the curve $y = 9 - x^2$, the *x*-axis and the lines $x = 1$ and $x = 2$. Find the volume, V, of the solid formed when R is rotated through 2π radians about the *x*-axis.

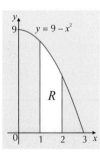

- If $y = 9 - x^2$, then $y^2 = 81 - 18x^2 + x^4$.
- Putting this into the formula gives:

$$V = \pi \int_{x_1}^{x_2} y^2 \, dx$$

$$= \pi \int_1^2 81 - 18x^2 + x^4 \, dx$$

$$= \pi \left[81x - 6x^3 + \frac{x^5}{5} \right]_1^2$$

$$= \pi \left[\left(81(2) - 6(8) + \frac{32}{5} \right) - \left(81(1) - 6(1) + \frac{1}{5} \right) \right]$$

$$= \pi \left[\left(162 - 48 + \frac{32}{5} \right) - \left(81 - 6 + \frac{1}{5} \right) \right]$$

$$= \pi \left[\frac{602}{5} - \frac{376}{5} \right] = \frac{226}{5} \pi$$

Example 2

Find the volume, V, of the solid formed when R, the area enclosed by the curve $y = \sqrt{6x^2 - 3x + 2}$, the x-axis and the lines $x = 1$ and $x = 2$, is rotated 2π radians about the x-axis.

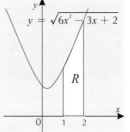

- If $y = \sqrt{6x^2 - 3x + 2}$, then $y^2 = 6x^2 - 3x + 2$.
- Putting this into the formula gives:

$$V = \pi \int_1^2 6x^2 - 3x + 2 \, dx$$

$$= \pi \left[2x^3 - \frac{3}{2}x^2 + 2x \right]_1^2$$

$$= \pi \left(\left[2(8) - \frac{3}{2}(4) + 2(2) \right] - \left[2(1) - \frac{3}{2}(1) + 2(1) \right] \right)$$

$$= \pi \left(14 - \frac{5}{2} \right) = \frac{23}{2}\pi$$

Tip: Don't forget to square y — you might think it's obvious, but it's a common mistake.

Exercise 8.1

Q1 For each of the following, find the exact volume of the solid generated when the area enclosed by the x-axis and the given curve and lines is rotated 2π radians about the x-axis.

a) $y = 4x$, $x = 1$ and $x = 2$ b) $y = \sqrt{x + 2}$, $x = 0$ and $x = 2$

c) $x^2 + y^2 = 4$, $x = 0$ and $x = 2$

Q2 For each of the following, the region R is enclosed by the curve $y = f(x)$, the lines $x = x_1$ and $x = x_2$ and the x-axis. In each case, find the exact volume of revolution formed when R is rotated $360°$ about the x-axis.

a) $f(x) = \frac{2}{x}$, $x_1 = 2$, $x_2 = 8$ b) $f(x) = e^x$, $x_1 = 0$, $x_2 = 2$

c) $f(x) = \frac{3}{\sqrt{x}}$, $x_1 = 1$, $x_2 = 2$ d) $f(x) = 1 + \sqrt{x}$, $x_1 = 0$, $x_2 = 1$

Q3 In each of the following questions, the given curve and lines enclose a region A. For each, find the exact volume of the solid formed by rotating region A about the x-axis by 2π radians.

a) $y = \sqrt{\sin 2x}$, $y = 0$, $x = 0$ and $x = \frac{\pi}{6}$

b) $y = \frac{2}{\sqrt{1 + 2x}}$, $y = 0$, $x = 0$ and $x = 3$

c) $y = \frac{1}{1 + 3x}$, $y = 0$, $x = 0$ and $x = 1$

d) $y = 2xe^x$, $y = 0$, $x = 0$ and $x = 1$

e) $y = x\sqrt{\sin x}$, $y = 0$, $x = 0$ and $x = \frac{\pi}{4}$

Q3 d)-e) Hint: You'll need to use integration by parts here.

Rotating about the *y*-axis

- As well as **rotating** about the *x*-axis, you can also find the **volume** of the **solid** formed when the area between a curve and the **y-axis** is rotated 2π **radians** about the **y-axis**.

- So if you take the **area** between the curve $y = 4 - x^2$, the *y*-axis and the lines $y = 0$ and $y = 4$, and **rotate** it about the **y-axis**, you end up with a solid shape that looks like this:

Tip: This is the curve that was used on page 130. Note that this time the area is bounded by the *y*-axis (between $y = 0$ and $y = 4$) rather than the *x*-axis (between $x = 0$ and $x = 2$).

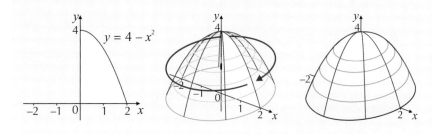

- The **method** is very similar to the one you used for rotating about the *x*-axis — you just use a slightly different **formula**:

$$V = \pi \int_{y_1}^{y_2} x^2 \, dy$$

where x is a function of y (i.e. $x = g(y)$) and y_1 and y_2 are the limits of y.

- So here, you need to **rearrange** the equation to get x^2 **on its own** — you'll end up with an equation in terms of y, which you integrate **with respect to** y. The **limits** are also in terms of y — they're **horizontal lines** at y_1 and y_2.

- Again, this formula isn't given to you in the exam, so you need to **learn** it (and make sure you don't get it mixed up with the formula for rotating about the *x*-axis).

Example 1

The region R is enclosed by the curve $y = 9 - x^2$, the *y*-axis and the lines $y = 2$ and $y = 6$.
Find the volume, V, of the solid formed when R is rotated 2π radians about the *y*-axis.

Tip: This is the same function as in the example on p.130 — but this time it's being rotated about the *y*-axis.

- First, rearrange the equation to make x^2 the subject: $y = 9 - x^2 \Rightarrow x^2 = 9 - y$.
- Putting this into the formula gives:

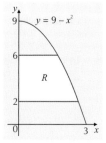

$$V = \pi \int_{y_1}^{y_2} x^2 \, dy$$

$$= \pi \int_{2}^{6} 9 - y \, dy$$

$$= \pi \left[9y - \frac{y^2}{2} \right]_2^6$$

$$= \pi[(54 - 18) - (18 - 2)]$$

$$= 20\pi$$

Example 2

Find the volume, V, of the solid formed when R, the area enclosed by the curve $y = \sqrt{x^2 + 5}$, the y-axis and the lines $y = 3$ and $y = 6$ is rotated 2π radians about the y-axis.

- First, rearrange the equation to get x^2 on its own:

$$y = \sqrt{x^2 + 5} \Rightarrow y^2 = x^2 + 5 \quad \text{so } x^2 = y^2 - 5.$$

- Now integrate:

$$V = \pi \int_3^6 y^2 - 5 \, dy$$
$$= \pi \left[\frac{1}{3}y^3 - 5y \right]_3^6$$
$$= \pi(42 - (-6))$$
$$= \boxed{48\pi}$$

Exercise 8.2

For all questions in this exercise, give your answers in terms of π.

Q1   Find the volume of the solid formed when the area bounded by the curve $y = x^2 + 2$, the y-axis and the lines $y = 3$ and $y = 6$ is rotated 2π radians about the y-axis.

Q2   The area bounded by the curve $y = \frac{x^2}{2} - 2$, the y-axis and the lines $y = 1$ and $y = 3$ is rotated 2π radians about the y-axis. Find the volume of the solid produced.

Q3   Find the volume of the solid formed when the area bounded by the curve $y^2 = x$, the y-axis and the lines $y = -1$ and $y = 2$ is rotated by 2π radians about the y-axis.

Q4   The area bounded by the ellipse $3y^2 + x^2 = 9$ between the y-axis and the lines $y = 1$ and $y = 2$ is rotated by 2π radians about the y-axis. Find the volume of the solid produced.

Q5   A curve is defined by $y = 3x^2 - 2$. The area bounded by the curve, the y-axis and the lines $y = -2$ and $y = 10$ is rotated by 2π radians about the y-axis. Find the volume of revolution of the curve between these lines.

Q6   The area bounded by the curve $y^2 - y = 10 - x^2$, the y-axis and the lines $y = 1$ and $y = 2$ is rotated through 2π radians about the y-axis. Show that the volume of revolution is $\frac{55}{6}\pi$.

Review Exercise — Chapter 5

Q1 a) Find $\int \dfrac{1}{\sqrt[3]{(2-11x)}}\,dx$

b) Show that the area under the curve $y = \dfrac{1}{\sqrt[3]{(2-11x)}}$ between
$x = -\dfrac{62}{11}$ and $x = -\dfrac{123}{11}$ is $\dfrac{27}{22}$.

Q2 Find the equation of the curve that has the derivative $\dfrac{dy}{dx} = (1-7x)^{\frac{1}{2}}$
and goes through the point $(0, 1)$.

Q3 Find the following integrals, giving your answers in terms of e or ln.

a) $\int 4e^{2x}\,dx$

b) $\int e^{3x-5}\,dx$

c) $\int \dfrac{2}{3x}\,dx$

d) $\int \dfrac{2}{2x+1}\,dx$

Q4 If $\int \dfrac{8}{2-x} - \dfrac{8}{x}\,dx = \ln P + C,$

where P is an expression in terms of x and C is a constant, find P.

Q5 Find the following integrals (A and B are constants):

a) $\int \cos(x+A)\,dx$

b) $\int \sin(A-x)\,dx$

c) $\int \csc^{2}((A+B)t + A + B)\,dt$

Q6 Find the following integrals:

a) $\int \cos 4x - \sec^{2}7x\,dx$

b) $\int 6\sec 3x\tan 3x - \csc^{2}\dfrac{x}{5}\,dx.$

Q7 Find the following integrals:

a) $\int \dfrac{\cos x}{\sin x}\,dx$

b) $\int \dfrac{20x^{4} + 12x^{2} - 12}{x^{5} + x^{3} - 3x}\,dx$

Q8 Find the following integrals:

a) $\int 3x^2 e^{x^3}\,dx$

b) $\int 2x\cos(x^2)e^{\sin(x^2)}\,dx$

c) $\int \sec 4x \tan 4x\, e^{\sec 4x}\,dx$

Q9 Find the following integrals, using the given substitution in each case.

a) $\int 16x(5 - x^2)^5\,dx$, using $u = 5 - x^2$

b) $\int 3\sin\theta\cos^4\theta\,d\theta$, using $u = \cos\theta$

c) $\int e^x(e^x + 1)(e^x - 1)^2\,dx$, using $u = e^x - 1$

Q10 Find the exact value of each of the following, using the given substitutions.

a) $\int_2^4 x(x^2 - 4)^3\,dx$, using $u = x^2 - 4$

b) $\int_{\frac{\pi}{4}}^{\frac{\pi}{3}} \sec^4 x\tan x\,dx$, using $u = \sec x$

c) $\int_3^{11} \dfrac{2x}{\sqrt{3x - 8}}\,dx$, using $u = \sqrt{3x - 8}$

Q11 Find $\displaystyle\int_1^{\sqrt{3}} \dfrac{4x}{\sqrt{1 + x^2}}\,dx$, using the substitution $x = \cot\theta$, $-\dfrac{\pi}{2} \le \theta \le \dfrac{\pi}{2}$

Q12 Use integration by parts to solve:

a) $\int 3x^2\ln x\,dx$

b) $\int 4x\cos 4x\,dx$

c) $\int_0^4 e^{\frac{x}{2}}x^2\,dx$

Q13 Region R is enclosed by the x-axis and the lines $y = 2x - 1$, $x = 1$ and $x = 3$. Find the exact volume of the solid generated when R is rotated 2π radians about the x-axis.

Q14 Find the exact volume of the solid formed when the area bounded by the curve $y = \dfrac{1}{x}$, the x-axis and the lines $x = 2$ and $x = 4$ is rotated 2π radians about the x-axis.

Q15 Find the exact volume of the solid formed when the region bounded by the curve $y = 4\sqrt{\ln x}$ and the lines $y = 0$, $x = 1$ and $x = 2$ is rotated 2π radians about the x-axis.

Q16 Find the volume of the solid formed when the area bounded by the curve $y = x^2 + 1$, the y-axis and the lines $y = 1$ and $y = 3$ is rotated 2π radians about the y-axis.

Q17 Find the volume of the solid formed when the area bounded by the curve $2y^3 - x^2 - 3 = 0$, the y-axis and the lines $y = 1$ and $y = 2$ is rotated 2π radians about the y-axis.

1   Find

  a) $\displaystyle\int 3e^{(5-6x)}\,dx$.

  (2 marks)

  b) $\displaystyle\int \frac{\csc^2 x - 2}{\cot x + 2x}\,dx$.

  (3 marks)

2   The graph below shows part of a curve with equation $y = \dfrac{2}{3\left(\sqrt[3]{5x-2}\right)}$.

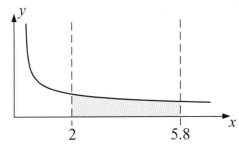

Find, using integration, the area of the shaded region bounded by the curve,
the x-axis, and the lines $x = 2$ and $x = 5.8$.

  (3 marks)

3   Find the volume of the solid formed when the region R, bounded by the curve $y = \csc x$,
the x-axis and the lines $x = \dfrac{\pi}{4}$ and $x = \dfrac{\pi}{3}$, is rotated 2π radians about the x-axis.
Give your answer to 3 decimal places.

  (3 marks)

4   Use integration by parts to find:

a) $\int x \sin 4x \, dx$

(3 marks)

b) $\int x^2 \cos 4x \, dx$

(4 marks)

5   Find the value of $\int_1^2 \frac{8}{x}(\ln x + 2)^3 \, dx$ using the substitution $u = \ln x$.
Give your answer to 4 s.f.

(6 marks)

6   Use integration by parts to calculate the exact value of $\int_1^4 \frac{\ln x}{x^2} \, dx$.

(5 marks)

7   The graph below shows the curve of $y = \frac{1}{x^2}$ for $x > 0$.

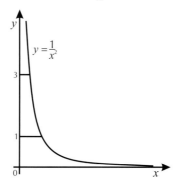

The region bounded by the curve, the y-axis and the lines $y = 1$ and $y = 3$ is rotated 2π
radians about the y-axis. Calculate the exact volume of the solid formed.

(5 marks)

1. Location of Roots

Sometimes finding the solutions of an equation algebraically is quite difficult. In these situations, it's often helpful to find roughly where the roots are (the points where f(x) = 0) by looking at the graph.

Locating roots by changes of sign

'Solving' or 'finding the roots of' an equation (where f(*x*) = 0) is the same as finding the values of *x* where the graph crosses the *x*-axis.

- The graph of the function gives you a rough idea of **how many** roots there are and **where** they are. E.g. the function f(*x*) = $3x^2 - x^3 - 2$ (below) has 3 roots, since it crosses the *x*-axis three times (i.e. there are 3 solutions to the equation $3x^2 - x^3 - 2 = 0$). From the graph you can see there's a root at *x* = 1 and two others near *x* = −1 and *x* = 3.

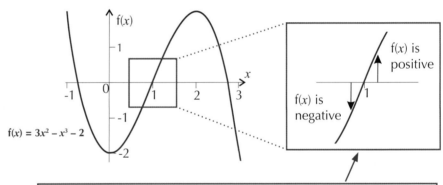

$$f(x) = 3x^2 - x^3 - 2$$

> For each root in the graph above, f(*x*) goes from positive to negative or vice versa — **f(x) changes sign as it passes through a root.** So to find if there's a root between two values 'a' and 'b', work out f(a) and f(b). If the signs are different, there's a root somewhere between them.

- Be careful though — this only applies to **continuous functions** (where there is no break or jump in the line of the graph). In some graphs, like tan *x*, the line jumps from positive to negative without actually crossing the *x*-axis, so you might get fooled into thinking there's a root when there isn't.

- Often you'll be given an **approximation** to a root and be asked to show that it's correct to a certain accuracy. To do this, choose the right **upper and lower bounds** and work out if there's a sign change between them.

> The **lower bound** is the **lowest** value a number could have and still be **rounded up** to the correct answer. The **upper bound** is the **upper limit** of the values which will be **rounded down** to the correct answer.

Tip: The graph doesn't have to be continuous throughout — only in the bit where you're trying to find a root.

Example

Show that one root of the equation $x^3 - x^2 - 9 = 0$ is $x = 2.472$ correct to 3 d.p.

- If $x = 2.472$ is a root rounded to 3 decimal places, the exact root must lie between the **upper and lower bounds** of this value — **2.4715** and **2.4725**. Any value in this interval would be rounded to 2.472 to 3 d.p.

$$2.471 \quad ^{2.4715} \quad 2.472 \quad ^{2.4725} \quad 2.473$$

Tip: Although 2.4725 would actually be rounded up to 2.473, everything below it would be rounded down to 2.472. It's just a limit.

- The function $f(x) = x^3 - x^2 - 9$ is **continuous**, so you know a root lies in the interval $2.4715 \leq x < 2.4725$ if $f(2.4715)$ and $f(2.4725)$ have **different signs**.

- $f(2.4715) = 2.4715^3 - 2.4715^2 - 9 = -0.0116...$

  $f(2.4725) = 2.4725^3 - 2.4725^2 - 9 = 0.0017...$

- $f(2.4715)$ and $f(2.4725)$ have different signs, so a root must lie between them.
  Since any value between them would be rounded to 2.472 to 3 d.p. this answer must be correct.

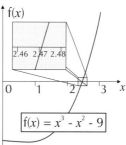

Tip: The function is continuous because it's just a cubic curve:

It has no breaks or jumps.

Exercise 1.1

Q1 $f(x) = x^3 - 5x + 1$
Show that there is a root of $f(x) = 0$ in the interval $2 < x < 3$.

Q2 $f(x) = \sin 2x - x$ (x is in radians)
Show that there is a root of $f(x) = 0$ in the interval $0.9 < x < 1.0$.

Q2 Hint: Remember to set your calculator to radians before doing this question.

Q3 $f(x) = x^3 + \ln x - 2$
Show that there is a root of $f(x) = 0$ in the interval $1.2 < x < 1.3$.

Q4 $f(x) = x^2 + \dfrac{1}{x} - 7$
Show that there is a root of $f(x)$ in the interval $2.5 < x < 2.6$.

Q5 Show that there is a root, α, of the equation $\cos x + x = 0$ which lies in the interval $-0.8 < \alpha < -0.7$ (α is in radians).

Q6 Show that there is a root, β, of the equation $e^x + x - 8 = 0$ which lies in the interval $1 < \beta < 2$.

Q7 Show that there are 2 solutions, α and β, to the equation $3x - x^4 + 3 = 0$, such that $1.6 < \alpha < 1.7$ and $-1 < \beta < 0$.

Q8 Show that there are 2 solutions, α and β, to the equation $e^{x-2} - \sqrt{x} = 0$, such that $0.01 < \alpha < 0.02$ and $2.4 < \beta < 2.5$.

Q9 Show that $x = 2.8$ is a solution to the equation $x^3 - 7x - 2 = 0$ to 1 d.p.

Q10 Show that $x = 0.7$ is a solution to the equation $2x - \frac{1}{x} = 0$ to 1 d.p.

Q11 $f(x) = e^x - x^3 - 5x$
Verify that a root of the equation $f(x) = 0$ is $x = 0.25$ correct to 2 d.p.

Q12 $f(x) = x^3 - 2x^2 - 3$
Verify that $x = 2.486$ is a root of the equation $f(x) = 0$ correct to 3 d.p.

Q13 Hint: Roots of f(x) are given when f(x) = 0, so you might need to rearrange the equation before doing any calculations.

Q13 Show that a solution to the equation $4x - 2x^3 = 15$ lies between -2.3 and -2.2.

Q14 Show that a solution to the equation $\ln(x + 3) = 5x$ lies between 0.23 and 0.24.

Q15 Shows that a solution to the equation $e^{3x}\sin x = 5$ lies between $x = 0$ and $x = 1$ (x is in radians).

Sketching graphs to find approximate roots

Sometimes it's easier to find the number of roots and roughly where they are if you **sketch** the graphs first.

- In questions like this you'll often be given **2 equations** to **sketch** on the same set of axes. Sketching graphs was first covered in C1 if you need a reminder.

Tip: Setting the equations equal to each other and then rearranging them to get f(x) = 0 gets you to where you were in the previous section.

- At the points where they **cross** each other, the two equations are equal. So for $y = x + 3$ and $y = x^2$, at the points of intersection you know that $x + 3 = x^2$, which you can rearrange to get $x^2 - x - 3 = 0$.

> The **number of roots** of this 'combined' equation is the same as the number of **points of intersection** of the original two graphs. The sketch you made will also show roughly **where** the roots are (it's the same x-value for both), so locating them is a bit easier.

Examples

a) **On the same set of axes, sketch the graphs $y = \ln x$ and $y = (x - 3)^2$.**

- Just sketch the two graphs on a set of axes. You don't need to draw perfectly accurate graphs, but do try and make sure they're as neat as possible.
- The important things are that they're the correct shape and that they cross the axes in the right places.

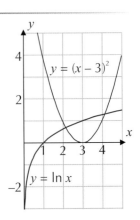

b) Hence work out the number of roots of the equation
   ln x – $(x$ – 3$)^2$ = 0.

- This equation is a combination of the previous two, so what it's asking is 'how many times do the two graphs cross each other?'. The graphs cross twice, so the equation has two roots.

c) Show that there is a solution between 2 and 3, and find this solution to 1 decimal place.

- You can see there's a solution there just by looking at the graph, but to make sure, work it out using the method from the previous topic — put 2 and 3 into the equation and check for a sign change.

$$\ln 2 - (2 - 3)^2 = -0.306...$$
$$\ln 3 - (3 - 3)^2 = 1.098...$$

- The sign has changed, so there is a root between 2 and 3.

- Looking at the picture, you can see that the root is very close to 2, so try again using $x = 2$ and $x = 2.2$.

$$\ln 2.2 - (2.2 - 3)^2 = 0.148...$$

- f(2.2) is positive, so the root is between 2 and 2.2. Trying again with $x = 2.1$ will tell you which it's closer to, as it's halfway between the two.

$$\ln 2.1 - (2.1 - 3)^2 = -0.068...$$ so the root is between 2.1 and 2.2.

- Now you just need to check if it rounds up to 2.2 or down to 2.1 — 2.15 is the upper bound for 2.1 and lower bound for 2.2, so try that.

$$\ln 2.15 - (2.15 - 3)^2 = 0.0429...$$ So the root is between 2.1 and 2.15.

- So the answer rounds down, and the value of the root to 1 d.p is 2.1.

> **Tip:** This is basically the trial and improvement method that you'll have used at GCSE for approximating solutions.

Exercise 1.2

Sketch all graphs in this exercise for $-5 < x < 5$ unless otherwise stated.

Q1 a) On the same axes, sketch the graphs of $y = \frac{1}{x}$ and $y = x - 2$.

   b) Using your graph from part a) write down the number of roots of the equation $\frac{1}{x} = x - 2$ in this interval.

   c) Show that one root of the equation $\frac{1}{x} = x - 2$ lies in the interval $2.4 < x < 2.5$.

> **Q1 Hint:** Remember, roots are solutions of an equation in the form f(x) = 0, so you might need to do some rearranging.

Q2 a) On the same axes, sketch the graphs of $y = 2x^3 - 7x$ and $y = x^2$.

   b) Using your graph from part a) write down the number of roots of the equation $2x^3 - x^2 - 7x = 0$ in this interval.

   c) Show that the equation $2x^3 - x^2 - 7x = 0$ has a root between $x = -2$ and $x = -1$.

Q3 a) On the same axes, sketch the graphs of $y = 2x^2 + 5$ and $y = x + 8$.

b) Write down the number of roots of the equation $2x^2 + 5 = x + 8$.

c) Show that the equation $2x^2 + 5 = x + 8$ has a root in the interval $(1, 2)$.

Q4 a) Sketch the graphs of $y = 2^x - 3$ and $y = \ln x$ on the same axes.

b) $f(x) = \ln x - 2^x + 3$. Using your graph write down the number of roots of the equation $f(x) = 0$.

c) Show that the equation $f(x) = 0$ has a root between 1.8 and 2.2 and find this root to 1 decimal place.

Q5 a) Sketch the graphs of $y = \sqrt{x+1}$ and $y = 2x$ on the same axes.

b) Write down the number of roots of the equation $\sqrt{x+1} = 2x$.

c) Show that the equation $\sqrt{x+1} = 2x$ has a root in the interval $(0.6, 0.7)$.

d) By rearranging the equation $\sqrt{x+1} = 2x$, use the quadratic formula to find the root of the equation from part c) to 3 s.f.

Q6 a) On the same axes sketch the graphs of $y = \sqrt[3]{x}$ and $y = \cos x$, where x is in radians, for $-2\pi < x < 2\pi$.

b) $f(x) = \cos x - \sqrt[3]{x}$. Write down the number of roots of the equation $f(x) = 0$ in this interval.

c) Show that a root of the equation $f(x) = 0$ lies in the interval $(0.5, 0.6)$.

d) Find the root from part c) to 2 significant figures.

Q7 a) Sketch the graphs of $y = e^{2x}$ and $y = 3 - x^2$ on the same axes.

b) Using your graph from part a), explain how you know that the equation $e^{2x} + x^2 = 3$ has two roots.

c) Show that the negative root of the equation $e^{2x} + x^2 = 3$ lies between $x = -2$ and $x = -1$, and find this root to 1 decimal place.

2. Iterative Methods

Another way of finding roots of an equation is with iteration formulas.
They can seem fiddly to work with but are actually pretty simple to use.

Learning Objectives

- Be able to use iteration formulas to find a solution of an equation to a given level of accuracy.
- Be able to find and rearrange iteration formulas and understand why some don't converge to a solution of an equation.
- Be able to draw staircase and cobweb diagrams to show the convergence or divergence of iterations.

Using iteration formulas

- Some equations are too difficult to solve algebraically, so you need to find **approximations** to the roots to a certain level of accuracy. In exam questions you'll usually be told the value of x that a root is close to, and then **iteration** does the rest.

- Iteration is a numerical method for **solving equations**, like **trial and improvement**. You put an approximate value of a root x into an iteration formula, and it gives you a **slightly more accurate** value. You then repeat as necessary until you have an answer that's to the **level of accuracy** that you want.

Example

Use the iteration formula $x_{n+1} = \sqrt[3]{x_n + 4}$ to solve $x^3 - 4 - x = 0$, to 2 d.p. Start with $x_0 = 2$.

- The notation x_n just means the approximation of x at the nth iteration. Putting x_0 in the formula for x_n gives you x_{n+1}, which is x_1 — the first iteration.

- $x_0 = 2$, so $x_1 = \sqrt[3]{x_0 + 4} = \sqrt[3]{2 + 4} = 1.8171...$

- This value now gets put back into the formula to find x_2:
  $x_1 = 1.8171...$, so $x_2 = \sqrt[3]{x_1 + 4} = \sqrt[3]{1.8171... + 4} = 1.7984...$

- Carry on until you get answers that are the same when rounded to 2 d.p:
  $x_2 = 1.7984...$, so $x_3 = \sqrt[3]{x_2 + 4} = \sqrt[3]{1.7984... + 4} = 1.7965...$

- x_2, x_3 and all further iterations are the same when rounded to 2 d.p., so the root is $x = 1.80$ to 2 d.p.

- Sometimes an iteration formula will just **not find a root**. In these cases, no matter how close to the root you have x_0, the iteration sequence **diverges** — the numbers get further and further apart.

- The iteration might also **stop working**, like if you have to take the square root of a negative number.

- However, you'll nearly always be given a formula that converges to a certain root, otherwise there's not much point in using it.

- If your formula diverges when it shouldn't, chances are you went wrong somewhere, so go back and double check every stage.

Example

The equation $x^3 - x^2 - 9 = 0$ has a root close to $x = 2.5$.
What is the result of using $x_{n+1} = \sqrt{x_n^3 - 9}$ with $x_0 = 2.5$ to find this root?

- Start with $x_1 = \sqrt{2.5^3 - 9} = 2.5739...$ (seems okay so far).

- Subsequent iterations give: $x_2 = 2.8376...$, $x_3 = 3.7214...$, $x_4 = 6.5221...$

- The results are getting further and further apart with each iteration.

- So the sequence diverges.

Exercise 2.1

Q1 a) Show that the equation $x^3 + 3x^2 - 7 = 0$ has a root in the interval $(1, 2)$.

   b) Use the iterative formula $x_{n+1} = \sqrt{\dfrac{7 - x_n^3}{3}}$ with starting value $x_0 = 1$ to find values for x_1, x_2, x_3 and x_4 to 3 decimal places.

Q2 An intersection of the curves $y = \ln x$ and $y = x - 2$ is at the point $x = \alpha$, where α is 3.1 to 1 decimal place.

   a) Starting with $x_0 = 3.1$, use the iterative formula $x_{n+1} = 2 + \ln x_n$ to find the first 5 iterations, giving your answers to 4 decimal places.

   b) Write down an estimate of the value of α to 3 decimal places.

Q3 a) Show that the equation $x^4 - 5x + 3 = 0$ has a root between $x = 1.4$ and $x = 1.5$.

   b) Use the iterative formula $x_{n+1} = \sqrt[3]{5 - \dfrac{3}{x_n}}$ and $x_0 = 1.4$ to find iterations x_1 to x_6 to 3 decimal places.

   c) Hence write down an approximation of the root from part a) to 2 decimal places.

Q4 $f(x) = x^2 - 5x - 2$

a) Show that a root of the equation $f(x) = 0$ lies between
   $x = 5$ and $x = 6$.

b) The root in part a) can be estimated using the iterative formula
   $x_{n+1} = \frac{2}{x_n} + 5$. Using a starting value of $x_0 = 5$ find the values of
   x_1, x_2, x_3 and x_4, giving your answers to 4 significant figures.

Q5 Use the iterative formula $x_{n+1} = 2 - \ln x_n$ with $x_0 = 1.5$ to find
    the root of the equation $\ln x = 2 - x$ to 2 decimal places.

Q6 a) Show that the equation $e^x - 10x = 0$ has a root in the
       interval $(3, 4)$.

    b) Using the iterative formula $x_{n+1} = \ln(10x_n)$ with an appropriate
       starting value find values for x_1, x_2, x_3 and x_4 to 3 d.p.

    c) Verify that the value of the root from part a) is $x = 3.577$ to 3 d.p.

    d) Describe what happens when you use the alternative formula
       $x_{n+1} = \frac{e^{x_n}}{10}$ with $x_0 = 3$.

Q7 $f(x) = x^2 - 5x - 10$

    The iterative formula $x_{n+1} = \frac{x_n^2 - 3x_n}{2} - 5$ can be used to find
    approximations to a root of the equation $f(x) = 0$.

    a) Find the values of x_1, x_2, x_3 and x_4, starting with $x_0 = -1$ and
       describe what is happening to the sequence $x_1, x_2, x_3, x_4 ...$

    b) Using the alternative iterative formula $x_{n+1} = \sqrt{5x_n + 10}$
       with starting value $x_0 = 6$, find a root to the equation $f(x) = 0$
       to 3 significant figures. Verify your answer is correct
       to this level of accuracy.

Finding iteration formulas

- The iteration formula is just a **rearrangement** of the equation, leaving a single 'x' on one side.

- There are often **lots of different ways** to rearrange the equation, so in the exam you'll usually be asked to '**show that**' it can be rearranged in a certain way, rather than starting from scratch.

- Sometimes a rearrangement of the equation leads to a **divergent iteration** when you come to working out the steps.

- This is the reason you won't be asked to both rearrange **and** use a formula to find a root without prompting.

Examples

Show that $x^3 - x^2 - 9 = 0$ can be rearranged into $x = \sqrt{\dfrac{9}{x-1}}$.
Use this to make an iteration formula and find the value of a root to 2 d.p. with starting value $x_0 = 2.5$.

- The '9' is on its own in the fraction so try:
  $x^3 - x^2 - 9 = 0 \Rightarrow x^3 - x^2 = 9$

- The LHS can be factorised now: $\quad x^2(x - 1) = 9$

- Get the x^2 on its own by dividing by $x - 1$: $\quad x^2 = \dfrac{9}{x-1}$

- Finally square root both sides: $\quad x = \sqrt{\dfrac{9}{x-1}}$

- You can now use the iteration formula $x_{n+1} = \sqrt{\dfrac{9}{x_n - 1}}$ to find approximations of the roots.

$$x_1 = \sqrt{\frac{9}{2.5 - 1}} = 2.449... \quad x_2 = \sqrt{\frac{9}{2.449 - 1}} = 2.491...$$

And so on. After 14 iterations, all the answers round to the same number, so the value of the root to 2 d.p. is:

$$x = 2.47.$$

Tip: Don't worry — you'll never have to carry out this many iterations in an exam.

Show that $x^3 - x^2 - 9 = 0$ can also be rearranged into $x = \sqrt{x^3 - 9}$ and use this to make an iteration formula.

- Start by isolating the x^2 term: $x^2 = x^3 - 9$

- Now just square root both sides: $x = \sqrt{x^3 - 9}$

- Which makes the iteration formula: $x_{n+1} = \sqrt{x_n^3 - 9}$

- This is the iteration formula used in the example on page 144, so if you tried to use it to find a root you'd end up with a diverging sequence and it wouldn't find a root.

Tip: This shows why you'll never just be given an equation and told to find a root by first making an iteration formula.

Exercise 2.2

Q1 Show that the equation $x^2 - 5x + 1 = 0$ can be written in the form:

a) $x = \sqrt{5x - 1}$

b) $x = 5 - \dfrac{1}{x}$

c) $x = \dfrac{x^2 + 1}{5}$

Q2 Show that the equation $x^4 + 7x - 3 = 0$ can be written in the form:

a) $x = \sqrt[4]{3 - 7x}$

b) $x = \dfrac{3}{x^3} - \dfrac{7}{x^2}$

c) $x = \dfrac{3 - 5x - x^4}{2}$

d) $x = \dfrac{\sqrt{3 - 7x}}{x}$

Q2 Hint: Think about which parts you need to get on their own before starting to rearrange the equation. In part c), for example, turn $7x$ into $5x + 2x$ to get where you want.

Q3 a) Show that the equation $x^3 - 2x^2 - 5 = 0$ can be rewritten as $x = 2 + \dfrac{5}{x^2}$.

b) Use the iterative formula $x_{n+1} = 2 + \dfrac{5}{x_n^2}$ with starting value $x_0 = 2$ to find x_5 to 1 decimal place.

c) Verify that the value found in part b) is a root of the equation $x^3 - 2x^2 - 5 = 0$ to 1 decimal place.

Q4 a) Rearrange the equation $x^2 + 3x - 8 = 0$ into the form $x = \frac{a}{x} + b$ where a and b are values to be found.

b) Verify that a root of the equation $x^2 + 3x - 8 = 0$ lies in the interval $(-5, -4)$.

c) Use the iterative formula $x_{n+1} = \frac{a}{x_n} + b$ with $x_0 = -5$ to find the values for $x_1 - x_6$, giving your answers to 3 d.p. Hence find a value of the root of the equation $x^2 + 3x - 8 = 0$ to 2 d.p.

Q5 Hint: Start by rewriting everything as powers of 2 or x if you're struggling. You're going to need the rules for multiplying powers for this question.

Q5 a) Show that the equation $2^{x-1} = 4\sqrt{x}$ can be written as $x = 2^{2x-6}$.

b) Use the iterative formula $x_{n+1} = 2^{2x_n - 6}$ starting with $x_0 = 1$ to find the values of x_1, x_2, x_3 and x_4, giving your answers to 4 d.p.

c) Verify that the value for x_4 is a correct approximation to 4 d.p. for the root of the equation $2^{x-1} = 4\sqrt{x}$.

Q6 Hint: Remember that $\ln e^x = x$.

Q6 $f(x) = \ln 2x + x^3$

a) Show that $f(x) = 0$ has a solution in the interval $0.4 < x < 0.5$.

b) Show that $f(x) = 0$ can be rewritten in the form $x = \frac{e^{-x^3}}{2}$.

c) Using an iterative formula based on part b) and an appropriate value for x_0 find an approximation of the root of the equation $f(x) = 0$ to 3 decimal places.

Q7 $f(x) = x^2 - 9x - 20$

a) Find an iterative formula for $f(x) = 0$ in the form $x_{n+1} = \sqrt{px_n + q}$ where p and q are constants to be found.

Q1-7 Hint: You can generate hundreds of iterations really fast using a basic computer spreadsheet. It's quick to set up and can even round automatically to a certain number of decimal places. See what happens if you try it with a few of these examples.

b) By using the formula in part a) and a starting value of $x_0 = 10$, find an approximation to a root of the equation $f(x) = 0$. Give your answer to 3 significant figures.

c) Show that an alternative iterative formula is $x_{n+1} = \frac{x_n^2 - 4x_n}{5} - 4$.

d) By using the iterative formula in part c) with starting value $x_0 = 1$ find the value of $x_1, x_2 ... x_8$.

e) Describe the behaviour of this sequence.

Sketching iterations

Once you've calculated a sequence of iterations, you can show on a **diagram** whether your sequence **converges** or **diverges**.

- First, sketch the graphs of $y = x$ and $y = f(x)$ (where f(x) is the iterative formula). The point where the two graphs **meet** is the **root** you're aiming for.
- Draw a **vertical line** from the x-value of your starting point (x_0) until it meets the curve $y = f(x)$.
- Now draw a **horizontal line** from this point to the line $y = x$. At this point, the x-value is x_1, the value of your first iteration. This is one **step**.
- Draw another step — a **vertical line** from this point to the curve, and a **horizontal line** joining it to the line $y = x$. Repeat this for each of your iterations.
- If your steps are getting **closer and closer** to the root, the sequence of iterations is **converging**.
- If the steps are moving **further and further away** from the root, the sequence is **diverging**.

Tip: In the exam you'll usually be given the graphs of $y = x$ and $y = f(x)$ and you'll just have to draw in the iteration steps between the two.

The method above produces two different types of diagrams — **cobweb** diagrams and **staircase** diagrams.

Cobweb diagrams

Cobweb diagrams look like they're **spiralling** in to the root (or away from it). The example below shows a **convergent cobweb diagram**.

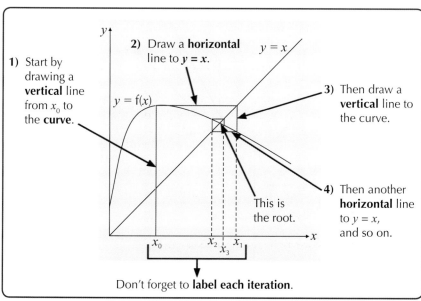

1) Start by drawing a **vertical** line from x_0 to the **curve**.

2) Draw a **horizontal** line to $y = x$.

$y = x$

$y = f(x)$

3) Then draw a **vertical** line to the curve.

4) Then another **horizontal** line to $y = x$, and so on.

This is the root.

x_0 x_2 x_3 x_1

Don't forget to **label each iteration**.

Tip: In this case, the iterations alternate between being below the root and above the root, but are getting closer each time.

A **divergent** cobweb diagram would have a similar shape, but each iteration would **spiral away from the root** rather than towards it.

Staircase diagrams

Staircase diagrams look like a set of **steps** leading to (or away from) the root. The examples below show a **convergent** and a **divergent** staircase diagram.

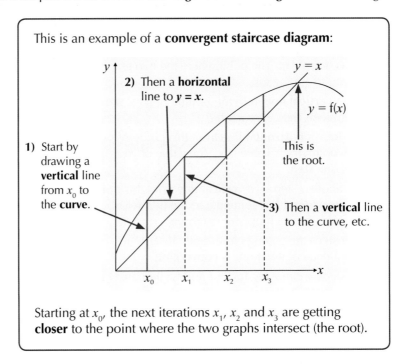

This is an example of a **convergent staircase diagram**:

2) Then a **horizontal** line to $y = x$.

1) Start by drawing a **vertical** line from x_0 to the **curve**.

This is the root.

3) Then a **vertical** line to the curve, etc.

$y = x$

$y = f(x)$

Starting at x_0, the next iterations x_1, x_2 and x_3 are getting **closer** to the point where the two graphs intersect (the root).

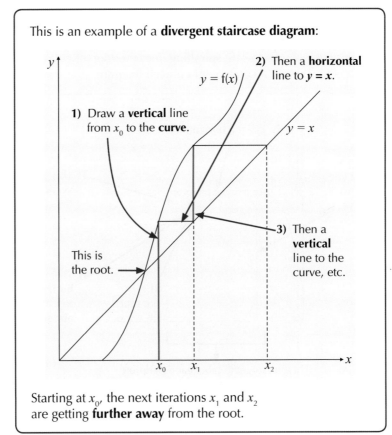

This is an example of a **divergent staircase diagram**:

2) Then a **horizontal** line to $y = x$.

$y = f(x)$

1) Draw a **vertical** line from x_0 to the **curve**.

$y = x$

3) Then a **vertical** line to the curve, etc.

This is the root.

Starting at x_0, the next iterations x_1 and x_2 are getting **further away** from the root.

Tip: The diagrams will be differently shaped depending on where you start your iterations — if you'd started with x_0 below the root here, you'd have got a convergent staircase diagram instead.

Q1 For each graph below, draw a diagram to show the convergence or divergence of the iterative sequence for the given value of x_0, and say whether it is a convergent or divergent staircase or cobweb diagram. Label x_0, x_1 and x_2 on each diagram where possible.

Q1 Hint: You'll need to draw the line $y = x$ on each diagram.

a) $x_0 = 3.5$

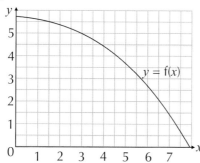

b) $x_0 = 3$

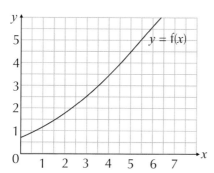

c) $x_0 = 1.75$

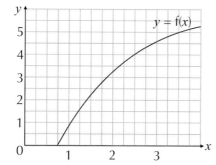

Q1 c) Hint: Take care with the scale on this diagram.

d) $x_0 = 4$

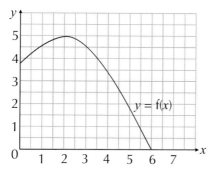

Combining the methods

When it comes to the exam, they'll often set you questions that **combine** all (or at least most) of the methods covered in this chapter into one long question.

Here you can see an **exam-style question** worked from start to finish, just how they'd want you to do it in the real thing.

Example

The graph below shows both roots of the continuous function $f(x) = 6x - x^2 + 13$.

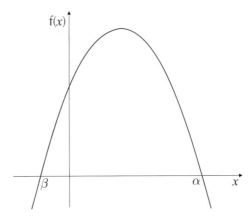

a) Show that the positive root, α, lies in the interval $7 < x < 8$.

b) Show that $6x - x^2 + 13 = 0$ can be rearranged into the formula:
$x = \sqrt{6x + 13}$

c) Use the iteration formula $x_{n+1} = \sqrt{6x_n + 13}$ and $x_0 = 7$ to find α to 1 d.p.

d) Sketch a diagram to show the convergence of the sequence for x_1, x_2 and x_3.

e) Show that the negative root, β, is -1.690 to 3 d.p.

a) $f(x)$ is a **continuous function**, so if $f(7)$ and $f(8)$ have **different signs** then there is a root in the interval $7 < x < 8$:

$$f(7) = (6 \times 7) - 7^2 + 13 = 6.$$

$$f(8) = (6 \times 8) - 8^2 + 13 = -3.$$

There is a **change of sign** so $7 < \alpha < 8$.

b) Get the x^2 **on its own** to make: $6x + 13 = x^2$

Now take the (positive) square root to leave: $x = \sqrt{6x + 13}$.

c) Using $x_{n+1} = \sqrt{6x_n + 13}$ with $x_0 = 7$, gives $x_1 = \sqrt{6 \times 7 + 13}$
$$= 7.4161...$$

Continuing the iterations:

$$x_2 = \sqrt{6 \times 7.4161... + 13} = 7.5826...$$

$$x_3 = \sqrt{6 \times 7.5826... + 13} = 7.6482...$$

$$x_4 = \sqrt{6 \times 7.6482... + 13} = 7.6739...$$

$$x_5 = \sqrt{6 \times 7.6739... + 13} = 7.6839...$$

$$x_6 = \sqrt{6 \times 7.6839... + 13} = 7.6879...$$

$$x_7 = \sqrt{6 \times 7.6879... + 13} = 7.6894...$$

x_4 to x_7 all round to 7.7 to 1 d.p., so to 1 d.p. $\alpha = 7.7$.

d) In an exam question, $y = \sqrt{6x + 13}$ and $y = x$ would usually be drawn for you, and the position of x_0 would be marked.

All you have to do is draw on the lines and label the values of x_1, x_2 and x_3.

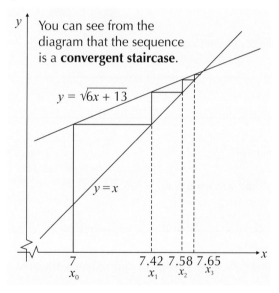

You can see from the diagram that the sequence is a **convergent staircase**.

$y = \sqrt{6x + 13}$

$y = x$

7 — x_0
7.42 — x_1
7.58 — x_2
7.65 — x_3

Tip: Here the values of x_1, x_2 and x_3 have been rounded to 2 d.p. to make it easier to label them on the graph.

e) If $\beta = -1.690$ to 3 d.p. the **upper and lower bounds** are -1.6895 and -1.6905. The root must lie **between** these values in order to be rounded to -1.690.

As the function is **continuous**, if $f(-1.6895)$ and $f(-1.6905)$ have **different signs** then $-1.6905 < \beta < -1.6895$:

$$f(-1.6895) = (6 \times -1.6895) - (-1.6895)^2 + 13 = 0.00858...$$
$$f(-1.6905) = (6 \times -1.6905) - (-1.6905)^2 + 13 = -0.00079...$$

There is a **change of sign**, so $-1.6905 < \beta < -1.6895$, and so

$$\beta = -1.690 \text{ to 3 d.p.}$$

3. Numerical Integration

Learning Objectives

- Be able to use Simpson's Rule to estimate the area under a curve.
- Be able to use the Mid-Ordinate Rule to estimate the area under a curve.
- Understand that increasing the number of steps improves the accuracy of the estimate.

You know how to find the area under a graph by integration, but sometimes you'll have a function that's too complicated to integrate. In these cases, you can estimate the area using Simpson's Rule or the Mid-Ordinate Rule.

Simpson's Rule

- **Simpson's Rule** is a bit like the Trapezium Rule that you met back in C2 (have a look at your AS notes if you need a reminder).

- It lets you **estimate** the **area under a curve** by dividing it up into **strips**, as shown in the diagram:

- The number of strips, n, must be **even** for Simpson's Rule to work.

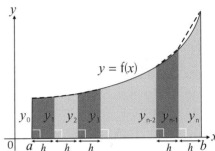

- The formula for the **integral** of y (i.e. the **area** underneath the curve) is given below:

Tip: The formula is given to you on the formula sheet in the exam, so you don't have to learn it. You do need to know what it means, and how to use it.

a and b are the **limits** of the integration, so $(b - a)$ is the **total width** of the area.

$$\int_a^b y \, dx \approx \frac{1}{3}h[(y_0 + y_n) + 4(y_1 + y_3 + \dots + y_{n-1}) + 2(y_2 + y_4 + \dots + y_{n-2})]$$

h is the **width** of each strip:

$$h = \frac{b - a}{n}$$

$y_0, y_1, y_2, \dots, y_n$ are the **heights** of the sides of each strip, as shown on the diagram above. You get these by putting the x-values into the equation of the curve, so $y_1 = f(x_1)$.

Example

Use Simpson's Rule with 4 strips to approximate the area of $\int_0^1 e^{2x^2 - 1} \, dx$.

- This function is too hard to integrate, so using Simpson's Rule will give you an **estimate** of the area under the curve.

- First find the **width** of each strip using $h = \frac{b - a}{n}$.
  Here $a = 0$, $b = 1$ and $n = 4$, so $h = \frac{1 - 0}{4} = 0.25$.

- Work out your **x-values**.
  $x_0 = a = 0$, then keep adding 0.25 until you get to $x_4 = b = 1$.
  So the x-values are 0, 0.25, 0.5, 0.75 and 1.

- Calculate the **y-values** from these x-values. Make sure you give them to enough decimal places (4 should be fine here).
  E.g. $y_0 = f(x_0) = e^{2(0^2) - 1} = 0.367879\dots$

Tip: Writing your x- and y-values in a table like this helps keep all your working organised. There are lots of messy looking numbers involved in these questions.

x	$y = e^{2x^2 - 1}$
$x_0 = 0$	$y_0 = 0.3679$
$x_1 = 0.25$	$y_1 = 0.4169$
$x_2 = 0.5$	$y_2 = 0.6065$
$x_3 = 0.75$	$y_3 = 1.1331$
$x_4 = 1$	$y_4 = 2.7183$

- Now put the y-values (and your value for h) into the **formula**:

Strip width h | First and last: $y_0 + y_4$ | Odds: $y_1 + y_3$ | Evens: y_2

$$\int_0^1 e^{2x^2-1}\,dx \approx \frac{1}{3}(0.25)[(0.3679 + 2.7183) + 4(0.4169 + 1.1331) + 2(0.6065)]$$

$$= \frac{1}{12}[3.0862 + 6.2 + 1.213] = \boxed{0.875 \text{ (to 3 d.p)}}$$

Choosing a value for n

- For Simpson's Rule, you must **always** use an **even number** of strips, n.

- Using **more** strips (i.e. a **larger** value for n) will almost certainly give you a **more accurate** approximation — closer to the actual area under the curve.

- If you know the **real value** for the area under the curve, you can calculate the **percentage error** of an estimate to determine its accuracy. Just find the **difference** between the real value and the estimate, and give it as a **percentage of the real value** — see the formula on page 157.

Tip: Although using more strips gives you a better estimate of the integral, it makes the calculation longer as you have more y-values to work out and put into the formula. Computer spreadsheets can be used to speed things up for large values of n.

Exercise 3.1

Give all answers to this exercise to 4 decimal places.

Q1 Use Simpson's Rule with 4 strips to find an approximate value for $\int_1^2 (\ln x)^2\,dx$.

Q2 Use Simpson's Rule with 4 strips to estimate the area under the curve $y = \sqrt{\tan\theta}$ between $x = 0$ and $x = \frac{\pi}{3}$.

Q3 a) Use Simpson's Rule with 4 strips to estimate the value of $\int_1^3 e^x \ln x\,dx$.
   b) Repeat part a) using 8 strips.
   c) (i) Which estimate, a) or b), is likely to be closer to the exact value?
      (ii) To how many decimal places are the estimates the same?

Q4 Using Simpson's Rule with 6 strips, estimate the area of the circle $y^2 + (x + 4)^2 = 25$ between $x = -3$ and $x = 0$ and above $y = 0$.

Q4 Hint: You need to rearrange the equation so that you can work out the y-values from the x-values.

Q5 a) Use Simpson's Rule with 6 strips to estimate the value of $\int_0^{\frac{\pi}{2}} \sin\theta \cos\theta\,d\theta$.
   b) Repeat part a) using 4 strips.
   c) An exact formula for the above integral is:
      $\int_a^b \sin\theta \cos\theta\,d\theta = \left[-\frac{1}{4}\cos 2\theta\right]_a^b$.
      (i) Use this formula to calculate the value of the integral.
      (ii) To how many decimal places do your answers to parts a) and b) agree with this value?

The Mid-Ordinate Rule

- Like Simpson's Rule, the **Mid-Ordinate Rule** lets you **estimate** the **area under a curve** by dividing it up into **strips**.

- It works in a similar way to the Trapezium Rule — except that instead of adding up the areas of lots of trapeziums, you add the areas of lots of **rectangles**, as shown in the diagram:

- The **height** of each rectangular strip is given by the **y-value** at the **midpoint** of the strip. So the **total area** of all the strips is the **sum** of the **heights** multiplied by the **width** (h) of each strip.

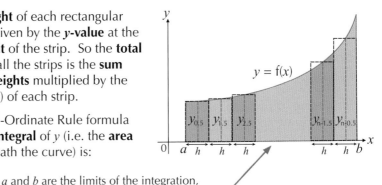

- The Mid-Ordinate Rule formula for the **integral** of y (i.e. the **area** underneath the curve) is:

a and b are the limits of the integration, so $(b - a)$ is the total width of the area.

$$\int_a^b y \, dx \approx h\big(y_{0.5} + y_{1.5} + \ldots + y_{n-1.5} + y_{n-0.5}\big)$$

Tip: This rule is also given on the formula sheet in the exam.

h is the width of each strip: $h = \dfrac{b - a}{n}$
(n is the number of strips.)

$y_{0.5}, y_{1.5}, y_{2.5}, \ldots, y_{n-0.5}$ are the **heights** of the **midpoints** of each strip. You get these by putting the **x-values** of the **midpoints** into the equation of the curve, so $y_{0.5} = f(x_{0.5})$.

Tip: If you prefer, once you've found $x_{0.5}$, you can find the other midpoints by repeatedly adding h onto your value for $x_{0.5}$.

- To work out the **midpoints** of each strip, take $x_0 = a$ and keep adding on h to get x_1, x_2 etc. up to x_n $(= b)$. Then $x_{0.5}$ is **halfway** between x_0 and x_1, $x_{1.5}$ is halfway between x_1 and x_2... and so on, up to $x_{n-0.5}$.

Example

Use the Mid-Ordinate Rule to approximate the area of $\int_1^4 \ln(x^3 + 2x) \, dx$, where $n = 3$.

- First find the **width** of each strip using $h = \dfrac{b - a}{n}$.
  Here $a = 1$, $b = 4$ and $n = 3$, so $h = \dfrac{4 - 1}{3} = 1$.

- The area starts at $x_0 = a = 1$, and so keep **adding on $h = 1$** to get values for x_1, x_2 and x_3: $x_0 = 1$, $x_1 = 2$, $x_2 = 3$ and $x_3 = 4$.

- For the Mid-Ordinate Rule, you need to use the values of x at the **midpoints**. $x_{0.5}$ is halfway between $x_0 = 1$ and $x_1 = 2$, so $x_{0.5} = 1.5$. Working out the other midpoints in the same way gives $x_{1.5} = 2.5$ and $x_{2.5} = 3.5$.

- Calculate the **midpoint y-values** from these x-values.
  E.g. $y_{0.5} = f(x_{0.5}) = \ln(1.5^3 + 2(1.5))$
  $= 1.852384\ldots$

x	$y = \ln(x^3 + 2x)$
$x_{0.5} = 1.5$	$y_{0.5} = 1.8524$
$x_{1.5} = 2.5$	$y_{1.5} = 3.0265$
$x_{2.5} = 3.5$	$y_{2.5} = 3.9095$

- Now put the y-values (and your value for h) into the **formula**:

Strip width
h

Sum of the midpoint y-values:
$y_{0.5} + y_{1.5} + y_{2.5}$

$$\int_{1}^{4} \ln(x^3 + 2x)\,dx \approx 1(1.8524 + 3.0265 + 3.9095) = 8.788 \text{ to 3 d.p.}$$

Choosing a value for n

- For the Mid-Ordinate Rule, you can use an **odd or even number** of strips, n.
- As for Simpson's Rule, using **more** strips (a **larger** value for n) will almost always give you a **more accurate** approximation for the area under the curve. You can show this by finding the **percentage error** of each estimate, as shown:

Example

Compare the accuracy of estimates using the Mid-Ordinate Rule with 4 strips (area = 0.57) and 8 strips (area = 0.61) if the actual area is 0.6.

% error $= \left| \dfrac{\text{real value} - \text{estimate}}{\text{real value}} \right| \times 100$, so for the two estimates:

% error (4 strips) $= \left| \dfrac{0.6 - 0.57}{0.6} \right| \times 100 = 5\%$

% error (8 strips) $= \left| \dfrac{0.6 - 0.61}{0.6} \right| \times 100 = 1.67\%$

The estimate using **8 strips** has a smaller % error so it's **more accurate**.

Tip: The modulus sign (see page 16) means you get a positive percentage error whether the estimate was bigger or smaller than the real value.

Exercise 3.2

Unless stated otherwise, give your answers to 4 decimal places.

Q1 Use the Mid-Ordinate Rule with 4 strips to estimate $\int_{1}^{5} \sqrt{x^3 + x^2}\,dx$.

Q2 Use the Mid-Ordinate Rule with 6 strips to estimate $\int_{2}^{5} (x^2 + x)^{-1}\,dx$.

Q3 a) Use the Mid-Ordinate Rule with 4 strips to estimate the area of the semicircle $(x - 4)^2 + y^2 = 16$, $y \geq 0$, to 1 decimal place.

b) Find the actual area of the semicircle (radius $r = 4$), to 1 d.p.

c) What is the percentage error of your estimate in part a)? How could you improve the accuracy of the estimate?

Q3 a) Hint: Rearrange the equation first so you can calculate y-values from your x-values.

Q4 a) Estimate the area under the curve $y = e^x \cos x$, $0 \leq x \leq 2$, using the Mid-Ordinate Rule with 4 strips.

b) Repeat part a) using 8 strips.

c) Compare the results for parts a) and b). To how many decimal places do the results agree?

Q5 A curve is defined by $y^2 = \ln x + 2x$.

a) Use the Mid-Ordinate Rule with 4 strips to estimate the area under this curve, $2 \leq x \leq 10$, $y \geq 0$. Round your answer to 2 d.p.

b) Repeat part a) using 8 strips.

c) Which is likely to be the more accurate estimate? Explain your answer.

Review Exercise — Chapter 6

Q1 The graph shows the function $f(x) = e^x - x^3$ for $0 \le x \le 5$.
How many roots does the equation $e^x - x^3 = 0$ have
in the interval $0 \le x \le 5$?

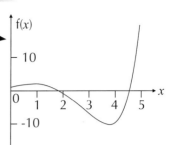

Q2 Show that there is a root in the interval:

a) $3 < x < 4$ for $\sin(2x) = 0$ (where x is in radians).

b) $2.1 < x < 2.2$ for $\ln(x - 2) + 2 = 0$.

c) $4.3 < x < 4.5$ for $x^3 - 4x^2 = 7$.

Q3 By selecting an appropriate interval show that, to 1 d.p., $x = 1.2$
is a root of the equation $x^3 + x - 3 = 0$.

Q4 Use the formula $x_{n+1} = -\frac{1}{2}\cos x_n$, with $x_0 = -1$, to find a root of $\cos x + 2x = 0$ to 2 d.p.

Q5 Use the formula $x_{n+1} = \sqrt{\ln x_n + 4}$, with $x_0 = 2$, to find a root of $x^2 - \ln x - 4 = 0$ to 3 d.p.

Q6 a) Show that the equation $2x^2 - x^3 + 1 = 0$ can be written in the form:

(i) $x = \sqrt{\dfrac{-1}{2 - x}}$

(ii) $x = \sqrt[3]{2x^2 + 1}$

(iii) $x = \sqrt{\dfrac{x^3 - 1}{2}}$

b) Use iteration formulas based on each of the above rearrangements with $x_0 = 2.3$ to find
a root of $2x^2 - x^3 + 1 = 0$ to 2 d.p. Which of the three formulas converge to a root?

Q7 a) On the same axes sketch the graphs of $y = \ln x$ and $y = \frac{2}{x}$.

Hence find the number of roots of the equation $\ln x - \frac{2}{x} = 0$.

b) Show that there is a root of the equation $\ln x - \frac{2}{x} = 0$ between $x = 2$ and $x = 3$.

Q8 a) Sketch the graphs of $y = \dfrac{1}{x + 1}$ and $y = x - 2$ on the same axes.

b) $f(x) = \dfrac{1}{x + 1} - x + 2$

Show that a root of the equation $f(x) = 0$ lies between $x = -1.4$ and $x = -1.3$.

c) Show that the equation $f(x) = 0$ can be written in the form $x^2 - x - 3 = 0$.

Q9 a) Show that the equation $x^x = 3$ has a root between $x = 1.5$ and $x = 2$.

b) Using the iterative formula $x_{n+1} = 3^{\frac{1}{x_n}}$, with an appropriate value for x_0, find
an approximation for the root of the equation $x^x = 3$ to 1 decimal place.

c) An alternative iterative formula is $x_{n+1} = 3x_n^{1 - x_n}$.
Using a starting value of $x_0 = 1.5$, find x_n values up to and including x_5.
What happens if you use this formula?

Q9 Hint: x^x
looks scary but
it's no harder than
others — just put
the numbers in
as usual.

Q10 a) Show that a solution to the equation $2x - 5\cos x = 0$ (where x is in radians) lies in the interval $(1.1, 1.2)$.

b) Show that the equation in part a) can be written as $x = p\cos x$, stating the value of p.

c) Using an iterative formula based on part b) and a starting value of $x_0 = 1.1$, find the values up to and including x_8, giving your answers to 4 decimal places. Comment on your findings.

Q10 d) Hint: You're going to need to take $\cos^{-1}$ of both sides here.

d) Find an alternative iterative formula that will find an approximation to the root in part a) and give the value of that root to 3 significant figures. Verify your solution.

Q11 Using the position of x_0 as given on the graph below, draw a staircase or cobweb diagram showing how the sequence converges. Label x_1 and x_2 on the diagram.

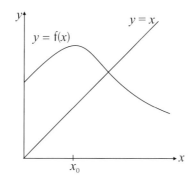

Q12 Using f(x) as shown on the graph below with $x_0 = 2$, draw a staircase or cobweb diagram to show how the sequence converges. Label x_1 and x_2 on the diagram.

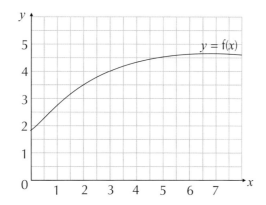

Q13 a) Use Simpson's Rule with 6 strips to approximate the area of $\int_1^4 \ln(\sqrt{x} + 2)\, dx$.

b) Why can't you use Simpson's Rule with 5 strips to find an estimate?

c) Use the Mid-Ordinate Rule with 6 strips to approximate the area of $\int_1^4 \ln(\sqrt{x} + 2)\, dx$.

Q14 a) Use the Mid-Ordinate Rule to estimate the value of $\int_2^4 x^2 e^{x-2}\, dx$, using $n = 4$.

b) Use Simpson's Rule to estimate the value of $\int_2^4 x^2 e^{x-2}\, dx$, using $n = 4$.

1   The sketch below shows part of the graph of the function $f(x) = 2xe^x - 3$.
The curve crosses the x-axis at the point P $(p, 0)$, as shown, so p is a root
of the equation $f(x) = 0$.

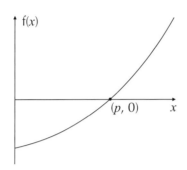

a)   Show that $0.7 < p < 0.8$.

(3 marks)

b)   Show that $f(x) = 0$ can be rewritten as $x = \frac{3}{2}e^{-x}$.

(2 marks)

c)   Starting with $x_0 = 0.7$, use the iteration

$$x_{n+1} = \frac{3}{2}e^{-x_n}$$

to find x_1, x_2, x_3 and x_4 to 4 d.p.

(3 marks)

d)   Show that $p = 0.726$ to 3 d.p.

(3 marks)

2   The graph of the function:
$$y = \sin 3x + 3x, \quad 0 < x < \pi$$
meets the line $y = 1$ when $x = a$.

a)   Show that $0.1 < a < 0.2$.

(4 marks)

b)   Show that the equation:
$$\sin 3x + 3x = 1$$
can be written as:
$$x = \frac{1}{3}(1 - \sin 3x).$$

(2 marks)

c)   Starting with $x_0 = 0.2$, use the iteration:
$$x_{n+1} = \frac{1}{3}(1 - \sin 3x_n)$$
to find x_4 to 3 d.p.

(2 marks)

3   The sequence given by
$$x_{n+1} = \sqrt[3]{x_n^2 - 4}, \quad x_0 = -1$$
converges to a number b.

a)   Find the values of x_1, x_2, x_3 and x_4 correct to 4 decimal places.

(3 marks)

b)   Show that $x = b$ is a root of the equation:
$$x^3 - x^2 + 4 = 0$$

(2 marks)

c)   Show that $b = -1.315$ to 3 decimal places, by choosing an appropriate interval.

(3 marks)

4   The function
$$f(x) = \ln(x + 3) - x + 2, \quad x > -3$$
has a root at $x = m$.

a)   Show that m lies between 3 and 4.

(3 marks)

b)   Find, using iteration, the value of m correct to 2 decimal places.
    Use the iteration formula $x_{n+1} = \ln(x_n + 3) + 2$ with $x_0 = 3$.

(3 marks)

c)   Use a suitable interval to verify that your answer to part b) is correct to 2 decimal places.

(3 marks)

d)   The graph below shows part of the curve $y = \ln(x + 3) + 2$, the line $y = x$ and the position of x_0. Complete the diagram showing the convergence of the iteration sequence, showing the locations of x_1 and x_2 on the graph.

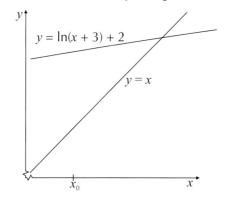

(2 marks)

5   Using Simpson's Rule with 4 strips, approximate the area of $\int_1^5 \dfrac{1}{x^2 + 3x} \, dx$.
    Give your answer to 3 s.f.

(4 marks)

6   Use the Mid-Ordinate Rule to approximate the area of $\int_1^3 2^x \, dx$, with 4 strips.
    Give your answer to 4 s.f.

(3 marks)

1. Proof

Mathematical proofs are all about showing that a statement is true (or false). There are a number of different ways to do this, and you need to know how they work in case you have to prove something for yourself.

Different types of proof

Simple proofs — odd and even numbers

Before you get onto the trickier proofs, there are some nice simple proofs about **odd** and **even numbers** that are really useful. But first you need to know these 'proper' definitions for them:

> Any **even** number can be written as $2a$, where a is an integer.

> Any **odd** number can be written as $2b + 1$, where b is an integer.

In the proofs below, $2j + 1$ and $2k + 1$ represent any two **odd numbers**, and $2l$ and $2m$ represent any two **even numbers** (where j, k, l and m are integers).

Examples

a) **Prove that the sum of two odd numbers is even.**

    Proof: $(2j + 1) + (2k + 1) = 2j + 2k + 2 = 2(j + k + 1) = $ even

    so odd + odd = even

b) **Prove that the sum of an odd number and an even number is odd.**

    Proof: $(2j + 1) + (2l) = 2j + 2l + 1 = 2(j + l) + 1 = $ odd

    so odd + even = odd

c) **Prove that the sum of two even numbers is even.**

    Proof: $2l + 2m = 2(l + m) = $ even

    so even + even = even

d) **Prove that the product of two odd numbers is odd.**

    Proof: $(2j + 1)(2k + 1) = 4jk + 2j + 2k + 1 = 2(2jk + j + k) + 1 = $ odd

    so odd × odd = odd

Tip: You can prove that e.g. the product of two even numbers is even in a similar way.

Direct proof

A **direct proof** (or 'proof by direct argument') is when you use **known facts** to build up your argument and show a statement **must** be true.

Example

A definition of a rational number is 'a number that can be written as a quotient of two integers, where the denominator is non-zero'.

Use this definition to prove that the following statement is true:
   "The product of two rational numbers is always a rational number."

- Take **any two** rational numbers and call them a and b.

- By the **definition** of rational numbers you can write them in the form $a = \frac{p}{q}$ and $b = \frac{r}{s}$, where p, q, r and s are all integers, and q and s are non-zero.

- The **product** of a and b is $ab = \frac{p}{q} \times \frac{r}{s} = \frac{pr}{qs}$.

- pr and qs are the products of integers, so they must also be integers, and because q and s are non-zero, qs must also be non-zero.

- We've shown that ab is a quotient of two integers and has a non-zero denominator, so by definition, **ab is rational**.

- Hence the original statement is **true**.

Tip: Remember — a quotient is what you get when you divide one number by another.

Tip: Here, the "known facts" are the definition of a rational number, the fact that the products of integers are integers, and the fact that the products of non-zero integers are also non-zero.

If you have to prove that an **identity** is true, it's enough to show that one side of the identity can be **rearranged** into the other — like for the proofs of the **trig identities** on pages 50-51, and in the example below.

Tip: Remember that an identity is true for all values of the unknown (e.g. x or θ) rather than just one particular value. An identity is shown by the symbol $\equiv$.

Example

Use the identity $\operatorname{cosec}^2 \theta \equiv 1 + \cot^2 \theta$ to prove that:
$$\left(1 + \frac{1}{\sin \theta}\right)\left(1 - \frac{1}{\sin \theta}\right) \equiv -\frac{1}{\tan^2 \theta}.$$

- Expand the left-hand side, writing in terms of $\operatorname{cosec} \theta$...

$$\left(1 + \frac{1}{\sin \theta}\right)\left(1 - \frac{1}{\sin \theta}\right) \equiv 1 - \frac{1}{\sin^2 \theta}$$
$$\equiv 1 - \operatorname{cosec}^2 \theta$$

- Now substitute in for $\operatorname{cosec}^2 \theta$ using the given identity:

$$\equiv 1 - (1 + \cot^2 \theta)$$
$$\equiv -\cot^2 \theta$$
$$\equiv -\frac{1}{\tan^2 \theta}$$

This is the same as the right-hand side, so the identity must be true.

Tip: Here, the "known facts" are the identities $\operatorname{cosec}^2 \theta \equiv 1 + \cot^2 \theta$, $\operatorname{cosec} \theta \equiv \frac{1}{\sin \theta}$ and $\cot \theta \equiv \frac{1}{\tan \theta}$.

Proof by contradiction

To prove a statement by **contradiction**, you say 'suppose the statement **isn't true**...', then prove that something **impossible** would have to be true for that to be the case.

Example

Prove the following statement: *"If x^2 is even, then x must be even."*

- You can prove the statement by contradiction. Suppose the statement is **not true**. Then there must be an **odd number** x for which x^2 is **even**.
- If x is odd, then you can write x as $2k + 1$, where k is an integer.
- Now, $x^2 = (2k + 1)^2 = 4k^2 + 4k + 1$
  $4k^2 + 4k = 2(2k^2 + 2k)$ is **even** because it is 2 × an integer
  $\Rightarrow 4k^2 + 4k + 1$ is **odd**.
- But this **isn't possible** if the statement that x^2 is even is true. You've **contradicted** the statement that there is an odd number x for which x^2 is even.
- So if x^2 is **even**, then x must be **even**, hence the original statement is **true**.

Tip: This proof uses the definitions of odd and even numbers from page 162.

Proof by exhaustion

In **proof by exhaustion** you break things down into two or more **cases**. You have to make sure that your cases cover **all possible situations**, then prove separately that the statement is true for **each case**.

Example

Prove the following statement:
"For any integer x, the value of $f(x) = x^3 + x + 1$ is an odd integer."

- To prove the statement, split the situation into **two cases**:

  (i) x is an **even number**, and (ii) x is an **odd number**.

- (i) If x is an **even integer**, then it can be written as $x = 2n$, for some integer n. Substitute $x = 2n$ into the function:
  $f(2n) = (2n)^3 + 2n + 1 = 8n^3 + 2n + 1 = 2(4n^3 + n) + 1$
  n is an integer $\Rightarrow (4n^3 + n)$ is an integer
  $\qquad\qquad\qquad\quad \Rightarrow 2(4n^3 + n)$ is an even integer
  $\qquad\qquad\qquad\quad \Rightarrow 2(4n^3 + n) + 1$ is an **odd integer**

  So $f(x)$ is **odd** when x is **even**.

- (ii) If x is an **odd integer**, then it can be written as $x = 2m + 1$, for some integer m. Substitute $x = 2m + 1$ into the function:
  $f(2m + 1) = (2m + 1)^3 + 2m + 1 + 1$
  $\qquad\qquad = (8m^3 + 12m^2 + 6m + 1) + 2m + 1 + 1$
  $\qquad\qquad = 8m^3 + 12m^2 + 8m + 3 = 2(4m^3 + 6m^2 + 4m) + 3$

  m is an integer $\Rightarrow (4m^3 + 6m^2 + 4m)$ is an integer
  $\qquad\qquad\qquad\quad \Rightarrow 2(4m^3 + 6m^2 + 4m)$ is an even integer
  $\qquad\qquad\qquad\quad \Rightarrow 2(4m^3 + 6m^2 + 4m) + 3$ is an **odd integer**

  So $f(x)$ is **odd** when x is **odd**.

- You have shown that $f(x)$ is **odd** when x is even **and** when x is odd. As any integer x **must** be either odd or even, you have therefore shown that $f(x)$ is **odd** for **any** integer x, so the statement is **true**.

Tip: These two cases cover all possible situations, because an integer is always either odd or even.

Tip: Again, you need to use the definitions of odd and even numbers — and the fact that sums and products of integers are also integers.

Disproof by counter-example

Disproof by **counter-example** is the easiest way to show a mathematical statement is **false**. All you have to do is find **one case** where the statement doesn't hold.

Example

Disprove the following statement:
"For any pair of real numbers x and y, if x > y, then $x^2 + x > y^2 + y$."

- To **disprove** the statement, it's enough to find just **one example** of x and y where $x > y$, but $x^2 + x \leq y^2 + y$.

- Let $x = 2$ and $y = -4$.
  Then $2 > -4 \Rightarrow x > y$
  but $x^2 + x = 2^2 + 2 = 6$
  and $y^2 + y = (-4)^2 + (-4) = 12$,
  so $x^2 + x < y^2 + y$

- So when $x = 2$ and $y = -4$, the first part of the statement holds, but the second part of the statement **doesn't**.

- So the statement is **not true**.

Tip: You might have to try a few different numbers before you come up with an example that doesn't work.

Exercise 1.1

Q1 a) Prove that the product of two even numbers is even.

  b) Prove that the product of an odd number and an even number is even.

Q1 Hint: These proofs are similar to the ones on p.162.

Q2 Prove by exhaustion that the product of any three consecutive integers is even.

Q3 Disprove the following statement:
"$n^2 - n - 1$ is a prime number for any integer $n > 2$."

Q4 "The graph of $y = \ln x$ has no turning points."
Use proof by contradiction to prove the statement above.

Q5 Disprove the following: $\sqrt{x^2 + y^2} < x + y$.

Q6 Prove that $\cos^2 \theta(1 + \tan^2 \theta) \equiv 1$, using the identity $\sec^2 \theta \equiv 1 + \tan^2 \theta$.

Q7 a) Prove the statement below:
      "For any integer n, $n^2 - n - 1$ is always odd."

  b) Hence prove that $(n^2 - n - 2)^3$ is always even.

Answers

Chapter 1: Functions

1. Functions and Mappings

Exercise 1.1 — Mappings and functions

Q1

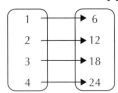

Q2

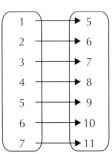

Q3

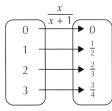

Range: $\left\{0, \frac{1}{2}, \frac{2}{3}, \frac{3}{4}\right\}$

Q4

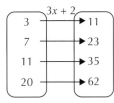

Domain: {3, 7, 11, 20}

Q5 $f(2) = 3(2) + 1 = 7$, $f(-1) = 3(-1) + 1 = -2$

Q6 $g(0) = \dfrac{1}{2(0) + 1} = 1$, $g(2) = \dfrac{1}{2(2) + 1} = \dfrac{1}{5}$

Q7 $h\left(\dfrac{\pi}{2}\right) = \sin\left(\dfrac{\pi}{2}\right) = 1$, $h\left(\dfrac{5\pi}{6}\right) = \sin\left(\dfrac{5\pi}{6}\right) = \dfrac{1}{2}$

Q8 $f(1) = \dfrac{1}{2 + \log_{10} 1} = \dfrac{1}{2 + 0} = \dfrac{1}{2}$

$f(100) = \dfrac{1}{2 + \log_{10} 100} = \dfrac{1}{2 + 2} = \dfrac{1}{4}$

Q9
  a) Yes, it is a function.

  b) No, because the map is not defined for elements 4 and 5 of the domain.

  c) No, because a value in the domain can map to more than one value in the range.

Exercise 1.2 — Graphs of functions

Q1
  a) Yes, it is a function.

  b) No, because a value of x can map to more than one value of $f(x)$.

Q2
  a)

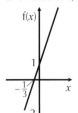

Range: $f(x) \geq -2$

  b)

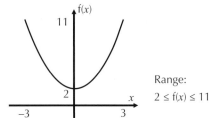

Range: $2 \leq f(x) \leq 11$

  c)

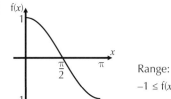

Range: $-1 \leq f(x) \leq 1$

  d)

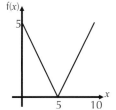

Range: $0 \leq f(x) \leq 5$

Q3
  a) The range shown is $3 \leq f(x) \leq 11$, so the domain is: $\dfrac{3 - 1}{2} \leq x \leq \dfrac{11 - 1}{2}$, which is $1 \leq x \leq 5$.

  b) The domain shown is $-1 \leq x \leq 4$.
The range is between $f(2)$ and $f(-1)$:
$((2)^2 - 4(2) + 5) \leq f(x) \leq ((-1)^2 - 4(-1) + 5)$, which is $1 \leq f(x) \leq 10$.

Q4 When $x = 0$, $f(x) = 2$.
For large x, $x + 2 \approx x + 1$ so as $x \to \infty$,
$\dfrac{x + 2}{x + 1} \to 1$. So $f(x) = 1$ is an asymptote.
So the range is $1 < f(x) \leq 2$.

Q5 The function $f(x) = \dfrac{1}{x - 2}$ is undefined when $x = 2$, so $a = 2$.

Q6 The function $f(x) = +\sqrt{9 - x^2}$ is only defined when $x^2 \leq 9$, i.e. when $-3 \leq x \leq 3$. So $a = -3$ and $b = 3$.

Q7 The graph of $h(x) = +\sqrt{x+1}$ is shown below.

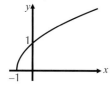

h(x) is undefined when x is less than –1.

Restricting the domain to $x \geq -1$ would make h(x) a function.

Q8 The graph of $k : x \rightarrow \tan x$ is shown below.

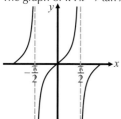

tan x is undefined at e.g. $-\frac{\pi}{2}$ and $\frac{\pi}{2}$

(it is also undefined periodically either side).

Restricting the domain to e.g. $-\frac{\pi}{2} < x < \frac{\pi}{2}$ would make this a function.

Q9 The function $m(x) = \frac{1}{x^2 - 4}$ is undefined when $x = 2$ and when $x = -2$.

So the largest continuous domain that makes it a function would be either $x > 2$ or $x < -2$.

Q10 a) It is not a function because it is not defined for all values of x in the domain (it's not defined at $x = 0$ or $x = 4$).

b) $x \in \mathbb{R}, x \neq 0, x \neq 4$

Exercise 1.3 — Types of function

It helps to sketch the graph of each function to identify its type.

Q1 a) One-to-one:

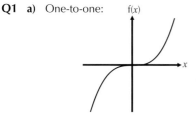

b) Many-to-one:

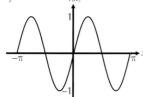

c) One-to-one:

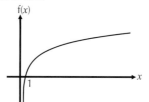

d) Many-to-one:

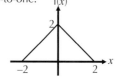

e) Many-to-one:

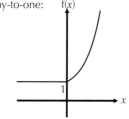

2. Composite Functions

Exercise 2.1 — Composite functions

Q1 a) Do $g(3) = 2(3) + 1 = 7$
then $f(7) = 7^2 = 49$, so fg(3) = 49.

b) $gf(3) = g(3^2) = g(9) = 2(9) + 1 = 19$

c) $f^2(5) = f(5^2) = f(25) = 25^2 = 625$

d) $g^2(2) = g(2(2) + 1) = g(5) = 2(5) + 1 = 11$

Q2 $fg\left(\frac{\pi}{2}\right) = f\left(2\left(\frac{\pi}{2}\right)\right) = f(\pi) = \sin \pi = 0$

$gf\left(\frac{\pi}{2}\right) = g\left(\sin\left(\frac{\pi}{2}\right)\right) = g(1) = 2(1) = 2$

Q3 a) $gf(1) = g\left(\frac{3}{1+2}\right) = g(1) = 2(1) = 2$.

$fg(1) = f(2(1)) = f(2) = \frac{3}{2+2} = \frac{3}{4}$.

$f^2(4) = f\left(\frac{3}{4+2}\right) = f\left(\frac{1}{2}\right) = \frac{3}{\frac{1}{2}+2} = \frac{6}{1+4} = 1\frac{1}{5}$

b) $g(-1) = -2$, and $f(-2)$ has a denominator of 0 which is undefined.

Q4 a) $fg(x) = f(x^2) = 2x^2 - 1$

b) $gf(x) = g(2x - 1) = (2x - 1)^2$

c) $f^2(x) = f(2x - 1) = 2(2x - 1) - 1 = 4x - 3$

Q5 a) $fg(x) = f(2x) = \cos 2x$

b) $gf(x) = 2 \cos x$

Q6 $fg(x) = f(x + 4) = \frac{2}{x + 4 - 1} = \frac{2}{x + 3}$

$gf(x) = g\left(\frac{2}{x - 1}\right) = \frac{2}{x - 1} + 4$

$= \frac{2}{x - 1} + \frac{4x - 4}{x - 1} = \frac{4x - 2}{x - 1} = \frac{2(2x - 1)}{x - 1}$

Q7 $f^2(x) = f\left(\dfrac{x}{1-x}\right) = \dfrac{\dfrac{x}{1-x}}{1 - \dfrac{x}{1-x}} = \dfrac{x}{(1-x)-x} = \dfrac{x}{1-2x}$

$gfg(x) = gf(x^2) = g\left(\dfrac{x^2}{1-x^2}\right) = \left(\dfrac{x^2}{1-x^2}\right)^2 = \dfrac{x^4}{(1-x^2)^2}$

Q8 **a)** $fg(x) = f(2x-3) = (2x-3)^2$, range: $fg(x) \geq 0$.

b) $gf(x) = g(x^2) = 2x^2 - 3$, range: $gf(x) \geq -3$.

Q9 **a)** $fg(x) = f(5x) = \dfrac{1}{5x}$, domain $x > 0$, range: $fg(x) > 0$.

b) $gf(x) = g\left(\dfrac{1}{x}\right) = \dfrac{5}{x}$, domain $x > 0$, range: $gf(x) > 0$.

Q10 $fgh(x) = fg(x^2 + 1) = f(5(x^2 + 1) - 1)$
$= f(5x^2 + 4) = 3(5x^2 + 4) + 2 = 15x^2 + 14$

Exercise 2.2 — Solving composite function equations

Q1 $fg(x) = f(3x - 4) = 2(3x - 4) + 1 = 6x - 7$
$6x - 7 = 23$
$x = 5$

Q2 $gf(x) = g\left(\dfrac{1}{x}\right) = \dfrac{2}{x} + 5$
$\dfrac{2}{x} + 5 = 6 \Rightarrow x = 2$

Q3 $gf(x) = g(x^2) = \dfrac{x^2}{x^2 - 3}$
$\dfrac{x^2}{x^2 - 3} = 4 \Rightarrow x^2 = 4x^2 - 12 \Rightarrow x^2 = 4$
$x = 2$ or $x = -2$

Q4 $gf(x) = g(x + 3) = (x + 3)^2 - 1$
$(x + 3)^2 - 1 = 3 \Rightarrow x = \pm\sqrt{4} - 3$
$x = -1$ or $x = -5$

Q5 $fg(x) = f(3x - 2) = (3x - 2)^2 + 1$
$(3x - 2)^2 + 1 = 50 \Rightarrow x = \dfrac{\pm\sqrt{49} + 2}{3}$
$x = 3$ or $x = -\dfrac{5}{3}$

Q6 $fg(x) = f(2x + 1) = 2^{(2x + 1)}$
$2^{(2x + 1)} = 32 = 2^5 \Rightarrow 2x + 1 = 5$
$x = 2$

Q7 $fg(x) = f(3 - x) = \log_{10}(3 - x)$
$\log_{10}(3 - x) = 0 \Rightarrow 3 - x = 1$
$x = 2$

Q8 $fg(x) = f(x^2 + 2x) = 2^{(x^2 + 2x)}$
$2^{(x^2 + 2x)} = 8 \Rightarrow x^2 + 2x = 3 \Rightarrow (x - 1)(x + 3) = 0$
$x = 1$ or $x = -3$

Q9 $fg(x) = f(2x - 1) = \dfrac{2x - 1}{2x - 1 + 1} = \dfrac{2x - 1}{2x} = 1 - \dfrac{1}{2x}$
$gf(x) = g\left(\dfrac{x}{x + 1}\right) = 2\left(\dfrac{x}{x + 1}\right) - 1 = \dfrac{x - 1}{x + 1}$
$1 - \dfrac{1}{2x} = \dfrac{x - 1}{x + 1} \Rightarrow 2x(x + 1) - (x + 1) = 2x(x - 1)$
$x = \dfrac{1}{3}$

Q10 $fg(x) = f(x + 1) = 2^{(x + 1)}$
$gf(x) = g(2^x) = 2^x + 1$
$2^{(x + 1)} = 2^x + 1$
$2 = 1 + \dfrac{1}{2^x} \Rightarrow 2^x = 1 \Rightarrow \log_2 1 = x$
$x = 0$

3. Inverse Functions

Exercise 3.1 — Inverse functions and their graphs

Q1 Yes, as the graph shows a one-to-one function.

Q2 No, as it is a many-to-one map, and many-to-one functions do not have inverse functions.

Q3 No, as $\sin x$ is a many-to-one function over the domain $x \in \mathbb{R}$.

Q4 No, as it is a many-to-one function over the domain $x \in \mathbb{R}$.

Q5 Yes, as it is a one-to-one function over the domain $x \geq 4$.

Q6 **a)** $f(x) = 3x + 4$ with domain $x \in \mathbb{R}$ has a range $f(x) \in \mathbb{R}$.
Replace $f(x)$ with y: $y = 3x + 4$
Rearrange: $x = \dfrac{y - 4}{3}$
Replace with $f^{-1}(x)$ and x: $f^{-1}(x) = \dfrac{x - 4}{3}$.
The domain of $f^{-1}(x)$ is $x \in \mathbb{R}$ and the range is $f^{-1}(x) \in \mathbb{R}$.

b) $f(x) = 5(x - 2)$ with domain $x \in \mathbb{R}$ has a range $f(x) \in \mathbb{R}$.
Replace $f(x)$ with y: $y = 5(x - 2)$
Rearrange: $x = \dfrac{y}{5} + 2$
Replace with $f^{-1}(x)$ and x: $f^{-1}(x) = \dfrac{x}{5} + 2$.
The domain of $f^{-1}(x)$ is $x \in \mathbb{R}$ and the range is $f^{-1}(x) \in \mathbb{R}$.

c) $f(x) = \dfrac{1}{x + 2}$ with domain $x > -2$ has a range $f(x) > 0$.
Replace $f(x)$ with y: $y = \dfrac{1}{x + 2}$
Rearrange: $x = \dfrac{1}{y} - 2$
Replace with $f^{-1}(x)$ and x: $f^{-1}(x) = \dfrac{1}{x} - 2$.
The domain of $f^{-1}(x)$ is the range of $f(x)$: $x > 0$.
The range of $f^{-1}(x)$ is the domain of $f(x)$: $f^{-1}(x) > -2$.

d) $f(x) = x^2 + 3$ with domain $x > 0$ has a range $f(x) > 3$.
Replace $f(x)$ with y: $y = x^2 + 3$
Rearrange: $x = \sqrt{y - 3}$
Replace with $f^{-1}(x)$ and x: $f^{-1}(x) = \sqrt{x - 3}$.
The domain of $f^{-1}(x)$ is the range of $f(x)$: $x > 3$.
The range of $f^{-1}(x)$ is the domain of $f(x)$: $f^{-1}(x) > 0$.

Q7 **a)** $f(x) = \dfrac{3x}{x + 1}$ with domain $x > -1$ has a range $f(x) < 3$ — you can work this out by sketching the graph. If you consider what happens as $x \to \infty$ you'll see that $f(x)$ approaches 3.
Replace $f(x)$ with y: $y = \dfrac{3x}{x + 1}$
Rearrange: $y(x + 1) = 3x \Rightarrow yx + y = 3x$
$\Rightarrow (3 - y)x = y \Rightarrow x = \dfrac{y}{3 - y}$
Replace with $f^{-1}(x)$ and x: $f^{-1}(x) = \dfrac{x}{3 - x}$.
The domain of $f^{-1}(x)$ is the range of $f(x)$: $x < 3$.
The range of $f^{-1}(x)$ is the domain of $f(x)$: $f^{-1}(x) > -1$.

b) $f^{-1}(2) = \dfrac{2}{3-2} = 2$

c) $f^{-1}\left(\dfrac{1}{2}\right) = \dfrac{\frac{1}{2}}{3-\frac{1}{2}} = \dfrac{1}{6-1} = \dfrac{1}{5}$

Q8 a) $f(x) = \dfrac{x-4}{x+3}$ with domain $x > -3$ has a range $f(x) < 1$ — again, sketching the graph will help. If you consider what happens as $x \to \infty$ you'll see that $f(x)$ approaches 1.

Replace $f(x)$ with y: $y = \dfrac{x-4}{x+3}$

Rearrange: $y(x+3) = x-4 \Rightarrow yx + 3y = x - 4$

$x(1-y) = 3y + 4 \Rightarrow x = \dfrac{3y+4}{1-y}$

Replace with $f^{-1}(x)$ and x: $f^{-1}(x) = \dfrac{3x+4}{1-x}$.

The domain of $f^{-1}(x)$ is the range of $f(x)$: $x < 1$.
The range of $f^{-1}(x)$ is the domain of $f(x)$: $f^{-1}(x) > -3$.

b) $f^{-1}(0) = \dfrac{3(0)+4}{1-0} = 4$

c) $f^{-1}\left(-\dfrac{2}{5}\right) = \dfrac{3\left(-\frac{2}{5}\right)+4}{1+\frac{2}{5}} = \dfrac{-6+20}{5+2} = \dfrac{14}{7} = 2$

Q9 $f(x)$ has a domain of $x > 3$, and a range of $f(x) \in \mathbb{R}$.
So $f^{-1}(x)$ has a domain $x \in \mathbb{R}$ and range $f^{-1}(x) > 3$.

Q10 $f(x)$ has a domain of $1 \le x \le 7$, which will give a range of $(4(1)-2) \le f(x) \le (4(7)-2)$, $2 \le f(x) \le 26$.
So $f^{-1}(x)$ has a domain $2 \le x \le 26$ and range $1 \le f^{-1}(x) \le 7$.

Q11 $f(x)$ has a domain of $x < 2$, and a range of $f(x) < 1$.
So $f^{-1}(x)$ has a domain $x < 1$ and range $f^{-1}(x) < 2$.

Q12

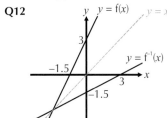

Q13 a)

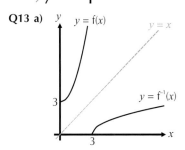

b) $f(x)$ has a domain of $x > 0$, which will give a range of $f(x) > 3$.
So $f^{-1}(x)$ has a domain $x > 3$ and range $f^{-1}(x) > 0$.

Q14 a)

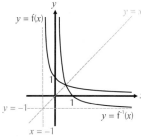

b) There is one point where the graphs intersect.

Q15 a) $f(x) = \dfrac{1}{x-3}$ with domain $x > 3$ has a range $f(x) > 0$.

Replace $f(x)$ with y: $y = \dfrac{1}{x-3}$

Rearrange: $x = \dfrac{1}{y} + 3$

Replace with $f^{-1}(x)$ and x: $f^{-1}(x) = \dfrac{1}{x} + 3$.

The domain of $f^{-1}(x)$ is the range of $f(x)$: $x > 0$.
The range of $f^{-1}(x)$ is the domain of $f(x)$: $f^{-1}(x) > 3$.

b)

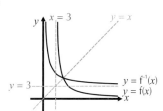

c) There is one solution as the graphs intersect once.

d) $\dfrac{1}{x-3} = \dfrac{1}{x} + 3$

$x^2 - 3x - 1 = 0$

So using the quadratic formula gives:

$x = \dfrac{3 + \sqrt{13}}{2}$

We ignore the negative solutions to the quadratic equation because we're only considering the domain $x > 3$.

4. Modulus

Exercise 4.1 — The graphs of | f(x) | and f(|x|)

Q1 a)

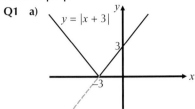

$y = |x + 3|$

b)

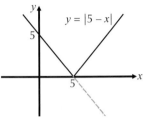

$y = |5 - x|$

c)

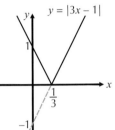

$y = |3x - 1|$

d)

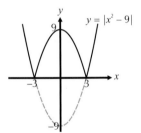

$y = |x^2 - 9|$

e)

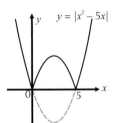

$y = |x^2 - 5x|$

Q2

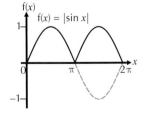

$f(x) = |\sin x|$

Q3

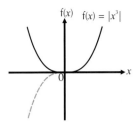

$f(x)$ $f(x) = |x^3|$

Q4

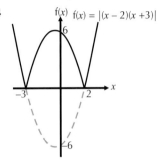

$f(x)$ $f(x) = |(x - 2)(x + 3)|$

Q5 a) $y = f(|x|)$

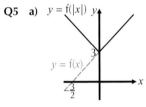

$y = f(x)$

b)

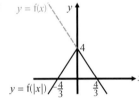

$y = f(x)$ $y = f(|x|)$

c) $y = f(|x|)$ $y = f(x)$

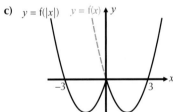

d) $y = f(|x|)$ $y = f(x)$

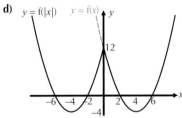

e)

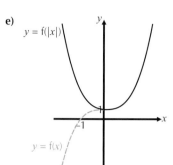

$y = f(|x|)$

$y = f(x)$

-1

f)

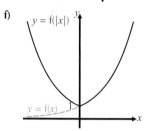

$y = f(|x|)$

$y = f(x)$

1

g)

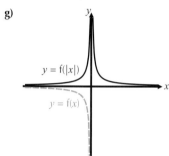

$y = f(|x|)$

$y = f(x)$

h)

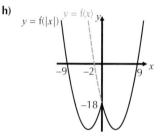

$y = f(x)$

$y = f(|x|)$

-9 -2 9

-18

i)

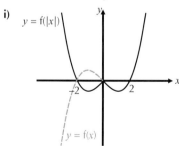

$y = f(|x|)$

-2 2

$y = f(x)$

Q6 1 = b), 2 = a), 3 = d), 4 = c)

Q7 a)

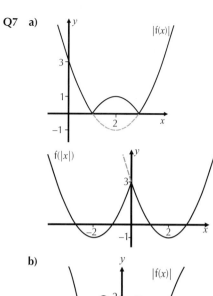

$|f(x)|$

3

1

2

-1

$f(|x|)$

3

-2 -1 2

b)

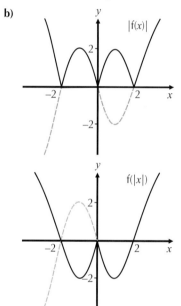

$|f(x)|$

2

-2 2

-2

$f(|x|)$

2

-2 2

-2

Q8 a)

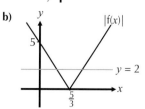

$|f(x)|$

5

$\frac{5}{3}$

-5 $f(x)$

b)

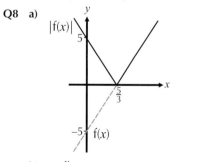

$|f(x)|$

5

$y = 2$

$\frac{5}{3}$

The line $y = 2$ intersects with the line $|3x - 5|$ in two places so there are 2 solutions to $|3x - 5| = 2$.

Q9

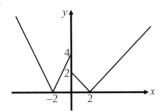

Q10 a)

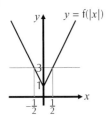

b) There are two solutions to $4|x| + 1 = 3$.
Reading off the graph, these are:
$x = \frac{1}{2}$ and $x = -\frac{1}{2}$.

Q11 1 = d), 2 = b), 3 = a), 4 = c)

Exercise 4.2 — Solving modulus equations and inequalities

Q1 a) Draw the line $y = 2$ to show how many times it intersects with the curve:

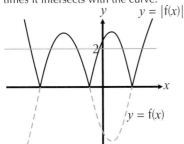

There are 6 points of intersection, so there are 6 solutions to the equation $|f(x)| = 2$.

b) The graph shows that 3 of the points of intersection occur where $y = |f(x)|$ is the same as $y = f(x)$, so 3 solutions could be found by solving $f(x) = 2$.

c) The other 3 solutions can be found by solving $-f(x) = 2$.

Q2

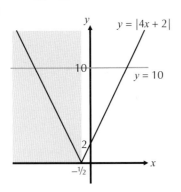

The graph shows that there are two solutions to $|4x + 2| = 10$.

$4x + 2 \geq 0$ for $x \geq -\frac{1}{2}$

$4x + 2 < 0$ for $x < -\frac{1}{2}$ (shaded)

So there are two equations to solve:

(1) $4x + 2 = 10 \Rightarrow x = 2$

(this is valid as it's in the range $x \geq -\frac{1}{2}$)

(2) $-(4x + 2) = 10 \Rightarrow x = -3$

(this is also valid as it's in the range $x < -\frac{1}{2}$)

So the two solutions are $x = 2$ and $x = -3$.

Q3 Rearranging the equation gives $|3x - 4| = 1$.

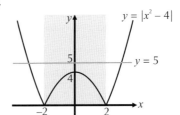

The graph shows that there are two solutions to $|3x - 4| = 1$.

$3x - 4 \geq 0$ for $x \geq \frac{4}{3}$

$3x - 4 < 0$ for $x < \frac{4}{3}$ (shaded)

So there are two equations to solve:

(1) $3x - 4 = 1 \Rightarrow x = \frac{5}{3}$

(this is valid as it's in the range $x \geq \frac{4}{3}$)

(2) $-(3x - 4) = 1 \Rightarrow x = 1$

(this is also valid as it's in the range $x < \frac{4}{3}$)

So the two solutions are $x = \frac{5}{3}$ and $x = 1$.

Q4

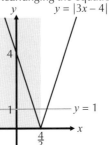

The graph shows that there are two solutions, both in the positive area of the graph where $x \leq -2$ or $x \geq 2$.

So there is just one equation to solve:

$x^2 - 4 = 5 \Rightarrow x = \pm 3$ (both of these solutions are valid as they are in the range $x \leq -2$ or $x \geq 2$).

Q5

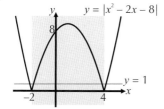

The graph shows that there are four solutions to $|x^2 - 2x - 8| = 1$.

$x^2 - 2x - 8 \geq 0$ for $x \leq -2$ and $x \geq 4$

$x^2 - 2x - 8 < 0$ for $-2 < x < 4$ (shaded)

So there are two equations to solve:

(1) $x^2 - 2x - 8 = 1 \Rightarrow x^2 - 2x - 9 = 0$

Using the quadratic formula $x = 1 \pm \sqrt{10}$ (both of these solutions are valid as they are in the range $x \leq -2$ or $x \geq 4$)

(2) $-(x^2 - 2x - 8) = 1 \Rightarrow x^2 - 2x - 7 = 0$

Using the quadratic formula $x = 1 \pm \sqrt{8}$ (both of these solutions are valid as they are in the range $-2 < x < 4$)

So the four solutions are $x = 1 + \sqrt{10}$, $x = 1 - \sqrt{10}$, $x = 1 + 2\sqrt{2}$ and $x = 1 - 2\sqrt{2}$.

Q6 Square both sides of the equation, factorise and solve:

$(2x - 1)^2 = (4x)^2 \Rightarrow 4x^2 - 4x + 1 = 16x^2$
$\Rightarrow 12x^2 + 4x - 1 = 0 \Rightarrow (6x - 1)(2x + 1) = 0$

So $x = \frac{1}{6}$ and $x = -\frac{1}{2}$.

Q7 a)

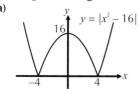

b)

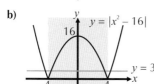

The graph shows that there are four solutions to $|x^2 - 16| = 3$.

$x^2 - 16 \geq 0$ for $x \leq -4$ and $x \geq 4$

$x^2 - 16 < 0$ for $-4 < x < 4$ (shaded)

So there are two equations to solve:

(1) $x^2 - 16 = 3 \Rightarrow x = \pm\sqrt{19}$ (both of these solutions are valid as they are in the range $x \leq -4$ or $x \geq 4$)

(2) $-(x^2 - 16) = 3 \Rightarrow x = \pm\sqrt{13}$ (both of these solutions are valid as they are in the range $-4 < x < 4$)

So the four solutions are $x = \sqrt{19}$, $x = -\sqrt{19}$, $x = \sqrt{13}$ and $x = -\sqrt{13}$.

Q8 a)

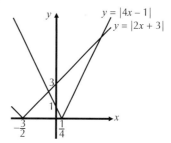

b) The graph shows that there are two solutions, one where both $2x + 3$ and $4x - 1$ are positive, and one where $2x + 3$ is positive but $4x - 1$ is negative.

So there are two equations to solve:

(1) $4x - 1 = 2x + 3 \Rightarrow x = 2$

(2) $-(4x - 1) = 2x + 3 \Rightarrow x = -\frac{1}{3}$

So the two solutions are $x = 2$ and $x = -\frac{1}{3}$.

Or using the algebraic method, solve:

$(2x + 3)^2 = (4x - 1)^2$
$4x^2 + 12x + 9 = 16x^2 - 8x + 1$
$3x^2 - 5x - 2 = 0$
$(3x + 1)(x - 2) = 0$

So $x = 2$ and $x = -\frac{1}{3}$.

Q9 $|4x - 2| \leq 6 \Rightarrow -6 \leq 4x - 2 \leq 6 \Rightarrow -4 \leq 4x \leq 8$
$\Rightarrow -1 \leq x \leq 2$.

Q10 a)

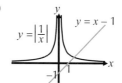

b) The graph shows that there is just one solution to $|f(x)| = g(x)$, in the positive area of the graph where $x > 0$.

So there is just one equation to solve to find the point of intersection of the graphs (which will help you find the range of x for the inequality):

$\frac{1}{x} = x - 1 \Rightarrow x^2 - x - 1 = 0 \Rightarrow x = \frac{1 \pm \sqrt{5}}{2}$.

But only $\frac{1 + \sqrt{5}}{2}$ is valid (i.e. in the range $x > 0$).

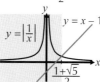

For $|f(x)| \geq g(x)$, we want the bit of the graph where the black line is above the grey line (shaded grey), so $x \leq \frac{1 + \sqrt{5}}{2}$.

Q11 a)

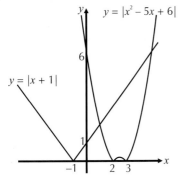

$y = |x^2 - 5x + 6|$

$y = |x + 1|$

b) The graph shows that there are two solutions to $|f(x)| = |g(x)|$, both of which are where both $f(x)$ and $g(x)$ are positive.

So there is one equation to solve to find the limits of the inequality:
$x^2 - 5x + 6 = x + 1 \Rightarrow x^2 - 6x + 5 = 0$
$\Rightarrow (x - 5)(x - 1) = 0$

So the graphs cross at $x = 5$ and $x = 1$.

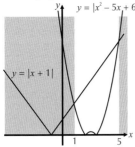

$y = |x^2 - 5x + 6|$

$y = |x + 1|$

$|f(x)| > |g(x)|$ where the line for $|x^2 - 5x + 6|$ is above the line for $|x + 1|$ (shaded grey on the graph), which is when $x < 1$ and when $x > 5$.

5. Transformations of Graphs

Exercise 5.1 — Transformations of graphs

Q1

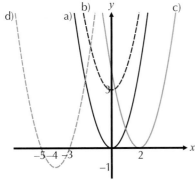

The coordinates of the turning points are:

a) (0, 0)   **b)** (0, 3)
c) (2, 0)   **d)** (−4, −1)

Q2 **a)**

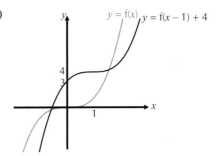

$y = f(x)$ $y = f(x - 1) + 4$

b) $y = (x - 1)^3 + 4$

Q3

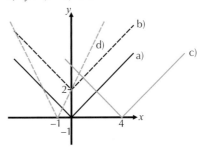

The transformations can be described as follows:

b) A translation of 2 up.

c) A translation of 4 right.

d) A translation of 1 left and a stretch vertically by a scale factor of 2.

Q4

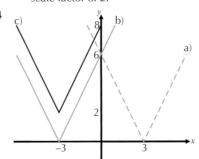

Q5

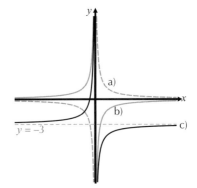

$y = -3$

Q6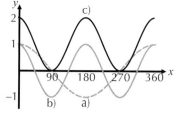

d) The minimum points on graph c) are at (90, 0) and (270, 0).

Q7 The maximum value of sin x is 1, and the minimum value is –1, so:

Transformed Function	New equation	Max value	Min value
f(x) + 2	sin x + 2	3	1
f(x – 90°)	sin(x – 90°)	1	–1
f(3x)	sin 3x	1	–1
4f(x)	4 sin x	4	–4

Q8 The point of inflection of x^3 is at (0, 0), so:

Transformed Function	New equation	Coordinates of point of inflection
f(x) + 1	x^3 + 1	(0, 1)
f(x – 2)	(x – 2)^3	(2, 0)
–f(x) – 3	$-x^3$ – 3	(0, –3)
f(–x) + 4	$-x^3$ + 4	(0, 4)

Q9 a)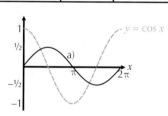

b) $y = \frac{1}{2}\cos\left(x - \frac{\pi}{2}\right)$

Q10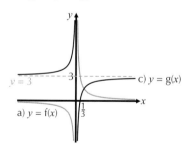

b) Reflect in the y-axis (or x-axis) and translate 3 up.

Q11

Original graph	New graph	Sequence of transformations
$y = x^3$	$y = (x - 4)^3 + 5$	Translate 4 right and 5 up.
$y = 4^x$	$y = 4^{3x} - 1$	Stretch horizontally by a factor of $\frac{1}{3}$ and translate 1 down.
$y = |x + 1|$	$y = 1 - |2x + 1|$	Stretch horizontally by a factor of $\frac{1}{2}$, reflect in the x-axis and translate 1 up.
$y = \sin x$	$y = -3 \sin 2x + 1$	Stretch horizontally by a factor of $\frac{1}{2}$, stretch vertically by a factor of 3, reflect in the x-axis and translate 1 up.

Q12 a) $y = 2x^2 - 4x + 6 = 2[x^2 - 2x + 3] = 2[(x - 1)^2 + 2]$

b) Translate 1 right, then translate 2 up, then stretch vertically by a factor of 2.

c)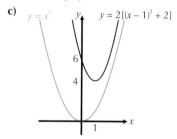

d) The minimum point is at (1, 4).
You can work out the minimum point by performing the transformations on the minimum point of the graph $y = x^2$ (which is (0, 0)).

Q13 a) Stretch horizontally, scale factor $\frac{1}{3}$, then stretch vertically, scale factor 4.

b) Stretch horizontally, scale factor $\frac{1}{2}$, then reflect in the x-axis, then translate 4 up.

c) Translate $\frac{\pi}{3}$ right, then stretch vertically, scale factor 2.

Q14 a)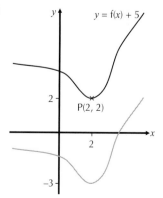

b)

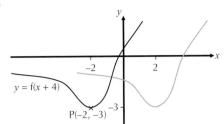

$y = f(x + 4)$

$P(-2, -3)$ -3

c)

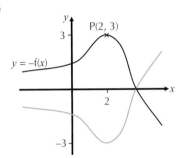

$P(2, 3)$

$y = -f(x)$

Q15 a)

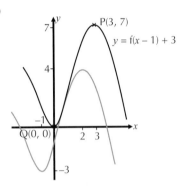

$P(3, 7)$

$y = f(x - 1) + 3$

$Q(0, 0)$

b)

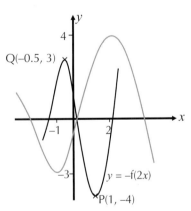

$Q(-0.5, 3)$

$y = -f(2x)$

$P(1, -4)$

c)

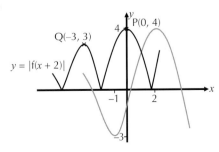

$P(0, 4)$

$Q(-3, 3)$

$y = |f(x + 2)|$

Review Exercise — Chapter 1

Q1 **a)** Range $f(x) \geq -16$. This is a function, and it's one-to-one (the domain is restricted so every x-value is mapped to only one value of $f(x)$).

b) To find the range of this function, you need to find the minimum point of $x^2 - 7x + 10$ — do this by completing the square:
$x^2 - 7x + 10 = (x - 3.5)^2 - 12.25 + 10$
$= (x - 3.5)^2 - 2.25$.
As $(x - 3.5)^2 \geq 0$ the minimum value of $x^2 - 7x + 10$ is -2.25, so the range is $f(x) \geq -2.25$. This is a function, and it's many-to-one (as more than one x-value is mapped to the same value of $f(x)$).
You could also have found the minimum point by differentiating, setting the derivative equal to 0 and solving for x.

c) Range $f(x) \geq 0$. This is not a function as $f(x)$ doesn't exist for $x < 0$.

d) Sketch the graph for this one:

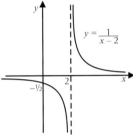

$y = \dfrac{1}{x - 2}$

$-\frac{1}{2}$

From the graph, the range is $f(x) \in \mathbb{R}$, $f(x) \neq 0$. This is not a function as it's not defined for $x = 2$.
If you're not sure about any of the domains or ranges for the other parts, draw the graphs and see if that helps.

Q2 **a)** $f(0) = \dfrac{5}{(2 \times 0) + 1} = 5$

$f\left(\frac{1}{2}\right) = \dfrac{5}{\left(2 \times \frac{1}{2}\right) + 1} = 2\frac{1}{2}$

b)

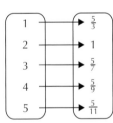

1	→	$\frac{5}{3}$
2	→	1
3	→	$\frac{5}{7}$
4	→	$\frac{5}{9}$
5	→	$\frac{5}{11}$

Range $\{\frac{5}{3}, 1, \frac{5}{7}, \frac{5}{9}, \frac{5}{11}\}$

c) Yes.

d) No — the map is not defined for $x = -\frac{1}{2}$.

Q3 **a)**

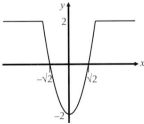

$-\sqrt{2}$ $\sqrt{2}$

b) $-2 \leq f(x) \leq 2$

Q4 a) $fg(2) = f(2(2) + 3) = f(7) = \frac{3}{7}$.
$gf(1) = g(3/1) = g(3) = 2(3) + 3 = 9$.
$fg(x) = f(2x + 3) = \frac{3}{2x + 3}$.

b) $fg(2) = f(2 + 4) = f(6) = 3(6^2) = 3 \times 36 = 108$.

$gf(1) = g(3(1^2)) = g(3) = 3 + 4 = 7$.
$fg(x) = f(x + 4) = 3(x + 4)^2$.

Q5 a) $fg(1) = f(10^{1+1}) = \log_{10}(10^2) = 2$
$gf(1) = g(\log_{10}1) = g(0) = 10^{0+1} = 10$
$f^2(10) = f(\log_{10}10) = f(1) = \log_{10}1 = 0$
$g^2(-1) = g(10^{-1+1}) = g(1) = 10^{1+1} = 100$

b) Because $f(1) = \log_{10}1 = 0$, and $f(0) = \log_{10}0$, which is undefined.

Q6 $fg(x) = f(x + 7) = 3(x + 7) = 3x + 21$
$gf(x) = g(3x) = 3x + 7$
$g^2(x) = g(x + 7) = (x + 7) + 7 = x + 14$

Q7 a) The domain of $fg(x)$ must be $x \le 12$ since this is the domain of $g(x)$. But $x + 3$ (the input into $f(x)$) must also be ≥ 2, so $x + 3 \ge 2 \Rightarrow x \ge -1$. So the complete domain for $fg(x)$ is $-1 \le x \le 12$.
The range can be found by putting the limits of the domain into $fg(x)$:
$(4(-1) + 12) \le fg(x) \le (4(12) + 12)$
$8 \le fg(x) \le 60$

b) $fg(x) = f(x + 3) = 4(x + 3) = 4x + 12$

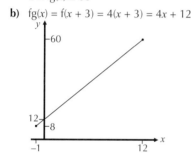

c) The domain of $gf(x)$ must be $x \ge 2$ since this is the domain of $f(x)$. But $4x$ (the input into $g(x)$) must also be ≤ 12, so $4x \le 12 \Rightarrow x \le 3$. So the complete domain for $gf(x)$ is $2 \le x \le 3$.
The range can be found by putting the limits of the domain into $gf(x)$:
$(4(2) + 3) \le gf(x) \le (4(3) + 3)$
$11 \le gf(x) \le 15$

d) $gf(x) = g(4x) = 4x + 3$

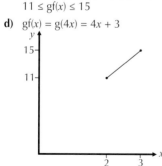

Q8 f is a one-to-one function so it has an inverse. The domain of the inverse is the range of the function and vice versa, so the domain of $f^{-1}(x)$ is $x \ge 3$ and the range is $f^{-1}(x) \in \mathbb{R}$.

Q9 First replace $f(x)$ with y to get an equation for y in terms of x, then rearrange to make x the subject:
$$y = \sqrt{2x - 4}$$
$$y^2 = 2x - 4$$
$$y^2 + 4 = 2x$$
$$x = \frac{y^2 + 4}{2} = \frac{y^2}{2} + 2$$
Finally replace x with $f^{-1}(x)$ and y with x:
$f^{-1}(x) = \frac{x^2}{2} + 2$, which has domain $x \ge 0$
(as the range of f is $f(x) \ge 0$) and range $f^{-1}(x) \ge 2$ (as the domain of f is $x \ge 2$).

Q10 In the domain $0 \le x \le \frac{\pi}{2}$, $\cos x$ is a one-to-one function, as shown:

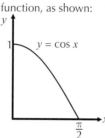

One-to-one functions have inverses, so $f^{-1}(x)$ does exist.

Q11 First replace $f(x)$ with y to get an equation for y in terms of x: $y = \log_{10}(x + 4)$.
Then rearrange the equation to make x the subject. First do 10 to the power of each side to get rid of the log, then rearrange:
$10^y = x + 4 \Rightarrow x = 10^y - 4$.
Finally replace x with $f^{-1}(x)$ and y with x:
$f^{-1}(x) = 10^x - 4$.
The question doesn't ask for the domain and range but the range is the domain of f(x): $f^{-1}(x) > -4$ and the domain is the range of f(x): $x \in \mathbb{R}$.

Q12 a) $f^{-1}(x) = x - 4$.

b) $g(x) = \frac{3}{x + 1}$
Replace $g(x)$ with y: $y = \frac{3}{x + 1}$
Rearrange: $x = \frac{3}{y} - 1$
Replace with $g^{-1}(x)$ and x: $g^{-1}(x) = \frac{3}{x} - 1$.

c) $f^{-1}g^{-1}(x) = f^{-1}(\frac{3}{x} - 1) = \frac{3}{x} - 1 - 4 = \frac{3}{x} - 5$

d) $gf(x) = g(x + 4) = \frac{3}{(x + 4) + 1} = \frac{3}{x + 5}$.

e) Let $h(x)$ be the inverse of $gf(x)$.
Replace with y: $y = \frac{3}{x + 5}$
Rearrange: $x = \frac{3}{y} - 5$
Replace with $h(x)$ and x: $h(x) = \frac{3}{x} - 5$.
This is the same as $f^{-1}g^{-1}(x)$.

Q13 a)

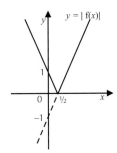

b)

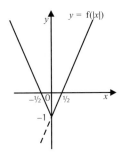

Q14 Using the algebraic (squaring) method:
$(3x - 1)^2 = (4 - x)^2$
$9x^2 - 6x + 1 = 16 - 8x + x^2$
$8x^2 + 2x - 15 = 0$
$(4x - 5)(2x + 3) = 0$

So the two solutions are: $x = \frac{5}{4}$ and $x = -\frac{3}{2}$.

You could also solve this by sketching the graphs of $f(x) = |3x - 1|$ and $g(x) = |4 - x|$ and solving $f(x) = g(x)$ or $-f(x) = g(x)$ depending on where the roots lie.

Q15 Using the algebraic (squaring) method:
$(4x + 3)^2 = (5x)^2$
$16x^2 + 24x + 9 = 25x^2$
$9x^2 - 24x - 9 = 0$
$3x^2 - 8x - 3 = 0$
$(3x + 1)(x - 3)$

So the two solutions are $x = -\frac{1}{3}$ and $x = 3$.

Again, you could have used the graphical method to solve this, but the algebraic way is quicker.

Q16 a) $-17 \leq x \leq 17$

b) $-2 < x + 8 < 2 \Rightarrow -10 < x < -6$

c) $-5 < 4x + 3 < 5 \Rightarrow -8 < 4x < 2 \Rightarrow -2 < x < \frac{1}{2}$

Q17 a) $f(x) = x^2 - 2x - 8 = (x + 2)(x - 4)$
So the graph of $f(x)$ touches the x-axis at -2 and 4, crosses the y-axis at -8 ($f(0) = -8$), and has a minimum point at $(1, -9)$.
You could use calculus to find the coordinates of the turning point.

For $y = |f(x)|$ reflect the negative part in the x-axis, and for $y = f(|x|)$ reflect the $x > 0$ part in the y-axis:

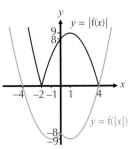

b) The graph below shows there are 2 solutions, one for $f(x) = -5$ (in the region $x \geq 0$) and one for $f(-x) = -5$ (in the region $x < 0$).

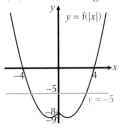

Since the graph is symmetrical about the y-axis we can find the positive solution and then use this to find the negative solution:
$x^2 - 2x - 8 = -5 \Rightarrow x^2 - 2x - 3 = 0$
$\Rightarrow (x + 1)(x - 3) = 0$
$\Rightarrow x = -1$ (not valid as x must be positive)
and $x = 3$ (valid).
So the valid solutions are $x = 3$ and $x = -3$ (for the negative part of the graph).

Solving algebraically: For $x < 0$, $f(-x) = -5 \Rightarrow$
$(-x)^2 - 2(-x) - 8 = -5 \Rightarrow x^2 + 2x - 8 = -5$
$\Rightarrow (x - 1)(x + 3) = 0 \Rightarrow x = 1$ (not valid for $x < 0$)
or $x = -3$ (valid)

c) Just look at the graph and see where $f(|x|) \geq -5$.

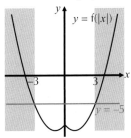

This is where the black line is above the grey line (shaded grey), and using the solutions from part b), this is true for $x \leq -3$ or $x \geq 3$.

Q18 a)

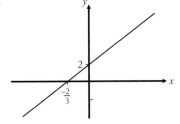

b)

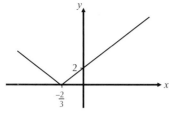

c)

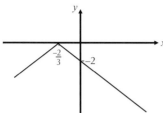

Q19

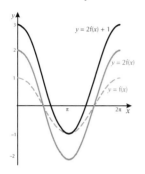

Exam-Style Questions — Chapter 1

Q1 To transform the curve $y = x^3$ into $y = (x - 1)^3$, translate it 1 unit horizontally to the right *[1 mark]*. To transform this into the curve $y = 2(x - 1)^3$, stretch it vertically by a scale factor of 2 *[1 mark]*. Finally, to transform into the curve $y = 2(x - 1)^3 + 4$, the whole curve is translated 4 units upwards *[1 mark]*.

Q2 a) $gf(x) = g(x^2 - 3)$ *[1 mark]* $= \dfrac{1}{x^2 - 3}$ *[1 mark]*

b) $\dfrac{1}{x^2 - 3} = \dfrac{1}{6} \Rightarrow x^2 - 3 = 6 \Rightarrow x^2 = 9$

$\Rightarrow x = 3, x = -3$

[3 marks available — 1 mark for rearranging to solve equation, 1 mark for each correct solution]

c) (i) f(x) is a many-to-one function, so the inverse would be one-to-many, which is not a function, so $f^{-1}(x)$ does not exist *[1 mark]*.

(ii) f(x) is a one-to-one function over the domain $x \geq 0$ *[1 mark]*, so $f^{-1}(x)$ would exist if f(x) had this restricted domain.

There are other restricted domains which would work so you could have another answer here.

Q3 a) $fg(6) = f(\sqrt{(3 \times 6) - 2}) = f(\sqrt{16})$ *[1 mark]*

$= f(4) = 2^4 = 16$ *[1 mark]*

b) $gf(2) = g(2^2) = g(4)$ *[1 mark]*

$= \sqrt{(3 \times 4) - 2} = \sqrt{10}$ *[1 mark]*

c) (i) First, write $y = g(x)$ and rearrange to make x the subject:

$y = \sqrt{3x - 2}$

$\Rightarrow y^2 = 3x - 2$

$\Rightarrow y^2 + 2 = 3x$

$\Rightarrow \dfrac{y^2 + 2}{3} = x$ *[1 mark]*

Then replace x with $g^{-1}(x)$ and y with x:

$g^{-1}(x) = \dfrac{x^2 + 2}{3}$ *[1 mark]*.

(ii) $fg^{-1}(x) = f\left(\dfrac{x^2 + 2}{3}\right)$ *[1 mark]*

$= 2^{\frac{x^2+2}{3}}$ *[1 mark]*

Q4 a)

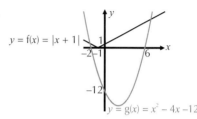

[2 marks available — 1 mark for each graph sketched with the intercepts]

$x^2 - 4x - 12 = (x + 2)(x - 6)$, so the x-intercepts are -2 and 6. To draw $|x + 1|$, just reflect the negative part of the graph of $y = x + 1$ in the x-axis.

b) The two graphs intersect twice, so there are two valid solutions to $x^2 - 4x - 12 = |x + 1|$. Looking at where f(x) ≥ 0 and where f(x) < 0 gives:

(1) $x^2 - 4x - 12 = x + 1$ for $x \geq -1$ *[1 mark]*.

$\Rightarrow x^2 - 5x - 13 = 0$

(2) $x^2 - 4x - 12 = -x - 1$ for $x < -1$ *[1 mark]*.

$\Rightarrow x^2 - 3x - 11 = 0$

Solving (1) using the quadratic formula gives:

$x = \dfrac{5 \pm \sqrt{77}}{2}$.

Since $x \geq -1$, the only valid solution is

$x = \dfrac{5 + \sqrt{77}}{2}$ *[1 mark]*.

Solving (2) using the quadratic formula gives:

$x = \dfrac{3 \pm \sqrt{53}}{2}$.

Since $x < -1$, the only valid solution is

$x = \dfrac{3 - \sqrt{53}}{2}$ *[1 mark]*.

c) We want the bits of the graph where the grey curve is above the black line (shaded grey).

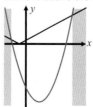

From part b), we know that the graphs intersect at

$x = \dfrac{5 + \sqrt{77}}{2}$ and $x = \dfrac{3 - \sqrt{53}}{2}$,

so $x^2 - 4x - 12 > |x + 1|$ when $x < \dfrac{3 - \sqrt{53}}{2}$

[1 mark] or when $x > \dfrac{5 + \sqrt{77}}{2}$ *[1 mark]*.

Q5 a) A reflection in the *y*-axis is a transformation of the form f(–*x*) *[1 mark]*. A translation of 3 up becomes f(–*x*) + 3 *[1 mark]*, then a translation of 2 right becomes f(–(*x* – 2)) + 3 *[1 mark]*.
So g(*x*) = f(2 – *x*) + 3.
Make sure you do f(–(x – 2)) instead of f(–x – 2) here.

b) Original coordinates of P: (1, 2).
After reflection in the *y*-axis: (–1, 2).
After translation of 3 up and 2 right: (1, 5) *[1 mark]*.
Original coordinates of Q: (3, 6).
After reflection in the *y*-axis: (–3, 6).
After translation of 3 up and 2 right: (–1, 9) *[1 mark]*.
Do a quick sketch of the graph if you need to.

Q6 a) The range of f is f(*x*) > 0 *[1 mark]*.

b) (i) Let *y* = f(*x*). Then $y = \dfrac{1}{x + 5}$.
Rearrange this to make *x* the subject:
$$y(x + 5) = 1 \Rightarrow x + 5 = \frac{1}{y}$$
$$\Rightarrow x = \frac{1}{y} - 5 \quad \textbf{[1 mark]}$$
Finally, write out in terms of *x* and f^{-1}(*x*):
$f^{-1}(x) = \dfrac{1}{x} - 5$ *[1 mark]*.

(ii) The domain of the inverse is the same as the range of the function, so *x* > 0 *[1 mark]*. The range of the inverse is the same as the domain of the function, so f^{-1}(*x*) > –5 *[1 mark]*.

c)

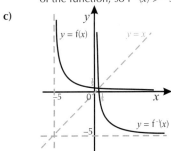

[2 marks available — 1 mark for each correct curve, each with correct intersections and asymptotes as shown]

Q7 a)

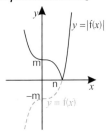

[2 marks available — 1 mark for reflecting in x-axis at x = n, 1 mark for crossing y-axis at y = m]

b)

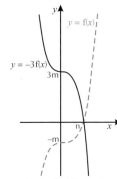

[2 marks available — 1 mark for reflecting in x-axis and 1 mark for crossing y-axis at y = 3m (due to stretch by scale factor 3)]

c)

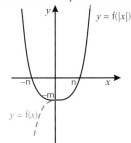

[2 marks available — 1 mark for reflecting in y-axis and 1 mark for crossing the x-axis at –n]

Chapter 2: Trigonometry

1. Inverse Trig Functions

Exercise 1.1 — Sin⁻¹, cos⁻¹ and tan⁻¹

Q1 **a)** If $x = \cos^{-1} 1$, then $1 = \cos x$ so $x = 0$.

    b) If $x = \sin^{-1} \frac{\sqrt{3}}{2}$ then $\frac{\sqrt{3}}{2} = \sin x$ so $x = \frac{\pi}{3}$.

    c) If $x = \tan^{-1} \sqrt{3}$ then $\sqrt{3} = \tan x$ so $x = \frac{\pi}{3}$.

Q2 **a)**

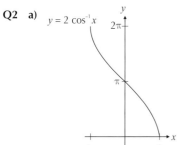

    The graph is the same as y = cos⁻¹ x but stretched vertically by a factor of 2, so the y-coordinates of the endpoints and y-intercept are doubled.

    b)

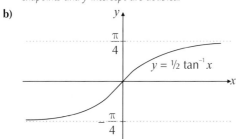

    The range is $-\frac{\pi}{4} < \frac{1}{2}\tan^{-1} x < \frac{\pi}{4}$.

    The graph is the same as y = tan⁻¹ x but stretched vertically by a factor of ½, so the y-coordinates of the asymptotes are halved.

Q3

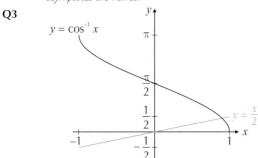

    The graphs intersect once, so there is one real root of the equation $\cos^{-1} x = \frac{x}{2}$.

Q4 **a)** $\sin^{-1}(-1) = -\frac{\pi}{2}$.

    This is one of the endpoints of the sin⁻¹ x graph.

    b) To find $\cos^{-1}\left(-\frac{\sqrt{3}}{2}\right)$, first find the angle a for which $\cos a = \frac{\sqrt{3}}{2}$:

So $\cos \frac{\pi}{6} = \frac{\sqrt{3}}{2}$:

Now use the CAST diagram to find the negative solutions that lie in the domain $0 \le x \le \pi$:

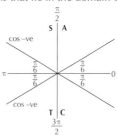

The only negative solution in that domain is $\pi - \frac{\pi}{6} = \frac{5\pi}{6}$.

So $\cos^{-1}\left(-\frac{\sqrt{3}}{2}\right) = \frac{5\pi}{6}$.

Q5 **a)** $\sin^{-1} \frac{1}{2} = \frac{\pi}{6}$, so $\tan(\sin^{-1} \frac{1}{2}) = \tan \frac{\pi}{6} = \frac{1}{\sqrt{3}}$.

    b) This is just the cos function followed by its inverse function so the answer is $\frac{2\pi}{3}$.

    c) $\sin^{-1} \frac{1}{2} = \frac{\pi}{6}$, so $\cos(\sin^{-1} \frac{1}{2}) = \cos \frac{\pi}{6} = \frac{\sqrt{3}}{2}$.

Q6 To find the inverse of the function, first write as $y = 1 + \sin 2x$, then rearrange to make x the subject:

$\sin 2x = y - 1 \Rightarrow 2x = \sin^{-1}(y - 1) \Rightarrow x = \frac{1}{2}\sin^{-1}(y - 1)$.

Now replace x with $f^{-1}(x)$ and y with x:

$f^{-1}(x) = \frac{1}{2}\sin^{-1}(x - 1)$

2. Cosec, Sec and Cot

Exercise 2.1 — Graphs of cosec, sec and cot

Q1 **a)**

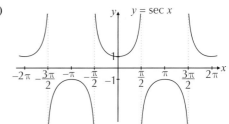

    b) The minimum points are at $(-2\pi, 1)$, $(0, 1)$ and $(2\pi, 1)$.

    c) The maximum points are at $(-\pi, -1)$ and $(\pi, -1)$.

    d) The range is $y \in \mathbb{R}$, $y \ge 1$ or $y \le -1$.

    You could also say that y is undefined for −1 < y < 1.

Q2 a)

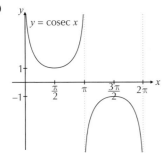

b) There is a maximum at $(\frac{3\pi}{2}, -1)$ and a minimum at $(\frac{\pi}{2}, 1)$.

c) The domain is $x \in \mathbb{R}$, $x \neq n\pi$ (where n is an integer). The range is $y \in \mathbb{R}$, $y \geq 1$ or $y \leq -1$.

The domain is all real numbers except those for which cosec x is undefined (i.e. at the asymptotes).

Q3 A horizontal translation right by $\frac{\pi}{2}$ (or 90°) or a horizontal translation left by $\frac{3\pi}{2}$ (or 270°).

Q4 a) If $f(x) = \cot x$, then $y = \cot \frac{x}{4} = f(\frac{x}{4})$. This is a horizontal stretch scale factor 4.

b) The period of $y = \cot x$ is 180°, so the period of $y = \cot \frac{x}{4}$ is 180° × 4 = 720°.

c)

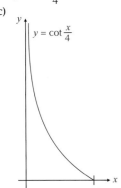

Q5 a) $y = 2 + \sec x$ is the graph of $y = \sec x$ translated vertically up by 2:

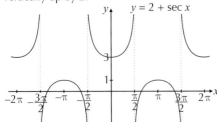

b) The minimum points are at $(-2\pi, 3)$, $(0, 3)$ and $(2\pi, 3)$. The maximum points are at $(-\pi, 1)$ and $(\pi, 1)$.

The maximum and minimum points have the same x-coordinates as on the graph of y = sec x, but the y-coordinates have all been increased by 2.

c) The domain is $x \in \mathbb{R}$, $x \neq \left(n\pi + \frac{\pi}{2}\right)$ (where n is an integer). The range is $y \in \mathbb{R}$, $y \geq 3$ or $y \leq 1$.

Q6 a) $y = 2 \operatorname{cosec} 2x$ is the graph of $y = \operatorname{cosec} x$ stretched horizontally by a factor of $\frac{1}{2}$ and stretched vertically by a factor of 2.

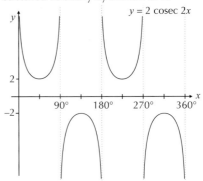

b) The minimum points are at (45°, 2) and (225°, 2).

c) The maximum points are at (135°, −2) and (315°, −2).

d) $y = 2 \operatorname{cosec} 2x$ is undefined when $x = 0°$, 90°, 180°, 270° and 360°.

Q7 a) If $f(x) = \operatorname{cosec} x$, then $y = 2 + 3 \operatorname{cosec} x = 3f(x) + 2$, which is a vertical stretch scale factor 3, followed by a vertical translation of 2 up. Vertical transformations do not affect the position of the asymptotes, so they are in the same position as for the graph of $y = \operatorname{cosec} x$, i.e. at $n\pi$ or 180n°, where n is an integer.

b) The period of the graph will be the same as for the graph of $y = \operatorname{cosec} x$, i.e. 360°.

Vertical transformations will not affect how often the graph repeats itself.

c)

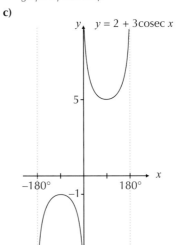

d) The range is $y \in \mathbb{R}$, $y \geq 5$ or $y \leq -1$.

Exercise 2.2 — Evaluating cosec, sec and cot

Q1 **a)** $\csc 80° = \dfrac{1}{\sin 80°} = 1.02$

b) $\sec 75° = \dfrac{1}{\cos 75°} = 3.86$

c) $\cot 30° = \dfrac{1}{\tan 30°} = 1.73$

d) $\sec(-70)° = \dfrac{1}{\cos(-70°)} = 2.92$

e) $3 - \cot 250° = 3 - \dfrac{1}{\tan 250°} = 2.64$

f) $2\csc 25° = \dfrac{2}{\sin 25°} = 4.73$

Q2 **a)** $\sec 3 = \dfrac{1}{\cos 3} = -1.01$

b) $\cot 0.6 = \dfrac{1}{\tan 0.6} = 1.46$

c) $\csc 1.8 = \dfrac{1}{\sin 1.8} = 1.03$

d) $\sec(-1) = \dfrac{1}{\cos(-1)} = 1.85$

e) $\csc \dfrac{\pi}{8} = \dfrac{1}{\sin \frac{\pi}{8}} = 2.61$

f) $8 + \cot \dfrac{\pi}{8} = 8 + \dfrac{1}{\tan \frac{\pi}{8}} = 10.4$

g) $\dfrac{1}{1 + \sec \frac{\pi}{10}} = \dfrac{1}{1 + \frac{1}{\cos \frac{\pi}{10}}} = 0.487$

h) $\dfrac{1}{6 + \cot \frac{\pi}{5}} = \dfrac{1}{6 + \frac{1}{\tan \frac{\pi}{5}}} = 0.136$

Q3 **a)** $\sec 60° = \dfrac{1}{\cos 60°} = \dfrac{1}{\left(\frac{1}{2}\right)} = 2$

b) $\csc 30° = \dfrac{1}{\sin 30°} = \dfrac{1}{\left(\frac{1}{2}\right)} = 2$

c) $\cot 45° = \dfrac{1}{\tan 45°} = \dfrac{1}{1} = 1$

d) $\csc \dfrac{\pi}{3} = \dfrac{1}{\sin\left(\frac{\pi}{3}\right)} = \dfrac{1}{\left(\frac{\sqrt{3}}{2}\right)} = \dfrac{2}{\sqrt{3}}$

e) $\sec(-180°) = \dfrac{1}{\cos(-180°)} = \dfrac{1}{\cos 180°} = -1$

The graph of y = cos x is symmetrical about the y-axis, so cos (−x) = cos x.

f) $\csc 135° = \csc(180° - 45°)$
$= \dfrac{1}{\sin(180° - 45°)}$

The CAST diagram below shows that sin 135° is the same size as sin 45°, and also lies in a positive quadrant for sin:

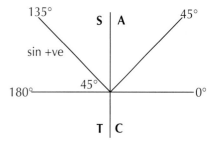

So $\csc 135° = \dfrac{1}{\sin 45°} = \dfrac{1}{\left(\frac{1}{\sqrt{2}}\right)} = \sqrt{2}$.

g) $\cot 330° = \cot(360° - 30°) = \dfrac{1}{\tan(360° - 30°)}$

The CAST diagram below shows that tan 330° is the same size as tan 30°, but lies in a negative quadrant for tan:

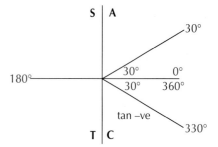

So $\cot 330° = \dfrac{1}{-\tan 30°} = \dfrac{1}{\left(-\frac{1}{\sqrt{3}}\right)} = -\sqrt{3}$.

h) $\sec \dfrac{5\pi}{4} = \sec\left(\pi + \dfrac{\pi}{4}\right) = \dfrac{1}{\cos\left(\pi + \frac{\pi}{4}\right)}$

The CAST diagram below shows that $\cos\left(\pi + \frac{\pi}{4}\right)$ is the same size as $\cos \frac{\pi}{4}$, but lies in a negative quadrant for cos:

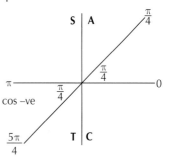

So $\sec \dfrac{5\pi}{4} = \dfrac{1}{-\cos \frac{\pi}{4}} = \dfrac{1}{\left(-\frac{1}{\sqrt{2}}\right)} = -\sqrt{2}$.

i) $\csc \dfrac{5\pi}{3} = \csc\left(2\pi - \dfrac{\pi}{3}\right) = \dfrac{1}{\sin\left(2\pi - \frac{\pi}{3}\right)}$

The CAST diagram shows that $\sin\left(2\pi - \frac{\pi}{3}\right) = -\sin \frac{\pi}{3}$, so:

$$\dfrac{1}{\sin\left(2\pi - \frac{\pi}{3}\right)} = \dfrac{1}{-\sin \frac{\pi}{3}} = \dfrac{1}{-\left(\frac{\sqrt{3}}{2}\right)} = -\dfrac{2}{\sqrt{3}}$$

j) $\operatorname{cosec}\frac{2\pi}{3} = \operatorname{cosec}\left(\pi - \frac{\pi}{3}\right) = \dfrac{1}{\sin\left(\pi - \frac{\pi}{3}\right)}$

The CAST diagram shows that
$\sin\left(\pi - \frac{\pi}{3}\right) = \sin\frac{\pi}{3}$, so:

$$\dfrac{1}{\sin\left(\pi - \frac{\pi}{3}\right)} = \dfrac{1}{\sin\frac{\pi}{3}} = \dfrac{1}{\left(\frac{\sqrt{3}}{2}\right)} = \dfrac{2}{\sqrt{3}}$$

k) $3 - \cot\frac{3\pi}{4} = 3 - \cot\left(\pi - \frac{\pi}{4}\right) = 3 - \dfrac{1}{\tan\left(\pi - \frac{\pi}{4}\right)}$

$= 3 - \dfrac{1}{-\tan\frac{\pi}{4}} = 3 - \left(\frac{1}{-1}\right) = 4$

l) $\dfrac{\sqrt{3}}{\cot\frac{\pi}{6}} = \dfrac{\sqrt{3}}{\left(\frac{1}{\tan\frac{\pi}{6}}\right)} = \sqrt{3}\left(\tan\frac{\pi}{6}\right)$

$= \sqrt{3} \times \dfrac{1}{\sqrt{3}} = 1$

Q4 a) $\dfrac{1}{1 + \sec 60°} = \dfrac{1}{1 + \left(\frac{1}{\cos 60°}\right)}$

$= \dfrac{1}{1 + \dfrac{1}{\left(\frac{1}{2}\right)}} = \dfrac{1}{3}$

b) $\cot 315° = \cot(360° - 45°) = \dfrac{1}{\tan(360° - 45°)}$

$= \dfrac{1}{-\tan 45°} = -1$, so:

$\dfrac{2}{6 + \cot 315°} = \dfrac{2}{6 + (-1)} = \dfrac{2}{5}$

c) $\dfrac{1}{\sqrt{3} - \sec 30°} = \dfrac{1}{\sqrt{3} - \left(\frac{1}{\cos 30°}\right)}$

$= \dfrac{\cos 30°}{\sqrt{3}(\cos 30°) - 1} = \dfrac{\left(\frac{\sqrt{3}}{2}\right)}{\sqrt{3}\left(\frac{\sqrt{3}}{2}\right) - 1}$

$= \dfrac{\frac{\sqrt{3}}{2}}{3 - 2} = \sqrt{3}$

d) $1 + \cot 420° = 1 + \cot(360° + 60°) = 1 + \cot 60°$

$= 1 + \dfrac{1}{\tan 60°} = 1 + \dfrac{1}{\sqrt{3}} = \dfrac{3 + \sqrt{3}}{3}$

e) $\cot 150° = \cot(180° - 30°) = \dfrac{1}{\tan(180° - 30°)}$

$= \dfrac{1}{-\tan 30°} = \dfrac{1}{-\left(\frac{1}{\sqrt{3}}\right)} = -\sqrt{3}$

So:

$\dfrac{2}{7 + \sqrt{3}\cot 150°} = \dfrac{2}{7 + \sqrt{3}(-\sqrt{3})} = \dfrac{2}{7 - 3} = \dfrac{1}{2}$

Exercise 2.3 — Simplifying expressions and solving equations

Q1 a) $\dfrac{1}{\cos x} = \sec x$, so $\sec x + \sec x = 2\sec x$

b) $(\operatorname{cosec}^2 x)(\sin^2 x) = \dfrac{1}{\sin^2 x}(\sin^2 x) = 1$

c) $\dfrac{1}{\tan x} = \cot x$, so $2\cot x + \cot x = 3\cot x$

d) $\dfrac{\sec x}{\operatorname{cosec} x} = \dfrac{\left(\frac{1}{\cos x}\right)}{\left(\frac{1}{\sin x}\right)} = \dfrac{\sin x}{\cos x} = \tan x$

e) $(\cos x)(\operatorname{cosec} x) = \dfrac{\cos x}{\sin x} = \dfrac{1}{\left(\frac{\sin x}{\cos x}\right)}$

$= \dfrac{1}{\tan x} = \cot x$

f) $\dfrac{\operatorname{cosec}^2 x}{\cot x} = \dfrac{\left(\frac{1}{\sin^2 x}\right)}{\left(\frac{1}{\tan x}\right)} = \dfrac{\tan x}{\sin^2 x}$

$= \dfrac{\left(\frac{\sin x}{\cos x}\right)}{\sin^2 x} = \dfrac{\sin x}{\cos x \sin^2 x}$

$= \dfrac{1}{\cos x \sin x} = \sec x \operatorname{cosec} x$

Q2 a) $\sin x \cot x = \sin x\left(\dfrac{1}{\tan x}\right) = \sin x\left(\dfrac{\cos x}{\sin x}\right)$

$= \cos x$

b) $\sec x - \cos x = \dfrac{1}{\cos x} - \cos x$

$= \dfrac{1 - \cos^2 x}{\cos x}$

Use the identity $\sin^2 x + \cos^2 x \equiv 1$:

$= \dfrac{\sin^2 x}{\cos x} = \left(\dfrac{\sin x}{\cos x}\right)\sin x = \tan x \sin x$

c) $\tan x \operatorname{cosec} x = \left(\dfrac{\sin x}{\cos x}\right)\left(\dfrac{1}{\sin x}\right)$

$= \dfrac{1}{\cos x} = \sec x$

d) $\dfrac{(\tan^2 x)(\operatorname{cosec} x)}{\sin x} = \dfrac{\left(\frac{\sin^2 x}{\cos^2 x}\right)\left(\frac{1}{\sin x}\right)}{\sin x}$

$= \dfrac{\left(\frac{\sin x}{\cos^2 x}\right)}{\sin x} = \dfrac{1}{\cos^2 x} = \sec^2 x$

Q3 a) $\sec x = 1.9 \Rightarrow \cos x = \dfrac{1}{1.9} = 0.52631...$

$x = \cos^{-1}(0.52631...) = 58.2°$ to 1 d.p.

There is another positive solution in the interval $0 \leq x \leq 360°$ at $(360° - 58.2°)$,
so $x = 301.8°$ to 1 d.p.
Remember, you can use the graphs or the CAST diagram to find other solutions in the interval.

b) $\cot x = 2.4 \Rightarrow \tan x = 0.41666...$

$x = 22.6°$ to 1 d.p.

There is another positive solution in the interval $0 \leq x \leq 360°$ at $(180° + 22.6°)$,
so $x = 202.6°$ to 1 d.p.

c) $\operatorname{cosec} x = -2 \Rightarrow \sin x = -0.5$

$\sin^{-1}(-0.5) = -30°$ which is not in the interval $0° \leq x \leq 360°$

There are two negative solutions in the interval $0 \leq x \leq 360°$ at $(180° + 30°)$ and $(360° - 30°)$,
so $x = 210°$ and $330°$

d) $\sec x = -1.3 \Rightarrow \cos x = -0.76923...$

$\cos^{-1}(-0.76923...) = 140.3°$ to 1 d.p.

There are two negative solutions in the interval $0 \le x \le 360°$ at $140.3°$ and $(360° - 140.3°)$, so $x = 140.3°$ and $219.7°$

e) $\cot x = -2.4 \Rightarrow \tan x = -0.41666...$

$\tan^{-1}(-0.41666...) = -22.6°$ to 1 d.p.

There are two negative solutions in the interval $0 \le x \le 360°$ at $(-22.6° + 180°)$ and $(-22.6° + 360°)$, so $x = 157.4°$ and $337.4°$

f) $4 \sec 2x = -7 \Rightarrow \cos 2x = -0.57142...$

$\cos^{-1}(-0.57142...) = 124.84990...$

You need to find all solutions for x in the interval $0 \le x \le 360°$ so $0 \le 2x \le 2 \times 360°$ so you'll need to look for solutions for 2x in the interval $0 \le 2x \le 720°$.

There are four negative solutions for $2x$ in the interval $0 \le x \le 720°$ at $124.849...$, $(360° - 124.849...°)$, $(360° + 124.849...°)$ and $(720° - 124.849...°)$ and each of these needs to be divided by 2 to give x.
So $x = 62.4°$, $117.6°$, $242.4°$ and $297.6°$.

Q4 a) $\sec x = 2 \Rightarrow \cos x = 0.5 \Rightarrow x = \cos^{-1}(0.5) = \frac{\pi}{3}$

There is another positive solution in the interval $0 \le x \le 2\pi$ at $(2\pi - \frac{\pi}{3})$, so $x = \frac{5\pi}{3}$

b) $\csc x = -2 \Rightarrow \sin x = -0.5 \Rightarrow \sin^{-1}(-0.5) = -\frac{\pi}{6}$

There are two negative solutions in the interval $0 \le x \le 2\pi$ at $(\pi + \frac{\pi}{6})$ and $(2\pi - \frac{\pi}{6})$, so $x = \frac{7\pi}{6}$ and $\frac{11\pi}{6}$

c) $\cot 2x = 1 \Rightarrow \tan 2x = 1 \Rightarrow 2x = \tan^{-1}(1) = \frac{\pi}{4}$

Don't forget to double the interval for the next bit because you're looking for solutions for 2x instead of x...

There are 3 other positive solutions for $2x$ in the interval $0 \le 2x \le 4\pi$, at $(\pi + \frac{\pi}{4})$, $(2\pi + \frac{\pi}{4})$ and $(3\pi + \frac{\pi}{4})$, so $x = \frac{\pi}{8}, \frac{5\pi}{8}, \frac{9\pi}{8}$ and $\frac{13\pi}{8}$

d) $\sec 5x = -1 \Rightarrow \cos 5x = -1$

$5x = \cos^{-1}(-1) = \pi$

In this case you're looking for solutions for 5x — the interval you'll need to look in is $0 \le 5x \le 10\pi$ since $0 \le x \le 2\pi$. And use the fact that the cos graph repeats itself every 2π. $(\pi, -1)$ is a minimum point on the graph, so this will be repeated every 2π.

There are 4 other solutions for $5x$ in the interval $0 \le 5x \le 10\pi$, at 3π, 5π, 7π, and 9π, so $x = \frac{\pi}{5}, \frac{3\pi}{5}, \pi, \frac{7\pi}{5}$ and $\frac{9\pi}{5}$

Q5 $\cot 2x - 4 = -5 \Rightarrow \tan 2x = -1$

$\tan^{-1}(1) = \frac{\pi}{4}$

There are 4 negative solutions for $2x$ in the interval $0 \le 2x \le 4\pi$, at $(\pi - \frac{\pi}{4})$, $(2\pi - \frac{\pi}{4})$, $(3\pi - \frac{\pi}{4})$ and $(4\pi - \frac{\pi}{4})$, so $x = \frac{3\pi}{8}, \frac{7\pi}{8}, \frac{11\pi}{8}$ and $\frac{15\pi}{8}$

Q6 $2 \csc 2x = 3 \Rightarrow \sin 2x = \frac{2}{3}$

$2x = \sin^{-1}\left(\frac{2}{3}\right) = 41.81031...°$

There are three other positive solutions for $2x$ in the interval $0 \le 2x \le 720°$ at $(180° - 41.81...°)$, $(360° + 41.81...°)$ and $(540° - 41.81...°)$, so $x = 20.9°$, $69.1°$, $200.9°$ and $249.1°$ to 1 d.p.

Q7 $-2 \sec x = 4 \Rightarrow \cos x = -0.5$

$\cos^{-1}(-0.5) = \frac{2\pi}{3}$

There are 2 negative solutions in the interval $0 \le x \le 2\pi$ at $\frac{2\pi}{3}$ and $(2\pi - \frac{2\pi}{3})$, so $x = \frac{2\pi}{3}$ and $\frac{4\pi}{3}$.

Q8 $\sqrt{3} \csc 3x = 2 \Rightarrow \sin 3x = \frac{\sqrt{3}}{2}$

$3x = \sin^{-1}\left(\frac{\sqrt{3}}{2}\right) = \frac{\pi}{3}$

There are 5 other positive solutions in the interval $0 \le 3x \le 6\pi$, at $(\pi - \frac{\pi}{3})$, $(2\pi + \frac{\pi}{3})$, $(3\pi - \frac{\pi}{3})$, $(4\pi + \frac{\pi}{3})$ and $(5\pi - \frac{\pi}{3})$, so $x = \frac{\pi}{9}, \frac{2\pi}{9}, \frac{7\pi}{9}, \frac{8\pi}{9}, \frac{13\pi}{9}$ and $\frac{14\pi}{9}$

Q9 a) $\sec^2 x - 2\sqrt{2} \sec x + 2$ factorises to $(\sec x - \sqrt{2})^2$.

$(\sec x - \sqrt{2})^2 = 0$

$\sec x = \sqrt{2}$

$\cos x = \frac{1}{\sqrt{2}}$

$x = 45°$

b) $\cot^2 x - \frac{4}{\sqrt{3}} \cot x + 1$ factorises to $(\cot x - \sqrt{3})(\cot x - \frac{1}{\sqrt{3}})$

So $(\cot x - \sqrt{3})(\cot x - \frac{1}{\sqrt{3}}) = 0$

$\Rightarrow \cot x = \sqrt{3}$ and $\cot x = \frac{1}{\sqrt{3}}$

$\Rightarrow \tan x = \frac{1}{\sqrt{3}}$ and $\tan x = \sqrt{3}$

So $x = 30°$ and $60°$

Q10 $(\csc x - 3)(2 \tan x + 1) = 0$ means that either $\csc x = 3$ (and so $\sin x = \frac{1}{3}$) or $\tan x = -\frac{1}{2}$.

The solutions for $\sin x = \frac{1}{3}$ are $x = 19.5°$ or $x = 180° - 19.5° = 160.5°$.

The solutions for $\tan x = -\frac{1}{2}$ are $x = -26.6° + 180° = 153.4°$ or $x = -26.6° + 360° = 333.4°$.

So $x = 19.5°$, $160.5°$, $153.4°$, $333.4°$ are all solutions.

3. Identities Involving Cosec, Sec and Cot

Exercise 3.1 — Using the identities

Q1 $\cosec^2 x + 2 \cot^2 x$
$= \cosec^2 x + 2 (\cosec^2 x - 1)$
$= 3 \cosec^2 x - 2$

Q2 $\tan^2 x - \dfrac{1}{\cos^2 x} = \tan^2 x - \sec^2 x$
$= \tan^2 x - (1 + \tan^2 x) = -1$

Q3 $x + \dfrac{1}{x} = \sec\theta + \tan\theta + \dfrac{1}{\sec\theta + \tan\theta}$

$= \dfrac{(\sec\theta + \tan\theta)^2 + 1}{\sec\theta + \tan\theta}$

$= \dfrac{\sec^2\theta + 2\sec\theta\tan\theta + \tan^2\theta + 1}{\sec\theta + \tan\theta}$

But since $\sec^2\theta = \tan^2\theta + 1$:

$x + \dfrac{1}{x} = \dfrac{\sec^2\theta + 2\sec\theta\tan\theta + \sec^2\theta}{\sec\theta + \tan\theta}$

$= \dfrac{2\sec\theta(\sec\theta + \tan\theta)}{\sec\theta + \tan\theta} = 2\sec\theta$

Q4 a) $\tan^2 x = 2\sec x + 2$
$\Rightarrow \sec^2 x - 1 = 2\sec x + 2$
$\Rightarrow \sec^2 x - 2\sec x - 3 = 0$

b) Solve $\sec^2 x - 2\sec x - 3 = 0$

This factorises to give: $(\sec x - 3)(\sec x + 1) = 0$

So $\sec x = 3 \Rightarrow \cos x = \dfrac{1}{3}$
and $\sec x = -1 \Rightarrow \cos x = -1$

Solving these over the interval $0° \leq x \leq 360°$ gives:
$x = 70.5°, 180°$ and $289.5°$ (to 1 d.p.)
Just use the graph of cos x or the CAST diagram as usual to find all the solutions in the interval.

Q5 a) $2\cosec^2 x = 5 - 5\cot x$
$\Rightarrow 2(1 + \cot^2 x) = 5 - 5\cot x$
$\Rightarrow 2\cot^2 x + 5\cot x - 3 = 0$

b) Solve $2\cot^2 x + 5\cot x - 3 = 0$

This factorises to give: $(2\cot x - 1)(\cot x + 3) = 0$

So $\cot x = \dfrac{1}{2} \Rightarrow \tan x = 2$
and $\cot x = -3 \Rightarrow \tan x = -\dfrac{1}{3}$
Solving these over the interval $-\pi \leq x \leq \pi$ gives:
$x = -2.03, -0.32, 1.11, 2.82$ (to 2 d.p.)

Q6 a) $2\cot^2 A + 5\cosec A = 10$
$\Rightarrow 2(\cosec^2 A - 1) + 5\cosec A = 10$
$\Rightarrow 2\cosec^2 A - 2 + 5\cosec A = 10$
$\Rightarrow 2\cosec^2 A + 5\cosec A - 12 = 0$

b) Solve $2\cosec^2 A + 5\cosec A - 12 = 0$

This factorises to give:

$(\cosec A + 4)(2\cosec A - 3) = 0$

So $\cosec A = -4 \Rightarrow \sin A = -\dfrac{1}{4}$

Or $\cosec x = \dfrac{3}{2} \Rightarrow \sin A = \dfrac{2}{3}$
The solutions (to 1 d.p.) are
$A = 194.5°, 345.5°, 41.8°, 138.2°$.

Q7 $\sec^2 x + \tan x = 1$
$\Rightarrow 1 + \tan^2 x + \tan x = 1$
$\Rightarrow \tan^2 x + \tan x = 0$
$\Rightarrow \tan x(\tan x + 1) = 0$

So $\tan x = 0 \Rightarrow x = 0, \pi, 2\pi$.

And $\tan x = -1 \Rightarrow x = \dfrac{3\pi}{4}, \dfrac{7\pi}{4}$
The solutions are: $x = 0, \dfrac{3\pi}{4}, \pi, \dfrac{7\pi}{4}, 2\pi$.

Q8 a) $\cosec^2\theta + 2\cot^2\theta = 2$
$\Rightarrow \cosec^2\theta + 2(\cosec^2\theta - 1) = 2$
$\Rightarrow 3\cosec^2\theta - 2 = 2$
$\Rightarrow 3\cosec^2\theta = 4$
$\Rightarrow \cosec^2\theta = \dfrac{4}{3}$
$\Rightarrow \cosec\theta = \pm\dfrac{2}{\sqrt{3}} \Rightarrow \sin\theta = \pm\dfrac{\sqrt{3}}{2}$

b) Solving $\sin\theta = \pm\dfrac{\sqrt{3}}{2}$ over the interval
$0° \leq x \leq 180°$ gives: $\theta = 60°, 120°$.

Q9 $\sec^2 x = 3 + \tan x$
$\Rightarrow (1 + \tan^2 x) = 3 + \tan x$
$\Rightarrow \tan^2 x - \tan x - 2 = 0$
$\Rightarrow (\tan x - 2)(\tan x + 1) = 0$

So $\tan x = 2$ or $\tan x = -1$.

Solving over the interval $0° \leq x \leq 360°$ gives:
$x = 63.4°, 135°, 243.4°$ and $315°$ (to 1 d.p.)

Q10 $\cot^2 x + \cosec^2 x = 7$
$\Rightarrow \cot^2 x + (1 + \cot^2 x) = 7$
$\Rightarrow 2\cot^2 x + 1 = 7$
$\Rightarrow \cot^2 x = 3 \Rightarrow \cot x = \pm\sqrt{3} \Rightarrow \tan x = \pm\dfrac{1}{\sqrt{3}}$
Solving over the interval $0 \leq x \leq 2\pi$ gives:

$x = \dfrac{\pi}{6}$ and $\dfrac{7\pi}{6}$ when $\tan x = +\dfrac{1}{\sqrt{3}}$
and $x = \dfrac{5\pi}{6}$ and $\dfrac{11\pi}{6}$ when $\tan x = -\dfrac{1}{\sqrt{3}}$.

Q11 $\tan^2 x + 5\sec x + 7 = 0$
$\Rightarrow (\sec^2 x - 1) + 5\sec x + 7 = 0$
$\Rightarrow \sec^2 x + 5\sec x + 6 = 0$
$\Rightarrow (\sec x + 2)(\sec x + 3) = 0$

So $\sec x = -2 \Rightarrow \cos x = -\dfrac{1}{2}$
and $\sec x = -3 \Rightarrow \cos x = -\dfrac{1}{3}$
Solving over the interval $0 \leq x \leq 2\pi$ gives:
$x = 1.91, 2.09, 4.19$ and 4.37 (to 2 d.p.)

Q12 Drawing a right angled triangle will help to solve this question:

$\tan\theta = \dfrac{60}{11}$

Notice that $180° \leq \theta \leq 270°$ — this puts us in the 3rd quadrant of the CAST diagram so sin will be –ve, cos will be –ve and tan will be +ve.

a) From the triangle, $\sin\theta = -\dfrac{\text{opp}}{\text{hyp}} = -\dfrac{60}{61}$.

b) $\cos\theta = -\dfrac{\text{adj}}{\text{hyp}} = -\dfrac{11}{61} \Rightarrow \sec\theta = \dfrac{1}{\left(-\frac{11}{61}\right)} = -\dfrac{61}{11}$.

c) $\operatorname{cosec} \theta = \dfrac{1}{\sin \theta} = \dfrac{1}{\left(-\frac{60}{61}\right)} = -\dfrac{61}{60}.$

Q13 Drawing a right angled triangle will help to solve this question:

$\operatorname{cosec} \theta = -\dfrac{17}{15}$

$\sin \theta = -\dfrac{15}{17}$

Notice that $180° \le \theta \le 270°$ — this puts us in the 3rd quadrant of the CAST diagram so sin will be –ve, cos will be –ve and tan will be +ve.

a) $\cos \theta = -\dfrac{\text{adj}}{\text{hyp}} = -\dfrac{8}{17}.$

b) $\sec \theta = \dfrac{1}{\cos \theta} = -\dfrac{17}{8}.$

c) $\tan \theta = \dfrac{\text{opp}}{\text{adj}} = \dfrac{15}{8}$ so $\cot \theta = \dfrac{1}{\tan \theta} = \dfrac{8}{15}.$

Q14 $\cos x = \dfrac{1}{6} \Rightarrow \sec x = 6$

So $\sec^2 x = 36$
$\Rightarrow 1 + \tan^2 x = 36$
$\Rightarrow \tan^2 x = 35$
$\Rightarrow \tan x = \pm\sqrt{35}$

Exercise 3.2 — Proving other identities

Q1 **a)** $\sec^2 \theta - \operatorname{cosec}^2 \theta \equiv (1 + \tan^2 \theta) - (1 + \cot^2 \theta)$
$$\equiv \tan^2 \theta - \cot^2 \theta$$

b) $\tan^2 \theta - \cot^2 \theta$ is the difference between two squares, and so can be written as:
$(\tan \theta + \cot \theta)(\tan \theta - \cot \theta).$
So is $\sec^2 \theta - \operatorname{cosec}^2 \theta$, so it can be written $(\sec \theta + \operatorname{cosec} \theta)(\sec \theta - \operatorname{cosec} \theta).$

So using the result from part a),
$(\sec \theta + \operatorname{cosec} \theta)(\sec \theta - \operatorname{cosec} \theta) \equiv (\tan \theta + \cot \theta)(\tan \theta - \cot \theta).$

Q2 First expand the bracket:
$(\tan x + \cot x)^2 \equiv \tan^2 x + \cot^2 x + 2 \tan x \cot x$
$$\equiv \tan^2 x + \cot^2 x + \dfrac{2 \tan x}{\tan x}$$
$$\equiv \tan^2 x + \cot^2 x + 2$$

Split up that '+2' into two lots of '+1' so it starts to resemble the identities...
$$\equiv (1 + \tan^2 x) + (1 + \cot^2 x)$$
$$\equiv \sec^2 x + \operatorname{cosec}^2 x$$

Q3 $\cot^2 x + \sin^2 x \equiv (\operatorname{cosec}^2 x - 1) + (1 - \cos^2 x)$
$$\equiv \operatorname{cosec}^2 x - \cos^2 x$$
This is the difference of two squares...
$$\equiv (\operatorname{cosec} x + \cos x)(\operatorname{cosec} x - \cos x)$$

Q4 $\dfrac{(\sec x - \tan x)(\tan x + \sec x)}{\operatorname{cosec} x - \cot x}$

$$\equiv \dfrac{\sec^2 x - \tan^2 x}{\operatorname{cosec} x - \cot x}$$

$$\equiv \dfrac{(1 + \tan^2 x) - \tan^2 x}{\operatorname{cosec} x - \cot x}$$

$$\equiv \dfrac{1}{\operatorname{cosec} x - \cot x}$$

Multiply top and bottom by (cosec x + cot x)...

$$\equiv \dfrac{\operatorname{cosec} x + \cot x}{(\operatorname{cosec} x - \cot x)(\operatorname{cosec} x + \cot x)}$$

$$\equiv \dfrac{\operatorname{cosec} x + \cot x}{\operatorname{cosec}^2 x - \cot^2 x}$$

$$\equiv \dfrac{\operatorname{cosec} x + \cot x}{(1 + \cot^2 x) - \cot^2 x}$$

$$\equiv \cot x + \operatorname{cosec} x$$

Q5 $\dfrac{\cot x}{1 + \operatorname{cosec} x} + \dfrac{1 + \operatorname{cosec} x}{\cot x}$

$$\equiv \dfrac{\cot^2 x + (1 + \operatorname{cosec} x)^2}{\cot x (1 + \operatorname{cosec} x)}$$

$$\equiv \dfrac{(\operatorname{cosec}^2 x - 1) + (1 + 2\operatorname{cosec} x + \operatorname{cosec}^2 x)}{\cot x (1 + \operatorname{cosec} x)}$$

$$\equiv \dfrac{2 \operatorname{cosec} x (1 + \operatorname{cosec} x)}{\cot x (1 + \operatorname{cosec} x)}$$

$$\equiv \dfrac{2 \operatorname{cosec} x}{\cot x} \equiv \dfrac{2 \tan x}{\sin x} \equiv \dfrac{2 \sin x}{\sin x \cos x} \equiv \dfrac{2}{\cos x} \equiv 2 \sec x$$

Q6 $\dfrac{\operatorname{cosec} x + 1}{\operatorname{cosec} x - 1} \equiv \dfrac{(\operatorname{cosec} x + 1)(\operatorname{cosec} x + 1)}{(\operatorname{cosec} x - 1)(\operatorname{cosec} x + 1)}$

$$\equiv \dfrac{\operatorname{cosec}^2 x + 2 \operatorname{cosec} x + 1}{\operatorname{cosec}^2 x - 1}$$

$$\equiv \dfrac{\operatorname{cosec}^2 x + 2 \operatorname{cosec} x + 1}{(1 + \cot^2 x) - 1}$$

$$\equiv \dfrac{\operatorname{cosec}^2 x + 2 \operatorname{cosec} x + 1}{\cot^2 x}$$

$$\equiv \dfrac{\operatorname{cosec}^2 x}{\cot^2 x} + \dfrac{2 \operatorname{cosec} x}{\cot^2 x} + \dfrac{1}{\cot^2 x}$$

$$\equiv \dfrac{\tan^2 x}{\sin^2 x} + \dfrac{2 \tan^2 x}{\sin x} + \tan^2 x$$

$$\equiv \dfrac{\sin^2 x}{\cos^2 x \sin^2 x} + \dfrac{2 \sin^2 x}{\cos^2 x \sin x} + \tan^2 x$$

$$\equiv \dfrac{1}{\cos^2 x} + \dfrac{2 \sin x}{\cos x \cos x} + \tan^2 x$$

$$\equiv \dfrac{1}{\cos^2 x} + \dfrac{2 \tan x}{\cos x} + \tan^2 x$$

$$\equiv \sec^2 x + 2 \tan x \sec x + (\sec^2 x - 1)$$

$$\equiv 2 \sec^2 x + 2 \tan x \sec x - 1$$

Review Exercise — Chapter 2

Q1 **a)** $\sin^{-1}\dfrac{1}{\sqrt{2}} = \dfrac{\pi}{4}$ **b)** $\cos^{-1}0 = \dfrac{\pi}{2}$

   c) $\tan^{-1}\sqrt{3} = \dfrac{\pi}{3}$

Q2

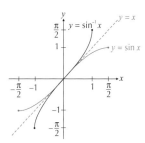

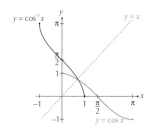

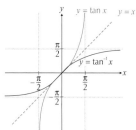

Q3 **a)** To find the inverse of $y = \dfrac{1}{1+\cos x}$,
   first rearrange to make x the subject:

   $1 + \cos x = \dfrac{1}{y} \Rightarrow \cos x = \dfrac{1}{y} - 1$

   $\Rightarrow x = \cos^{-1}\left(\dfrac{1}{y} - 1\right)$

   Then replace x with $f^{-1}(x)$ and y with x:

   $f^{-1}(x) = \cos^{-1}\left(\dfrac{1}{x} - 1\right)$.

   b) $f(x)$ has domain $0 \le x \le \dfrac{\pi}{2}$ and range $\dfrac{1}{2} \le f(x) \le 1$.

   The domain of $f(x)$ becomes the range of $f^{-1}(x)$ and
   the range of $f(x)$ becomes the domain of $f^{-1}(x)$, so
   the domain of $f^{-1}(x)$ is $\dfrac{1}{2} \le x \le 1$, and the range is
   $0 \le f^{-1}(x) \le \dfrac{\pi}{2}$.

   c) $f^{-1}(x)$ is the reflection of $f(x)$ in the line $y = x$:

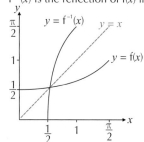

Q4 **a)** $\sin^{-1}1 = \dfrac{\pi}{2}$, $\cos^{-1}1 = 0$, $\tan^{-1}1 = \dfrac{\pi}{4}$,
   so $f(1) = \dfrac{\pi}{2} + 0 + \dfrac{\pi}{4} = \dfrac{3\pi}{4}$

   b) $\sin^{-1}(-1) = -\dfrac{\pi}{2}$, $\cos^{-1}(-1) = \pi$, $\tan^{-1}(-1) = -\dfrac{\pi}{4}$,
   so $f(-1) = -\dfrac{\pi}{2} + \pi - \dfrac{\pi}{4} = \dfrac{\pi}{4}$

Q5 **a)** $\operatorname{cosec} 30° = 2$ (since $\sin 30° = 0.5$)

   b) $\sec 30° = \dfrac{2}{\sqrt{3}}$ (since $\cos 30° = \dfrac{\sqrt{3}}{2}$)

   c) $\cot 30° = \sqrt{3}$ (since $\tan 30° = \dfrac{1}{\sqrt{3}}$)

Q6

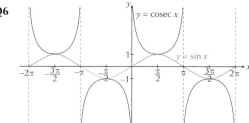

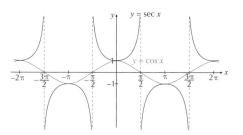

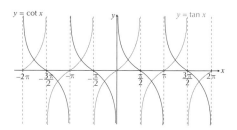

Q7 **a)** If $f(x) = \sec x$, then $y = \sec 4x = f(4x)$.
   This is a horizontal stretch scale factor $\dfrac{1}{4}$.

   b) The period of $y = \sec x$ is 2π, so the period of
   $y = \sec 4x$ is $2\pi \div 4 = \dfrac{\pi}{2}$.

   c)

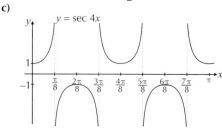

   d) $y = \sec 4x$ is undefined when $x = \dfrac{\pi}{8}, \dfrac{3\pi}{8}, \dfrac{5\pi}{8}$
   and $\dfrac{7\pi}{8}$.

Q8 Divide the whole identity by $\cos^2\theta$ to get:

$$\frac{\cos^2\theta}{\cos^2\theta} + \frac{\sin^2\theta}{\cos^2\theta} \equiv \frac{1}{\cos^2\theta}$$

$$\Rightarrow 1 + \tan^2\theta \equiv \sec^2\theta$$

(as sin/cos $\equiv$ tan and 1/cos $\equiv$ sec)

Q9 Using the identities $\text{cosec}^2\theta \equiv 1 + \cot^2\theta$ and $\sin^2\theta + \cos^2\theta \equiv 1$, the LHS becomes:
$(\text{cosec}^2\theta - 1) + (1 - \cos^2\theta) \equiv \text{cosec}^2\theta - \cos^2\theta$
which is the same as the RHS.

Q10 $y = \cot^2\theta = \text{cosec}^2\theta - 1 = x^2 - 1$

Q11 $y^2 = 4\tan^2\theta = 4(\sec^2\theta - 1) = 4(x^2 - 1)$

$$\Rightarrow y = \pm 2\sqrt{x^2 - 1}$$

Q12 a) $\text{cosec}^2 x = \dfrac{3\cot x + 4}{2}$

$\Rightarrow 2\,\text{cosec}^2 x = 3\cot x + 4$
$\Rightarrow 2(1 + \cot^2 x) = 3\cot x + 4$
$\Rightarrow 2\cot^2 x - 3\cot x + 2 - 4 = 0$
$\Rightarrow 2\cot^2 x - 3\cot x - 2 = 0$

b) Solve $2\cot^2 x - 3\cot x - 2 = 0$

This factorises to give $(2\cot x + 1)(\cot x - 2) = 0$

So $\cot x = -\dfrac{1}{2} \Rightarrow \tan x = -2$

and $\cot x = 2 \Rightarrow \tan x = \dfrac{1}{2}$

Solving these over the interval $0 \le x \le 2\pi$ gives:
$x = 0.46, 3.61, 2.03$ and 5.18 (to 2 d.p.)

Q13 a) $\sec\theta = \dfrac{1}{\cos\theta} = 2$

b) $\cos\theta = \dfrac{1}{2}$, so draw a right-angled triangle with the adjacent side having a length of 1 and the hypotenuse having a length of 2:

Using Pythagoras' Theorem, the missing side has a length of $\sqrt{(2^2 - 1^2)} = \sqrt{3}$.

So $\tan\theta = \dfrac{\text{OPP}}{\text{ADJ}} = \dfrac{\sqrt{3}}{1} = \sqrt{3}$

c) From a), $\sec\theta = 2$, so $\sec^2\theta = 4$
$\Rightarrow 1 + \tan^2\theta = 4$
$\Rightarrow \tan^2\theta = 3$
$\Rightarrow \tan\theta = \sqrt{3}$

d) $\cot\theta = \dfrac{1}{\tan\theta} = \dfrac{1}{\sqrt{3}}$

e) From d), $\cot\theta = \dfrac{1}{\sqrt{3}}$, so $\cot^2\theta = \dfrac{1}{3}$

$\Rightarrow \text{cosec}^2\theta - 1 = \dfrac{1}{3}$

$\Rightarrow \text{cosec}^2\theta = \dfrac{4}{3}$

$\Rightarrow \text{cosec}\,\theta = \dfrac{2}{\sqrt{3}} \Rightarrow \sin\theta = \dfrac{\sqrt{3}}{2}$

You can check that this is right by looking at the right-angled triangle in part b).

Exam-Style Questions — Chapter 2

Q1 a)

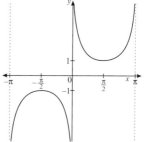

[3 marks available — 1 mark for n-shaped curve in third quadrant and u-shaped curve in first quadrant, 1 mark for asymptotes at 0 and $\pm\pi$ and 1 mark for max/min points of the curves at -1 and 1]

b) If $\text{cosec}\,x = \dfrac{5}{4} \Rightarrow \dfrac{1}{\sin x} = \dfrac{5}{4} \Rightarrow \sin x = \dfrac{4}{5}$
[1 mark]. Solving this for x gives $x = 0.927, 2.21$
[1 mark for each solution, lose a mark if answers aren't given to 3 s.f.].

The second solution can be found by sketching $y = \sin x$:

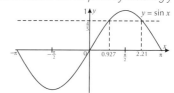

You can see that there are two solutions, one at 0.927, and the other at $\pi - 0.927 = 2.21$. You could also use the CAST diagram and find the other positive solution for sin in the 2nd quadrant.

c) $\text{cosec}\,x = 3\sec x \Rightarrow \dfrac{1}{\sin x} = \dfrac{3}{\cos x} \Rightarrow \dfrac{\cos x}{\sin x} = 3$

$\Rightarrow \dfrac{1}{\tan x} = 3$ so $\tan x = \dfrac{1}{3}$

Solving for x gives $x = -2.82, 0.322$,

[1 mark for appropriate rearranging, 1 mark for each solution.]

Again, you can sketch a graph to find the second solution (or use a CAST diagram).

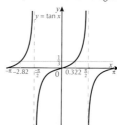

You can see that there are two solutions in the given range, one at 0.322 (this is the one you get from your calculator) and one at $-\pi + 0.322 = -2.82$.

Q2 a) The start and end points of the cos curve (with restricted domain) are $(0, 1)$ and $(\pi, -1)$, so the coordinates of the start point of $\cos^{-1}$ (point A) are $(-1, \pi)$ *[1 mark]* and the coordinates of the end point (point B) are $(1, 0)$ *[1 mark]*.

b) $y = \cos^{-1} x$, so $x = \cos y$ **[1 mark]**.

c) $\cos^{-1} x = 2$, so $x = \cos 2$ **[1 mark]**
so $x = -0.416$ **[1 mark]**.

Q3 a) $\dfrac{2\sin x}{1 - \cos x} - \dfrac{2\cos x}{\sin x}$

$\equiv \dfrac{2\sin^2 x - 2\cos x + 2\cos^2 x}{\sin x(1 - \cos x)}$ **[1 mark]**

$\equiv \dfrac{2 - 2\cos x}{\sin x(1 - \cos x)}$ **[1 mark]**

$\equiv \dfrac{2(1 - \cos x)}{\sin x(1 - \cos x)}$ **[1 mark]**

$\equiv \dfrac{2}{\sin x} \equiv 2\operatorname{cosec} x$ **[1 mark]**

b) $2\operatorname{cosec} x = 4$

$\operatorname{cosec} x = 2$ <u>OR</u> $\sin x = \dfrac{1}{2}$ **[1 mark]**

$x = \dfrac{\pi}{6}$ **[1 mark]**, $x = \dfrac{5\pi}{6}$ **[1 mark]**.

Q4 a) (i) Rearrange the identity $\sec^2\theta \equiv 1 + \tan^2\theta$ to get $\sec^2\theta - 1 \equiv \tan^2\theta$, then replace $\tan^2\theta$ in the equation:

$3\tan^2\theta - 2\sec\theta = 5$

$3(\sec^2\theta - 1) - 2\sec\theta - 5 = 0$ **[1 mark]**

$3\sec^2\theta - 3 - 2\sec\theta - 5 = 0$

so $3\sec^2\theta - 2\sec\theta - 8 = 0$ **[1 mark]**

(ii) To factorise this, let $y = \sec\theta$, so the equation becomes $3y^2 - 2y - 8 = 0$, so
$(3y + 4)(y - 2) = 0$ **[1 mark]**.

Solving for y gives $y = -\dfrac{4}{3}$ or $y = 2$.

As $y = \sec\theta$, this means that $\sec\theta = -\dfrac{4}{3}$
or $\sec\theta = 2$ **[1 mark]**.

$\sec\theta = \dfrac{1}{\cos\theta}$, so $\cos\theta = -\dfrac{3}{4}$ or $\cos\theta = \dfrac{1}{2}$
[1 mark].

b) Let $\theta = 2x$. From above, we know that the solutions to $3\tan^2\theta - 2\sec\theta = 5$ satisfy
$\cos\theta = -\dfrac{3}{4}$ or $\cos\theta = \dfrac{1}{2}$.
The range for x is $0 \le x \le 180°$, so as $\theta = 2x$, the range for θ is $0 \le \theta \le 360°$ **[1 mark]**.
Solving these equations for θ gives
$\theta = 138.59°, 221.41°$ and $\theta = 60°, 300°$ **[1 mark]**.
So, as $\theta = 2x$, $x = \dfrac{1}{2}\theta$,
so $x = 69.30°, 110.70°, 30°, 150°$ **[1 mark]**.

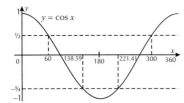

There is a solution at $360 - 60 = 300°$, and another at $360 - 138.59 = 221.41°$.

Chapter 3: Exponentials and Logarithms

1. Exponential and Logarithmic Graphs

Exercise 1.1 — Transformations

Q1 a) – c)

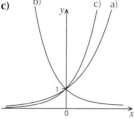

Q2 a)

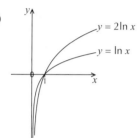

b)

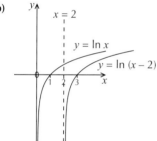

c)

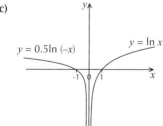

d)

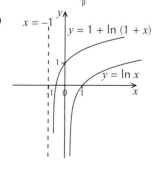

Q3 a)

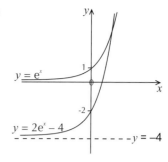

b)

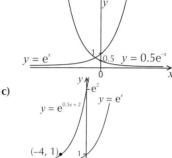

c)

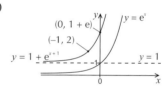

d)

Q4 a) $A = 2$ **b)** $B = -\frac{1}{3}$ **c)** $C = 3$

Q5 a) $A = (0, 3)$, D: $y = 0$.

   b) $B = (0, 3)$, E: $y = 2$.

   c) $C = (0, 2)$, F: $y = 3$.

Q6 a) Asymptote at $y = -3$ and y intercept at $(0, -2)$. So $y = e^x$ has been translated down the y-axis by 3 so the function is $f(x) = e^x - 3$.

   b) Asymptote at $x = -2$ and passes through the x-axis at $x = -1$. So $y = \ln x$ has been translated by 2 units left on the x-axis. So $g(x) = \ln (x + 2)$.

   c) Asymptote at $y = 0$ and goes through point $(-1, 1)$. So $y = e^x$ has been translated left on the x-axis by 1 so the function is $h(x) = e^{(x + 1)}$

2. Using Exponentials and Logarithms

Exercise 2.1 — Solving Equations

Q1 a) If $y = e^x$ then $x = \ln y$

b) If $a = \ln b$ then $b = e^a$

Q2 a) $e^x = 7 \Rightarrow \ln e^x = \ln 7 \Rightarrow x = \ln 7$.

b) $5e^{3t} = 11 \Rightarrow e^{3t} = \frac{11}{5} \Rightarrow \ln e^{3t} = \ln\left(\frac{11}{5}\right)$
$\Rightarrow 3t = \ln\left(\frac{11}{5}\right) \Rightarrow t = \frac{1}{3}\ln\left(\frac{11}{5}\right)$

c) $2e^{(-2x)} = 6 \Rightarrow e^{(-2x)} = 3 \Rightarrow \ln e^{(-2x)} = \ln 3$
$\Rightarrow -2x = \ln 3 \Rightarrow x = -\frac{1}{2}\ln 3$

d) $e^{(0.5x + 3)} = 9 \Rightarrow \ln e^{(0.5x+3)} = \ln 9 \Rightarrow 0.5x + 3 = \ln 9$
$\Rightarrow 0.5x = \ln 9 - 3 \Rightarrow x = 2(\ln 9 - 3)$

e) $10 - 3e^{(1-2x)} = 8 \Rightarrow 3e^{(1-2x)} = 2 \Rightarrow e^{(1-2x)} = \frac{2}{3}$
$\Rightarrow \ln e^{(1-2x)} = \ln \frac{2}{3} \Rightarrow 1 - 2x = \ln \frac{2}{3}$
$\Rightarrow -2x = \ln \frac{2}{3} - 1 \Rightarrow x = -\frac{1}{2}(\ln \frac{2}{3} - 1)$

Q3 a) (i) $\ln x = -2 \Rightarrow e^{\ln x} = e^{-2} \Rightarrow x = e^{-2}$

(ii) $x = 0.135$ to 3 s.f.

b) (i) $3 \ln (2x) = 7 \Rightarrow \ln (2x) = \frac{7}{3} \Rightarrow e^{\ln (2x)} = e^{\frac{7}{3}} \Rightarrow$
$2x = e^{\frac{7}{3}} \Rightarrow x = \frac{1}{2}e^{\frac{7}{3}}$

(ii) $x = 5.16$ to 3 s.f.

c) (i) $\ln (5t - 3) = 4 \Rightarrow e^{\ln (5t-3)} = e^4 \Rightarrow 5t - 3 = e^4 \Rightarrow$
$t = \frac{1}{5}(e^4 + 3)$

(ii) $t = 11.5$ to 3 s.f.

d) (i) $6 \ln (8 - 2t) = 10 \Rightarrow \ln (8 - 2t) = \frac{5}{3}$
$\Rightarrow e^{\ln (8 - 2t)} = e^{\frac{5}{3}} \Rightarrow 8 - 2t = e^{\frac{5}{3}}$
$\Rightarrow t = -\frac{1}{2}(e^{\frac{5}{3}} - 8)$

(ii) $t = 1.35$ to 3 s.f.

e) (i) $6 - \ln (0.5x) = 3 \Rightarrow \ln (0.5x) = 3 \Rightarrow e^{\ln (0.5x)} = e^3$
$\Rightarrow 0.5x = e^3 \Rightarrow x = 2e^3$

(ii) $x = 40.2$

Q4 a) $e^{3x} = 27 \Rightarrow \ln (e^{3x}) = \ln 27 \Rightarrow 3x = \ln 27 = \ln (3^3)$
$\Rightarrow 3x = 3 \ln 3 \Rightarrow x = \ln 3$.

If you're asked to give your answer in the form ln a where a is a number, try to write the number inside the logarithm as a power of a and use the third log law to get it in the form you want.

b) $e^{-4x} = 9 \Rightarrow \ln (e^{-4x}) = \ln 9 \Rightarrow -4x = \ln 9$
$\Rightarrow x = -\frac{1}{4}\ln 9 = -\frac{1}{4}\ln (3^2) = -\frac{1}{2}\ln 3$

c) $e^{(6x - 1)} = \frac{1}{3} \Rightarrow \ln e^{(6x-1)} = \ln\left(\frac{1}{3}\right) \Rightarrow 6x - 1 = \ln (3^{-1})$
$\Rightarrow 6x = 1 - \ln 3 \Rightarrow x = \frac{1}{6}(1 - \ln 3)$

d) $3e^{(2x + 3)} = \frac{1}{27} \Rightarrow e^{(2x+3)} = \frac{1}{81} \Rightarrow \ln e^{(2x+3)} = \ln\left(\frac{1}{81}\right)$
$\Rightarrow 2x + 3 = \ln (3^{-4}) \Rightarrow 2x + 3 = -4\ln (3)$
$\Rightarrow 2x = -4 \ln 3 - 3 \Rightarrow x = \frac{1}{2}(-4 \ln 3 - 3)$

e) $\frac{1}{3}e^{(1 - x)} - 3 = 0 \Rightarrow e^{(1 - x)} = 9 \Rightarrow \ln e^{(1 - x)} = \ln 9$
$\Rightarrow 1 - x = \ln 9 \Rightarrow x = 1 - \ln (3^2) \Rightarrow x = 1 - 2\ln 3$

Q5 a) (i) Substitute $y = e^x \Rightarrow y^2 - 7y + 12 = 0$
$\Rightarrow (y - 3)(y - 4) = 0 \Rightarrow y = 3$ or $y = 4$
$\Rightarrow e^x = 3$ or $e^x = 4 \Rightarrow x = \ln 3$ or $x = \ln 4$

(ii) $x = 1.10$ or $x = 1.39$

b) (i) $e^{7x} - 3e^{5x} = 0 \Rightarrow e^{5x} (e^{2x} - 3) = 0 \Rightarrow e^{5x} = 0$
or $e^{2x} = 3$. $e^{5x} = 0$ is impossible so $e^{2x} = 3$
$\Rightarrow 2x = \ln 3 \Rightarrow x = 0.5 \ln 3$

The graph of $y = be^{ax}$ has an asymptote at $y = O$ for any values of a or b, so it never reaches O. Therefore anytime you have $be^a = O$ where a and b are any real numbers, there's no solution.

(ii) $x = 0.549$

c) (i) Substitute $y = e^x \Rightarrow 3y^2 + 10y + 3 = 0$
$\Rightarrow (3y + 1)(y + 3) = 0 \Rightarrow e^x = -\frac{1}{3}$ or $e^x = -3$
both of which are impossible since $e^x > 0$.
There are no solutions.

(ii) No solutions.

d) (i) Substitute $y = e^{2x} \Rightarrow y^2 + 4y + 5 = 0$.
Using the quadratic formula:
$$x = \frac{-4 \pm \sqrt{4^2 - (4 \times 1 \times 5)}}{2}$$
$$= \frac{-4 \pm \sqrt{16 - 20}}{2} = \frac{-4 \pm \sqrt{-4}}{2}$$
there are no real solutions since there is a negative square root.

(ii) No solutions.

e) (i) $e^x + e^{-x} = 6 \Rightarrow e^{2x} + 1 - 6e^x = 0$

If you have an equation with e^{-x} in it, then you can multiply everything through by e^x to get rid of it.

$\Rightarrow$ Substitute $y = e^x \Rightarrow y^2 + 1 - 6y = 0$
The quadratic formula gives solutions:
$$y = \frac{6 \pm \sqrt{32}}{2} = 3 \pm 2\sqrt{2}$$
$\Rightarrow e^x = 3 \pm 2\sqrt{2}$
$\Rightarrow x = \ln (3 \pm 2\sqrt{2})$

(ii) $x = 1.76$ or -1.76

Q6 a) $\ln 5 + \ln x = 7 \Rightarrow \ln(5x) = 7 \Rightarrow e^{\ln (5x)} = e^7$
$\Rightarrow 5x = e^7 \Rightarrow x = \frac{e^7}{5}$

b) $\ln (2x) + \ln (3x) = 15 \Rightarrow \ln (2x \times 3x) = 15$
$\Rightarrow \ln(6x^2) = 15 \Rightarrow e^{\ln 6x^2} = e^{15} \Rightarrow 6x^2 = e^{15}$
$\Rightarrow x = \sqrt{\frac{1}{6}e^{15}} = \frac{1}{\sqrt{6}}e^{\frac{15}{2}}$ (since $x > 0$)

c) $\ln (x^2 - 4) - \ln (2x) = 0 \Rightarrow \ln \left(\frac{x^2 - 4}{2x}\right) = 0$
$\Rightarrow \frac{x^2 - 4}{2x} = e^0 = 1 \Rightarrow x^2 - 4 = 2x$
$\Rightarrow x^2 - 2x - 4 = 0$
$\Rightarrow x = \frac{2 \pm \sqrt{20}}{2} = 1 \pm \sqrt{5}$
But $x > 0$ otherwise $\ln 2x$ would be undefined so $x = 1 + \sqrt{5}$.

d) $3 \ln (x^2) + 5 \ln x = 2 \Rightarrow 6 \ln x + 5 \ln x = 2$
$\Rightarrow 11 \ln x = 2 \Rightarrow \ln x = \frac{2}{11} \Rightarrow x = e^{\frac{2}{11}}$

Review Exercise — Chapter 3

Q1 a) The graph still has an asymptote at $y = 0$ but it goes through (0, 2) instead of (0, 1) so the graph has been stretched by a factor of 2 along the y-axis, so the function is $y = 2e^x$.

b) The graph has a negative gradient and so it is a translation of $y = e^{-x}$. It has an asymptote at $y = 1$ and goes through the point (0, 2), so the graph $y = e^{-x}$ has been translated up the y-axis by 1 unit, so it is the function $y = 1 + e^{-x}$.

Q2 a) A = (–1, 0), C: $x = -2$

b) B = (1, 3), D: $x = 0$

Q3 a)-d)

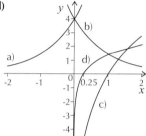

Q4 a) (i)

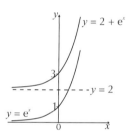

(ii)

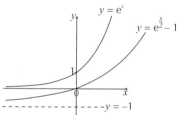

(iii)

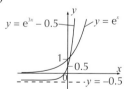

(iv)

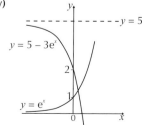

b) (i) The transformation from $y = e^x$ to $y = 2 + e^x$ is a translation 2 units vertically up.

(ii) The transformation from $y = e^x$ to $y = e^{\frac{x}{2}} - 1$ is a stretch horizontally by a scale factor of 2 and a translation 1 unit vertically down.

(iii) The transformation from $y = e^x$ to $y = e^{3x} - 0.5$ is a stretch horizontally by a scale factor of $\frac{1}{3}$ and a translation 0.5 units vertically down.

(iv) The transformation from $y = e^x$ to $y = 5 - 3e^x$ is a stretch vertically by a scale factor of 3, a reflection in the x-axis and a translation 5 units vertically up.

Q5 a) (i)

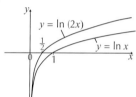

(ii)

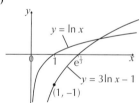

(iii)

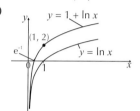

(iv)

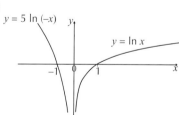

b) (i) The transformation from $y = \ln x$ to $y = 1 + \ln x$ is a translation 1 unit up.

(ii) The transformation from $y = \ln x$ to $y = \ln (2x)$ is a stretch horizontally of scale factor $\frac{1}{2}$.

(iii) The transformation from $y = \ln x$ to $y = 3\ln x - 1$ is a stretch vertically of scale factor 3 and a translation of 1 unit vertically down.

(iv) The transformation from $y = \ln x$ to $y = 5\ln (-x)$ is a reflection in the y-axis and a stretch vertically of scale factor 5.

Q6 a) $e^{2x} = 6 \Rightarrow 2x = \ln 6 \Rightarrow x = \ln 6 \div 2 = 0.8959$ to 4 d.p.

b) $\ln (x + 3) = 0.75 \Rightarrow x + 3 = e^{0.75} \Rightarrow x = e^{0.75} - 3$ $= -0.8830$ to 4 d.p.

c) $3e^{-4x+1} = 5 \Rightarrow e^{-4x+1} = \frac{5}{3} \Rightarrow e^{4x-1} = \frac{3}{5}$
$\Rightarrow 4x - 1 = \ln \frac{3}{5}$
$\Rightarrow x = (\ln \frac{3}{5} + 1) \div 4 = 0.1223$ to 4 d.p.

d) $\ln x + \ln 5 = \ln 4 \Rightarrow \ln (5x) = \ln 4 \Rightarrow 5x = 4$
$\Rightarrow x = 0.8000$ to 4 d.p.

Q7 a) $2\ln x - \ln (2x) = 2 \Rightarrow \ln (x^2) - \ln (2x) = 2$
$\Rightarrow \ln \left(\frac{x^2}{2x} \right) = 2 \Rightarrow \frac{x^2}{2x} = e^2 \Rightarrow \frac{x}{2} = e^2 \Rightarrow x = 2e^2$

b) $\ln (2x - 7) + \ln 4 = -3 \Rightarrow \ln (4(2x - 7)) = -3$
$\Rightarrow 8x - 28 = e^{-3} \Rightarrow x = \frac{e^{-3} + 28}{8}$ or $\frac{1}{8e^3} + \frac{7}{2}$.

Q8 a) $y = 2 - e^{x+1}$

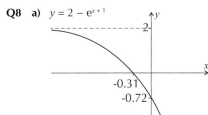

Goes through (0, −0.72) and (−0.31, 0), with asymptote at $y = 2$.

b) $y = 5e^{0.5x} + 5$

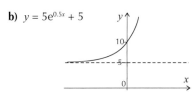

Goes through (0, 10), with asymptote at $y = 5$.

c) $y = \ln (2x) + 1$

Goes through (0.18, 0), with asymptote at $x = 0$.

d) $y = \ln (x + 5)$

Goes through (0, 1.61) and (−4, 0), with asymptote at $x = -5$.

You can use your 'graph transformation' skills to work out what they'll look like — e.g. d) is just $y = \ln x$ shifted 5 to the left.

Q9 a) $2e^{2x} + e^x = 3$. Let $y = e^x$, $2y^2 + y - 3 = 0$, which will factorise to: $(2y + 3)(y - 1) = 0$, so $e^x = -1.5$ (not possible), and $e^x = 1$, so $x = 0$ is the only solution.

b) $e^{8x} - e^{4x} - 6 = 0 \Rightarrow$ Substitute $y = e^{4x}$
$\Rightarrow y^2 - y - 6 = 0 \Rightarrow (y - 3)(y + 2) = 0 \Rightarrow y = 3$
or $y = -2 \Rightarrow e^{4x} = 3$ or $e^{4x} = -2$. $e^{4x} = -2$ is impossible since $e^{4x} > 0$, so $e^{4x} = 3 \Rightarrow 4x = \ln 3$
$\Rightarrow x = \frac{1}{4} \ln 3$.

Exam-Style Questions — Chapter 3

Q1 a) $6e^x = 3 \Rightarrow e^x = 0.5$ *[1 mark]*
$\Rightarrow x = \ln 0.5$ *[1 mark]*.

b) $e^{2x} - 8e^x + 7 = 0$.
(This looks like a quadratic, so use $y = e^x$...)
If $y = e^x$, then $y^2 - 8y + 7 = 0$. This will factorise to give: $(y - 7)(y - 1) = 0 \Rightarrow y = 7$ and $y = 1$.
So $e^x = 7 \Rightarrow x = \ln 7$, and $e^x = 1 \Rightarrow x = \ln 1 = 0$.
[4 marks available — 1 mark for factorisation of a quadratic, 1 mark for both solutions for e^x, and 1 mark for each correct solution for x.]

c) $4\ln x = 3 \Rightarrow \ln x = 0.75$ *[1 mark]*
$\Rightarrow x = e^{0.75}$ *[1 mark]*.

d) $\ln x + \frac{24}{\ln x} = 10$
(You need to get rid of the fraction, so multiply through by $\ln x$...)
$(\ln x)^2 + 24 = 10\ln x \Rightarrow (\ln x)^2 - 10\ln x + 24 = 0$
(...which looks like a quadratic, so use $y = \ln x$...)
$y^2 - 10y + 24 = 0 \Rightarrow (y - 6)(y - 4) = 0$
$\Rightarrow y = 6$ or $y = 4$.
So $\ln x = 6 \Rightarrow x = e^6$, or $\ln x = 4 \Rightarrow x = e^4$.
[4 marks available — 1 mark for factorisation of a quadratic, 1 mark for both solutions for $\ln x$, and 1 mark for each correct solution for x.]

Q2 $y = e^{ax} + b$
The sketch shows that when $x = 0$, $y = -6$, so:
$-6 = e^0 + b$ *[1 mark]* $-6 = 1 + b \Rightarrow b = -7$ *[1 mark]*.

The sketch also shows that when $y = 0$, $x = \frac{1}{4}\ln 7$, so:
$0 = e^{(\frac{a}{4}\ln 7)} - 7$ *[1 mark]* $\Rightarrow e^{(\frac{a}{4}\ln 7)} = 7$
$\Rightarrow \frac{a}{4}\ln 7 = \ln 7 \Rightarrow \frac{a}{4} = 1 \Rightarrow a = 4$ *[1 mark]*.
The asymptote occurs as $x \to -\infty$, so $e^{4x} \to 0$, and since $y = e^{4x} - 7$, $y \to -7$.
So the equation of the asymptote is $y = -7$ *[1 mark]*.

Q3 a) $2e^x + 18e^{-x} = 20$

(Multiply through by e^x to remove the e^{-x}, since $e^x \times e^{-x} = 1$)
$2e^{2x} + 18 = 20e^x$
$\Rightarrow 2e^{2x} - 20e^x + 18 = 0 \Rightarrow e^{2x} - 10e^x + 9 = 0$
(This now looks like a quadratic equation, so use $y = e^x$ to simplify...)
$y^2 - 10y + 9 = 0$
$\Rightarrow (y - 1)(y - 9) = 0 \Rightarrow y = 1$ or $y = 9$.
So $e^x = 1 \Rightarrow x = 0$ or $e^x = 9 \Rightarrow x = \ln 9$.

[4 marks available — 1 mark for factorisation of a quadratic, 1 mark for both solutions for e^x, and 1 mark for each correct exact solution for x.]

b) $2\ln x - \ln 3 = \ln 12 \Rightarrow 2\ln x = \ln 12 + \ln 3$

(Use the log laws to simplify at this point...)

$\Rightarrow \ln x^2 = \ln 36$ *[1 mark]* $\Rightarrow x^2 = 36$ *[1 mark]*
$\Rightarrow x = 6$ *[1 mark]* *(x must be positive as $\ln(-6)$ does not exist.)*

Q4 a) $y = \ln(4x - 3)$, and $x = a$ when $y = 1$.
$1 = \ln(4a - 3) \Rightarrow e^1 = 4a - 3$ *[1 mark]*
$\Rightarrow a = (e^1 + 3) \div 4 = 1.43$ to 2 d.p. *[1 mark]*.

b) The curve can only exist when $4x - 3 > 0$
[1 mark] so $x > 3 \div 4$, $x > 0.75$. If $x > b$, then $b = 0.75$ *[1 mark]*.

c)

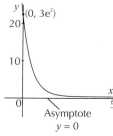

When $y = 0$, $4x - 3 = e^0 = 1$, so $x = 1$.
As $x \to \infty$, $y \to \infty$ gradually.
From (b), there will be an asymptote at $x = 0.75$.

[2 marks available — 1 mark for correct shape including asymptote at $x = 0.75$, 1 mark for (1, 0) as a point on the graph.]

Q5 a) $27 = 3e^{2-2x} \Rightarrow 9 = e^{2-2x} \Rightarrow \ln 9 = 2 - 2x$ *[1 mark]*
$\Rightarrow 2x = 2 - \ln 9 \Rightarrow x = 1 - 0.5\ln 9$ *[1 mark]*
$\Rightarrow x = 1 - 0.5\ln 3^2 = 1 - \ln 3$ *[1 mark]*.

b) Sketch of the graph $y = 3e^{2-2x}$ with asymptote and y-intercept labelled.

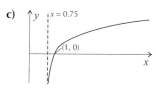

[3 marks available — 1 mark for correct shape of graph, 1 mark for (0, 3e²) as a point on the graph, 1 mark for asymptote at $y = 0$.]

c) $y = 3e^{2-2x} \Rightarrow e^{2-2x} = \dfrac{y}{3} \Rightarrow 2 - 2x = \ln\left(\dfrac{y}{3}\right)$
$\Rightarrow 2x = 2 - \ln\left(\dfrac{y}{3}\right) \Rightarrow x = 1 - 0.5\ln\left(\dfrac{y}{3}\right)$

[2 marks — 1 mark for taking logarithms of each side and 1 mark for the final answer.]

Q6 a) $y = 4\ln(x - A)$
The sketch shows that when $x = 6$, $y = 0$, so:
$0 = 4\ln(6 - A)$ *[1 mark]*
$6 - A = e^0 = 1 \Rightarrow A = 6 - 1 = 5$ *[1 mark]*.
The graph is a horizontal translation of $y = \ln x$, by 5 units right. $y = \ln x$ has an asymptote at $x = 0$, so $y = 4\ln(x - 5)$ will have an asymptote at $x = 5$ *[1 mark]*
The vertical stretch of scale factor 4 doesn't affect the horizontal position of the asymptote.

b) $y = 4\ln(x - 5)$
When $x = B$, $y = 8$, so:
$8 = 4\ln(B - 5)$ *[1 mark]*
$2 = \ln(B - 5)$
$B - 5 = e^2 \Rightarrow B = e^2 + 5$ *[1 mark]*.

Chapter 4: Differentiation

1. Chain Rule

Exercise 1.1 — The chain rule

Q1 a) $y = (x + 7)^2$, so let $y = u^2$ where $u = x + 7$

$\Rightarrow \dfrac{dy}{du} = 2u = 2(x + 7)$, $\dfrac{du}{dx} = 1$

$\dfrac{dy}{dx} = \dfrac{du}{dx} \times \dfrac{dy}{du} = 1 \times 2(x + 7) = 2(x + 7)$

b) $y = (2x - 1)^5$, so let $y = u^5$ where $u = 2x - 1$

$\Rightarrow \dfrac{dy}{du} = 5u^4 = 5(2x - 1)^4$, $\dfrac{du}{dx} = 2$

$\dfrac{dy}{dx} = \dfrac{du}{dx} \times \dfrac{dy}{du} = 2 \times 5(2x - 1)^4 = 10(2x - 1)^4$

c) $y = 3(4 - x)^8$, so let $y = 3u^8$ where $u = 4 - x$

$\Rightarrow \dfrac{dy}{du} = 24u^7 = 24(4 - x)^7$, $\dfrac{du}{dx} = -1$

$\dfrac{dy}{dx} = \dfrac{du}{dx} \times \dfrac{dy}{du} = (-1) \times 24(4 - x)^7 = -24(4 - x)^7$

d) $y = (3 - 2x)^7$, so let $y = u^7$ where $u = 3 - 2x$

$\Rightarrow \dfrac{dy}{du} = 7u^6 = 7(3 - 2x)^6$, $\dfrac{du}{dx} = -2$

$\dfrac{dy}{dx} = \dfrac{du}{dx} \times \dfrac{dy}{du} = (-2) \times 7(3 - 2x)^6 = -14(3 - 2x)^6$

e) $y = (x^2 + 3)^5$, so let $y = u^5$ where $u = x^2 + 3$

$\Rightarrow \dfrac{dy}{du} = 5u^4 = 5(x^2 + 3)^4$, $\dfrac{du}{dx} = 2x$

$\dfrac{dy}{dx} = \dfrac{du}{dx} \times \dfrac{dy}{du} = 2x \times 5(x^2 + 3)^4 = 10x(x^2 + 3)^4$

f) $y = (5x^2 + 3)^2$, so let $y = u^2$ where $u = 5x^2 + 3$

$\Rightarrow \dfrac{dy}{du} = 2u = 2(5x^2 + 3)$, $\dfrac{du}{dx} = 10x$

$\dfrac{dy}{dx} = \dfrac{du}{dx} \times \dfrac{dy}{du} = 10x \times 2(5x^2 + 3) = 20x(5x^2 + 3)$

Q2 a) $f(x) = (4x^3 - 9)^8$, so let $y = u^8$ where $u = 4x^3 - 9$

$\Rightarrow \dfrac{dy}{du} = 8u^7 = 8(4x^3 - 9)^7$, $\dfrac{du}{dx} = 12x^2$

$f'(x) = \dfrac{du}{dx} \times \dfrac{dy}{du} = 12x^2 \times 8(4x^3 - 9)^7$

$= 96x^2(4x^3 - 9)^7$

b) $f(x) = (6 - 7x^2)^4$, so let $y = u^4$ where $u = 6 - 7x^2$

$\Rightarrow \dfrac{dy}{du} = 4u^3 = 4(6 - 7x^2)^3$, $\dfrac{du}{dx} = -14x$

$f'(x) = \dfrac{du}{dx} \times \dfrac{dy}{du} = (-14x) \times 4(6 - 7x^2)^3$

$= -56x(6 - 7x^2)^3$

c) $f(x) = (x^2 + 5x + 7)^6$, so let $y = u^6$
where $u = x^2 + 5x + 7$

$\Rightarrow \dfrac{dy}{du} = 6u^5 = 6(x^2 + 5x + 7)^5$, $\dfrac{du}{dx} = 2x + 5$

$f'(x) = \dfrac{du}{dx} \times \dfrac{dy}{du} = (2x + 5) \times 6(x^2 + 5x + 7)^5$

$= (12x + 30)(x^2 + 5x + 7)^5$

d) $f(x) = (x + 4)^{-3}$, so let $y = u^{-3}$ where $u = x + 4$

$\Rightarrow \dfrac{dy}{du} = -3u^{-4} = -3(x + 4)^{-4}$, $\dfrac{du}{dx} = 1$

$f'(x) = \dfrac{du}{dx} \times \dfrac{dy}{du} = 1 \times (-3)(x + 4)^{-4} = -3(x + 4)^{-4}$

e) $f(x) = (5 - 3x)^{-2}$, so let $y = u^{-2}$ where $u = 5 - 3x$

$\Rightarrow \dfrac{dy}{du} = -2u^{-3} = -2(5 - 3x)^{-3}$, $\dfrac{du}{dx} = -3$

$f'(x) = \dfrac{du}{dx} \times \dfrac{dy}{du} = (-3) \times (-2)(5 - 3x)^{-3} = 6(5 - 3x)^{-3}$

f) $f(x) = \dfrac{1}{(5 - 3x)^4} = (5 - 3x)^{-4}$,

so let $y = u^{-4}$ where $u = 5 - 3x$

$\Rightarrow \dfrac{dy}{du} = -4u^{-5} = -4(5 - 3x)^{-5}$, $\dfrac{du}{dx} = -3$

$f'(x) = \dfrac{du}{dx} \times \dfrac{dy}{du} = (-3) \times (-4)(5 - 3x)^{-5} = \dfrac{12}{(5 - 3x)^5}$

g) $f(x) = (3x^2 + 4)^{\frac{3}{2}}$, so let $y = u^{\frac{3}{2}}$ where $u = 3x^2 + 4$

$\Rightarrow \dfrac{dy}{du} = \dfrac{3}{2}u^{\frac{1}{2}} = \dfrac{3}{2}(3x^2 + 4)^{\frac{1}{2}}$, $\dfrac{du}{dx} = 6x$

$f'(x) = \dfrac{du}{dx} \times \dfrac{dy}{du} = 6x \times \dfrac{3}{2}(3x^2 + 4)^{\frac{1}{2}} = 9x(3x^2 + 4)^{\frac{1}{2}}$

h) $f(x) = \dfrac{1}{\sqrt{5 - 3x}} = (5 - 3x)^{-\frac{1}{2}}$,

so let $y = u^{-\frac{1}{2}}$ where $u = 5 - 3x$

$\Rightarrow \dfrac{dy}{du} = -\dfrac{1}{2}u^{-\frac{3}{2}} = -\dfrac{1}{2}(5 - 3x)^{-\frac{3}{2}}$, $\dfrac{du}{dx} = -3$

$f'(x) = \dfrac{du}{dx} \times \dfrac{dy}{du} = (-3) \times (-\dfrac{1}{2})(5 - 3x)^{-\frac{3}{2}}$

$= \dfrac{3}{2(\sqrt{5 - 3x})^3}$

Q3 a) $y = (5x - 3x^2)^{-\frac{1}{2}}$, so let $y = u^{-\frac{1}{2}}$ where $u = 5x - 3x^2$

$\Rightarrow \dfrac{dy}{du} = -\dfrac{1}{2}u^{-\frac{3}{2}} = -\dfrac{1}{2}(5x - 3x^2)^{-\frac{3}{2}}$, $\dfrac{du}{dx} = 5 - 6x$

$\dfrac{dy}{dx} = \dfrac{du}{dx} \times \dfrac{dy}{du} = (5 - 6x) \times -\dfrac{1}{2}(5x - 3x^2)^{-\frac{3}{2}}$

$= -\dfrac{5 - 6x}{2(\sqrt{5x - 3x^2})^3}$

When $x = 1$, $\dfrac{dy}{dx} = -\dfrac{5 - (6 \times 1)}{2(\sqrt{(5 \times 1) - (3 \times 1^2)})^3} = \dfrac{1}{4\sqrt{2}}$

b) $y = \dfrac{12}{\sqrt[3]{x + 6}} = 12(x + 6)^{-\frac{1}{3}}$,

so let $y = 12u^{-\frac{1}{3}}$ where $u = x + 6$

$\Rightarrow \dfrac{dy}{du} = -4u^{-\frac{4}{3}} = -4(x + 6)^{-\frac{4}{3}}$, $\dfrac{du}{dx} = 1$

$\dfrac{dy}{dx} = \dfrac{du}{dx} \times \dfrac{dy}{du} = 1 \times -4(x + 6)^{-\frac{4}{3}} = -\dfrac{4}{\sqrt[3]{(x + 6)^4}}$

When $x = 1$, $\dfrac{dy}{dx} = -\dfrac{4}{\sqrt[3]{(1 + 6)^4}} = -\dfrac{4}{7(\sqrt[3]{7})}$

Q4 a) $(\sqrt{x} + \dfrac{1}{\sqrt{x}})^2 = \sqrt{x}\sqrt{x} + 2\sqrt{x}\dfrac{1}{\sqrt{x}} + \dfrac{1}{\sqrt{x}}\dfrac{1}{\sqrt{x}}$

$= x + \dfrac{1}{x} + 2$

$\dfrac{d}{dx}(x + \dfrac{1}{x} + 2) = 1 - \dfrac{1}{x^2}$

Remember $\dfrac{1}{x} = x^{-1}$

b) $y = (\sqrt{x} + \frac{1}{\sqrt{x}})^2$, so let $y = u^2$ where $u = \sqrt{x} + \frac{1}{\sqrt{x}}$

$\Rightarrow \dfrac{dy}{du} = 2u = 2(\sqrt{x} + \frac{1}{\sqrt{x}})$,

$\dfrac{du}{dx} = \frac{1}{2}x^{-\frac{1}{2}} - \frac{1}{2}x^{-\frac{3}{2}} = \dfrac{1}{2\sqrt{x}} - \dfrac{1}{2(\sqrt{x})^3}$

$\dfrac{dy}{dx} = \dfrac{du}{dx} \times \dfrac{dy}{du} = (\dfrac{1}{2\sqrt{x}} - \dfrac{1}{2(\sqrt{x})^3}) \times 2(\sqrt{x} + \frac{1}{\sqrt{x}})$

$= 2(\frac{1}{2} + \frac{1}{2x} - \frac{1}{2x} - \frac{1}{2x^2}) = 1 - \dfrac{1}{x^2}$

Using powers notation makes this question easier to handle.

Q5 $y = (x - 3)^5$, so let $y = u^5$ where $u = x - 3$

$\Rightarrow \dfrac{dy}{du} = 5u^4 = 5(x - 3)^4$, $\dfrac{du}{dx} = 1$

$\dfrac{dy}{dx} = \dfrac{du}{dx} \times \dfrac{dy}{du} = 1 \times 5(x - 3)^4 = 5(x - 3)^4$

At the point $(1, -32)$, gradient $= 5(1 - 3)^4 = 80$

The equation of a straight line is $y = mx + c$

$\Rightarrow -32 = (80 \times 1) + c \Rightarrow c = -112$

So the equation of the tangent is $y = 80x - 112$

Q6 $y = (2x - 3)^7$, so let $y = u^7$ where $u = 2x - 3$

$\Rightarrow \dfrac{dy}{du} = 7u^6 = 7(2x - 3)^6$, $\dfrac{du}{dx} = 2$

$\dfrac{dy}{dx} = \dfrac{du}{dx} \times \dfrac{dy}{du} = 2 \times 7(2x - 3)^6 = 14(2x - 3)^6$

At the point $(2, 1)$, gradient $= 14(4 - 3)^6 = 14$

The equation of a straight line is $y = mx + c$

$\Rightarrow 1 = (14 \times 2) + c \Rightarrow c = -27$

So the equation of the tangent is $y = 14x - 27$.

Q7 $y = \frac{1}{4}(x - 7)^4$, so let $y = \frac{1}{4}u^4$ where $u = x - 7$

$\Rightarrow \dfrac{dy}{du} = u^3 = (x - 7)^3$, $\dfrac{du}{dx} = 1$

$\dfrac{dy}{dx} = \dfrac{du}{dx} \times \dfrac{dy}{du} = 1 \times (x - 7)^3 = (x - 7)^3$

When $x = 6$, $y = \frac{1}{4}(6 - 7)^4 = \frac{1}{4}$

and $\dfrac{dy}{dx} = (6 - 7)^3 = -1$

The gradient of the normal is $-1 \div -1 = 1$

The equation of a straight line is $y = mx + c$

$\Rightarrow \frac{1}{4} = (1 \times 6) + c \Rightarrow c = -\frac{23}{4}$

So the equation of the normal is $y = x - \frac{23}{4}$

Q8 $y = (\frac{x}{4} - 2)^3$, so let $y = u^3$ where $u = \frac{x}{4} - 2$

$\Rightarrow \dfrac{dy}{du} = 3u^2 = 3(\frac{x}{4} - 2)^2$, $\dfrac{du}{dx} = \frac{1}{4}$

$\dfrac{dy}{dx} = \dfrac{du}{dx} \times \dfrac{dy}{du} = \frac{1}{4} \times 3(\frac{x}{4} - 2)^2 = \frac{3}{4}(\frac{x}{4} - 2)^2$

At the point $(4, -1)$, gradient $= \frac{3}{4}(\frac{4}{4} - 2)^2 = \frac{3}{4}$

So the gradient of the normal $= -\frac{4}{3}$

$-1 = (-\frac{4}{3} \times 4) + c \Rightarrow c = \frac{13}{3}$

So the equation of the normal is $y = -\frac{4}{3}x + \frac{13}{3}$

To write it in the form $ax + by + c = 0$, where a, b and c are integers, multiply by 3 and rearrange:

$y = -\frac{4}{3}x + \frac{13}{3} \Rightarrow 3y = -4x + 13 \Rightarrow 4x + 3y - 13 = 0$

Q9 $y = (7x^2 - 3)^{-4}$, so let $y = u^{-4}$ where $u = 7x^2 - 3$

$\Rightarrow \dfrac{dy}{du} = -4u^{-5} = -4(7x^2 - 3)^{-5}$, $\dfrac{du}{dx} = 14x$

$\dfrac{dy}{dx} = \dfrac{du}{dx} \times \dfrac{dy}{du} = 14x \times -4(7x^2 - 3)^{-5} = -56x(7x^2 - 3)^{-5}$

When $x = 1$, $\dfrac{dy}{dx} = -56(1)(7(1)^2 - 3)^{-5} = -56(4^{-5})$

$= -\dfrac{7}{128}$

Q10 $y = \dfrac{7}{\sqrt[3]{3 - 2x}}$, so let $y = 7u^{-\frac{1}{3}}$ where $u = 3 - 2x$

$\Rightarrow \dfrac{dy}{du} = -\frac{7}{3}u^{-\frac{4}{3}} = -\dfrac{7}{3(\sqrt[3]{3 - 2x})^4}$, $\dfrac{du}{dx} = -2$

$f'(x) = \dfrac{du}{dx} \times \dfrac{dy}{du} = -2 \times -\dfrac{7}{3(\sqrt[3]{3 - 2x})^4} = \dfrac{14}{3(\sqrt[3]{3 - 2x})^4}$

$f'(x)$ could also be written as $\frac{14}{3}(3 - 2x)^{-\frac{4}{3}}$.

Q11 $y = \sqrt{5x - 1}$, so let $y = u^{\frac{1}{2}}$ where $u = 5x - 1$

$\Rightarrow \dfrac{dy}{du} = \frac{1}{2}u^{-\frac{1}{2}} = \frac{1}{2}\dfrac{1}{\sqrt{5x - 1}}$, $\dfrac{du}{dx} = 5$

$\dfrac{dy}{dx} = \dfrac{du}{dx} \times \dfrac{dy}{du} = 5 \times \frac{1}{2}\dfrac{1}{\sqrt{5x - 1}} = \dfrac{5}{2\sqrt{5x - 1}}$

when $x = 2$, $\dfrac{dy}{dx} = \dfrac{5}{2\sqrt{10 - 1}} = \frac{5}{6}$

and $y = \sqrt{10 - 1} = 3$

$y = mx + c \Rightarrow 3 = (\frac{5}{6} \times 2) + c \Rightarrow c = \frac{4}{3}$

So the equation of the tangent is $y = \frac{5}{6}x + \frac{4}{3}$

In the form $ax + by + c = 0$, $5x - 6y + 8 = 0$

Q12 $y = \sqrt[3]{3x - 7}$, so let $y = u^{\frac{1}{3}}$ where $u = 3x - 7$

$\Rightarrow \dfrac{dy}{du} = \frac{1}{3}u^{-\frac{2}{3}} = \dfrac{1}{3(\sqrt[3]{3x - 7})^2}$, $\dfrac{du}{dx} = 3$

$\dfrac{dy}{dx} = \dfrac{du}{dx} \times \dfrac{dy}{du} = 3 \times \dfrac{1}{3(\sqrt[3]{3x - 7})^2} = \dfrac{1}{(\sqrt[3]{3x - 7})^2}$

when $x = 5$, $\dfrac{dy}{dx} = \dfrac{1}{(\sqrt[3]{(3 \times 5)} - 7)^2} = \frac{1}{4}$, $y = \sqrt[3]{15 - 7} = 2$

Gradient of normal $= \dfrac{-1}{\frac{1}{4}} = -4$

$y = mx + c \Rightarrow 2 = (-4 \times 5) + c \Rightarrow c = 22$

So the equation of the normal is $y = 22 - 4x$

Q13 $y = (x^4 + x^3 + x^2)^2$, so let $y = u^2$ where $u = x^4 + x^3 + x^2$

$\Rightarrow \dfrac{dy}{du} = 2u = 2(x^4 + x^3 + x^2)$, $\dfrac{du}{dx} = 4x^3 + 3x^2 + 2x$

$\dfrac{dy}{dx} = \dfrac{du}{dx} \times \dfrac{dy}{du} = (4x^3 + 3x^2 + 2x) \times 2(x^4 + x^3 + x^2)$

At $x = -1$ $\dfrac{dy}{dx} = (-4 + 3 + -2) \times 2(1 - 1 + 1) = -6$

$y = ((-1)^4 + (-1)^3 + (-1)^2)^2 = 1$

$y = mx + c \Rightarrow 1 = (-6 \times -1) + c \Rightarrow c = -5$

So the equation of the tangent is $y = -6x - 5$.

Exercise 1.2 — Finding $\dfrac{dy}{dx}$ when $x = f(y)$

Q1 a) $\dfrac{dx}{dy} = 6y + 5 \Rightarrow \dfrac{dy}{dx} = \dfrac{1}{6y + 5}$

At $(5, -1)$, $y = -1$ so $\dfrac{dy}{dx} = \dfrac{1}{-1} = -1$.

b) $\dfrac{dx}{dy} = 3y^2 - 2 \Rightarrow \dfrac{dy}{dx} = \dfrac{1}{3y^2 - 2}$

At $(-4, -2)$, $y = -2$ so $\dfrac{dy}{dx} = \dfrac{1}{10} = 0.1$.

c) $x = (2y + 1)(y - 2) = 2y^2 - 3y - 2$

$\dfrac{dx}{dy} = 4y - 3 \Rightarrow \dfrac{dy}{dx} = \dfrac{1}{4y - 3}$

At $(3, -1)$ $y = -1$ so $\dfrac{dy}{dx} = -\dfrac{1}{7}$.

d) $x = \dfrac{4 + y^2}{y} = 4y^{-1} + y$

$\dfrac{dx}{dy} = -4y^{-2} + 1 \Rightarrow \dfrac{dy}{dx} = \dfrac{1}{1 - 4y^{-2}} = \dfrac{y^2}{y^2 - 4}$

At $(5, 4)$, $y = 4$ so $\dfrac{dy}{dx} = \dfrac{4}{3}$.

Q2 $x = (2y^3 - 5)^3$, so let $x = u^3$ where $u = 2y^3 - 5$

$\Rightarrow \dfrac{dx}{du} = 3u^2 = 3(2y^3 - 5)^2$, $\dfrac{du}{dy} = 6y^2$

$\dfrac{dx}{dy} = \dfrac{du}{dy} \times \dfrac{dx}{du} = 6y^2 \times 3(2y^3 - 5)^2 = 18y^2(2y^3 - 5)^2$

$\dfrac{dy}{dx} = \dfrac{1}{18y^2(2y^3 - 5)^2}$

Q3 a) $x = \sqrt{4 + y} \Rightarrow x = u^{\frac{1}{2}}$, $u = 4 + y$

$\Rightarrow \dfrac{dx}{du} = \dfrac{1}{2}u^{-\frac{1}{2}} = \dfrac{1}{2}\dfrac{1}{\sqrt{4 + y}}$, $\dfrac{du}{dy} = 1$

$\dfrac{dx}{dy} = \dfrac{du}{dy} \times \dfrac{dx}{du} = 1 \times \dfrac{1}{2}\dfrac{1}{\sqrt{4 + y}} = \dfrac{1}{2\sqrt{4 + y}} = \dfrac{1}{2x}$

$\Rightarrow \dfrac{dy}{dx} = 2x$

If you look back at the question, $x = \sqrt{4 + y}$, so you can just replace this with x on the bottom row when finding dx/dy.

b) $x = \sqrt{4 + y} \Rightarrow x^2 = 4 + y \Rightarrow y = x^2 - 4$

$\dfrac{dy}{dx} = 2x$

2. Differentiation of e^x and $\ln x$

Exercise 2.1 — Differentiating e^x

Q1 a) $y = e^{f(x)}$, where $f(x) = 3x$, so $f'(x) = 3$

$\dfrac{dy}{dx} = f'(x)e^{f(x)} = 3 \times e^{3x} = 3e^{3x}$

b) $\dfrac{dy}{dx} = f'(x)e^{f(x)} = 2 \times e^{2x-5} = 2e^{2x-5}$

c) $\dfrac{dy}{dx} = f'(x)e^{f(x)} = 1 \times e^{x+7} = e^{x+7}$

d) $\dfrac{dy}{dx} = f'(x)e^{f(x)} = 3 \times e^{3x+9} = 3e^{3x+9}$

e) $\dfrac{dy}{dx} = f'(x)e^{f(x)} = (-2) \times e^{7-2x} = -2e^{7-2x}$

f) $\dfrac{dy}{dx} = f'(x)e^{f(x)} = 3x^2 \times e^{x^3} = 3x^2 e^{x^3}$

Q2 $f'(x) = g'(x)e^{g(x)} = (3x^2 + 3)e^{x^3 + 3x}$

Q3 $f'(x) = g'(x)e^{g(x)} = (3x^2 - 3)e^{x^3 - 3x - 5}$

Q4 $f(x) = e^{2x^2 + x}$, so:

$f'(x) = g'(x)e^{g(x)} = (4x + 1) \times e^{2x^2 + x} = (4x + 1)e^{x(2x + 1)}$

Q5 e^x differentiates to e^x and e^{-x} differentiates to $-e^{-x}$ so

$f'(x) = \dfrac{1}{2} \times (e^x - (-e^{-x})) = \dfrac{1}{2}(e^x + e^{-x})$

Q6 $f(x) = e^{x^2 + 7x + 12}$

$f'(x) = g'(x)e^{g(x)} = (2x + 7)e^{x^2 + 7x + 12}$

Q7 $\dfrac{d}{dx}(e^{x^4 + 3x^2}) = (4x^3 + 6x)e^{x^4 + 3x^2}$ and

$\dfrac{d}{dx}(2e^{2x}) = 4e^{2x}$

So $f'(x) = (4x^3 + 6x)e^{x^4 + 3x^2} + 4e^{2x}$

Q8 $\dfrac{dy}{dx} = f'(x)e^{f(x)} = 2 \times e^{2x} = 2e^{2x}$

At $x = 0$, $\dfrac{dy}{dx} = 2 \times e^{2 \times 0} = 2 \times 1 = 2$

$y = mx + c \Rightarrow 1 = (2 \times 0) + c \Rightarrow c = 1$

So the equation of the tangent is $y = 2x + 1$

There's no real need to use the $y = mx + c$ formula here as we already know the place it crosses the y-axis is $(0, 1)$ (it's given in the question), but it's good to be safe.

Q9 $\dfrac{dy}{dx} = f'(x)e^{f(x)} = 3 \times e^{3(x-2)} = 3e^{3(x-2)}$

When $x = 2$, $\dfrac{dy}{dx} = 3e^{3(2-2)} = 3e^0 = 3$

$y = mx + c \Rightarrow 1 = (3 \times 2) + c \Rightarrow c = -5$

So the equation of the tangent is $y = 3x - 5$.

Q10 $\dfrac{dy}{dx} = f'(x)e^{f(x)} = 4xe^{2x^2}$

At $x = 1$, $\dfrac{dy}{dx} = 4 \times 1 \times e^2 = 4e^2$ and $y = e^2$

$y = mx + c \Rightarrow e^2 = (4e^2 \times 1) + c \Rightarrow c = -3e^2$

So the equation of the tangent is $y = 4e^2 x - 3e^2$.

Q11 $\frac{dy}{dx} = f'(x)e^{f(x)} = 2e^{2x-4}$

When $x = 2$, $\frac{dy}{dx} = 2e^{4-4} = 2e^0 = 2$

$\Rightarrow$ Gradient of the normal $= -\frac{1}{2}$

$y = mx + c \Rightarrow 1 = (-\frac{1}{2} \times 2) + c \Rightarrow c = 1 - (-1) = 2$

So the equation of the normal is $y = 2 - \frac{1}{2}x$.

Q12 $\frac{dy}{dx} = f'(x)e^{f(x)} = (3 \times e^{3x}) = 3e^{3x}$

When it crosses the y-axis, $x = 0$, so $y = e^{3 \times 0} + 3 = 4$

$\frac{dy}{dx} = (3 \times e^{3 \times 0}) = (3 \times 1) = 3$

$\Rightarrow$ Gradient of the normal $= -\frac{1}{3}$

$y = mx + c \Rightarrow 4 = (-\frac{1}{3} \times 0) + c \Rightarrow c = 4$

So the equation of the normal is $y = -\frac{1}{3}x + 4$.

Q13 $\frac{dy}{dx} = f'(x)e^{f(x)} = 3 \times e^{3(x-1)} = 3e^{3(x-1)}$

When $x = 2$, $y = e^3$ and $\frac{dy}{dx} = 3e^3$

So the gradient of the normal is $-\frac{1}{3e^3} = -\frac{1}{3}e^{-3}$

$y = mx + c \Rightarrow e^3 = 2 \times -\frac{1}{3}e^{-3} + c$

$\Rightarrow c = e^3 + \frac{2}{3}e^{-3}$

So the equation of the normal is
$y = -\frac{1}{3}e^{-3}x + e^3 + \frac{2}{3}e^{-3}$.

Q14 If y has a stationary point the gradient $\frac{dy}{dx}$ will be 0.

$\frac{dy}{dx} = f'(x)e^{f(x)} = (3x^2 - 3)e^{x^3 - 3x - 5}$

So if $\frac{dy}{dx} = 0$, either $3x^2 - 3 = 0$ or $e^{x^3 - 3x - 5} = 0$.

If $3x^2 - 3 = 0 \Rightarrow 3(x^2 - 1) = 0 \Rightarrow x^2 = 1$

$\Rightarrow x = \pm 1$ and if $e^{x^3 - 3x - 5} = 0$, there are no solutions.

So the gradient is 0 when $x = \pm 1 \Rightarrow$ the curve has stationary points at $x = \pm 1$.

Q15 Stationary points occur when the gradient is 0.

$\frac{dy}{dx} = f'(x)e^{f(x)} - 6 = 3e^{3x} - 6$

$3e^{3x} - 6 = 0 \Rightarrow e^{3x} = 2 \Rightarrow 3x = \ln 2 \Rightarrow x = \frac{1}{3}\ln 2$

Take ln of both sides to get rid of the exponential.

To find the nature of the root, calculate $\frac{d^2y}{dx^2}$

$\frac{d^2y}{dx^2} = 3f'(x)e^{f(x)} = 9e^{3x}$

When $x = \frac{1}{3}\ln 2$, $\frac{d^2y}{dx^2} = 9e^{\ln 2} = 9 \times 2 = 18$

$\frac{d^2y}{dx^2}$ is positive, so it's a minimum stationary point.

Exercise 2.2 — Differentiating ln x

Q1 a) $y = \ln(3x) = \ln 3 + \ln x \Rightarrow \frac{dy}{dx} = \frac{1}{x}$

You could use that the derivative of $\ln(f(x))$ is $\frac{f'(x)}{f(x)}$ — it'd give the same answer.

b) $\frac{dy}{dx} = 3 \times \frac{1}{x} = \frac{3}{x}$

c) $\frac{dy}{dx} = \frac{f'(x)}{f(x)} = \frac{1}{1+x}$

The coefficient of x is 1 so it's a 1 on top of the fraction.

d) $\frac{dy}{dx} = \frac{f'(x)}{f(x)} = \frac{1}{5+x}$

e) $\frac{dy}{dx} = \frac{f'(x)}{f(x)} = \frac{5}{1+5x}$

f) $\frac{dy}{dx} = 4 \times \frac{f'(x)}{f(x)} = 4 \times \frac{4}{4x-2} = \frac{16}{4x-2} = \frac{8}{2x-1}$

Don't forget to simplify your answers if you can.

Q2 a) $\frac{dy}{dx} = \frac{f'(x)}{f(x)} = \frac{2x}{1+x^2}$

b) $\frac{dy}{dx} = \frac{f'(x)}{f(x)} = \frac{-4x}{4-2x^2} = \frac{-2x}{2-x^2}$

c) $y = \ln(2+x)^2 = 2\ln(2+x)$

$\frac{dy}{dx} = 2\frac{f'(x)}{f(x)} = 2 \times \frac{1}{2+x} = \frac{2}{2+x}$

d) $3\ln x^3 = 9\ln x \Rightarrow \frac{dy}{dx} = \frac{9}{x}$

e) $\frac{dy}{dx} = 2 \times \frac{f'(x)}{f(x)} = 2 \times \frac{6x+3}{3x^2+3x}$

$= \frac{12x+6}{3x^2+3x} = \frac{4x+2}{x^2+x}$

f) $\frac{dy}{dx} = \frac{f'(x)}{f(x)} = \frac{3x^2+2x}{x^3+x^2} = \frac{3x+2}{x^2+x}$

Q3 $f(x) = \ln\frac{1}{x} = \ln x^{-1} = -\ln x \Rightarrow f'(x) = -\frac{1}{x}$

Q4 $f(x) = \ln\sqrt{x} = \ln x^{\frac{1}{2}} = \frac{1}{2}\ln x \Rightarrow f'(x) = \frac{1}{2x}$

Q5 $\ln\left(\frac{\sqrt{1-x}}{\sqrt{1+x}}\right) = \ln\sqrt{1-x} - \ln\sqrt{1+x}$

First part:
$f(x) = \ln\sqrt{1-x} = \ln(1-x)^{\frac{1}{2}} = \frac{1}{2}\ln(1-x)$

$f'(x) = -\frac{1}{2(1-x)}$

Second part:
$f(x) = \ln\sqrt{1+x} = \ln(1+x)^{\frac{1}{2}} = \frac{1}{2}\ln(1+x)$

$f'(x) = \frac{1}{2(1+x)}$

Putting it all together:
$f'(x) = -\frac{1}{2(1-x)} - \frac{1}{2(1+x)} = \frac{-(1+x)-(1-x)}{2(1-x)(1+x)}$

$= -\frac{1}{(1-x)(1+x)}$

Q6 $\ln((2x + 1)^2 \sqrt{x - 4}) = \ln (2x + 1)^2 + \ln \sqrt{x - 4}$

$$= 2\ln (2x + 1) + \frac{1}{2}\ln (x - 4)$$

First part:

$f'(x) = 2 \times \dfrac{2}{2x + 1} = \dfrac{4}{2x + 1}$

Second part:

$f'(x) = \dfrac{1}{2} \times \dfrac{1}{x - 4} = \dfrac{1}{2(x - 4)}$

Putting it all together:

$f'(x) = \dfrac{4}{2x + 1} + \dfrac{1}{2(x - 4)} = \dfrac{8(x - 4) + 2x + 1}{2(2x + 1)(x - 4)}$

$$= \dfrac{10x - 31}{2(2x + 1)(x - 4)}$$

Q7 $g(x) = x - \sqrt{x - 4} \Rightarrow g'(x) = 1 - (\dfrac{dy}{du} \times \dfrac{du}{dx})$

$$= 1 - \dfrac{1}{2\sqrt{x - 4}}$$

$f'(x) = \dfrac{g'(x)}{g(x)} = \dfrac{1 - \dfrac{1}{2\sqrt{x - 4}}}{x - \sqrt{x - 4}} = \dfrac{2\sqrt{x - 4} - 1}{2(x\sqrt{x - 4} - x + 4)}$

Q8 $\ln \left(\dfrac{(3x + 1)^2}{\sqrt{2x + 1}}\right) = \ln (3x + 1)^2 - \ln \sqrt{2x + 1}$

$$= 2\ln (3x + 1) - \frac{1}{2}\ln (2x + 1)$$

First part:

$f'(x) = 2 \times \dfrac{3}{3x + 1} = \dfrac{6}{3x + 1}$

Second part:

$f'(x) = \dfrac{1}{2} \times \dfrac{2}{2x + 1} = \dfrac{1}{2x + 1}$

Putting it all together:

$f'(x) = \dfrac{6}{3x + 1} - \dfrac{1}{2x + 1} = \dfrac{6(2x + 1) - 3x - 1}{(3x + 1)(2x + 1)}$

$$= \dfrac{9x + 5}{(3x + 1)(2x + 1)}$$

You could have left your answer as 2 fractions.

Q9 $\ln (x\sqrt{x + 4}) = \ln x + \ln \sqrt{x + 4} = \ln x + \frac{1}{2}\ln (x + 4)$

First part:

$\dfrac{dy}{dx} = \dfrac{1}{x}$

Second part:

$\dfrac{dy}{dx} = \dfrac{1}{2} \times \dfrac{1}{x + 4} = \dfrac{1}{2(x + 4)}$

Putting it all together:

$f'(x) = \dfrac{1}{x} + \dfrac{1}{2(x + 4)} = \dfrac{2x + 8 + x}{2x(x + 4)} = \dfrac{3x + 8}{2x(x + 4)}$

Q10 $y = \ln (3x) = \ln 3 + \ln x \Rightarrow \dfrac{dy}{dx} = \dfrac{1}{x}$

This is just the derivative from 1 a).

When $x = \dfrac{1}{3}$, $\dfrac{dy}{dx} = \dfrac{1}{\left(\frac{1}{3}\right)} = 3$

$y = mx + c \Rightarrow 0 = (3 \times \frac{1}{3}) + c \Rightarrow c = -1$

So the equation of the tangent is $y = 3x - 1$.

Q11 a) $y = \ln (3x)^2 = 2\ln (3x) = 2\ln 3 + 2\ln x$

$\Rightarrow \dfrac{dy}{dx} = \dfrac{2}{x}$

When $x = -2$, $\dfrac{dy}{dx} = -1$ and $y = \ln 36$

$y = mx + c \Rightarrow \ln 36 = [(-1) \times (-2)] + c$

$\Rightarrow c = \ln 36 - 2$

So the equation of the tangent is

$y = -x + \ln 36 - 2$

b) When $x = 2$, $\dfrac{dy}{dx} = 1$ and $y = \ln 36$

$y = mx + c \Rightarrow \ln 36 = [1 \times 2] + c$

$\Rightarrow c = \ln 36 - 2$

So the equation of the tangent is

$y = x + \ln 36 - 2$

Q12 a) $y = \ln (x + 6)^2 = 2\ln (x + 6) \Rightarrow \dfrac{dy}{dx} = 2\dfrac{f'(x)}{f(x)} = \dfrac{2}{x + 6}$

When $x = -3$, $\dfrac{dy}{dx} = \dfrac{2}{3}$ and $y = \ln 9$

So the gradient of the normal $= -\dfrac{1}{\left(\frac{2}{3}\right)} = -\dfrac{3}{2}$

$y = mx + c \Rightarrow \ln 9 = (-\frac{3}{2} \times -3) + c$

$\Rightarrow c = \ln 9 - \dfrac{9}{2}$

so the equation of the normal is

$y = -\dfrac{3}{2}x + \ln 9 - \dfrac{9}{2}$.

b) When $x = 0$, $\dfrac{dy}{dx} = \dfrac{2}{6} = \dfrac{1}{3}$ and $y = \ln 36$

So the gradient of the normal $= -\dfrac{1}{\left(\frac{1}{3}\right)} = -3$

$y = mx + c \Rightarrow \ln 36 = (-3 \times 0) + c \Rightarrow c = \ln 36$

So the equation of the normal is

$y = -3x + \ln 36$

Q13 Stationary points occur when the gradient is 0.

$\dfrac{dy}{dx} = \dfrac{f'(x)}{f(x)} = \dfrac{3x^2 - 6x + 3}{x^3 - 3x^2 + 3x}$

so $3x^2 - 6x + 3 = 0 \Rightarrow 3(x - 1)(x - 1) = 0$

You can ignore the denominator here, as it's only the top part that affects when it's equal to O.

So the gradient is 0 when $x = 1$. When $x = 1$, $y = 0$ so the stationary point is at $(1, 0)$.

3. Differentiation of Trig Functions

Exercise 3.1 — Differentiating sin, cos and tan

Q1 **a)** $y = \sin(3x)$, so let $y = \sin u$ where $u = 3x$

$$\Rightarrow \frac{dy}{du} = \cos u = \cos(3x), \frac{du}{dx} = 3$$

$$\frac{dy}{dx} = \frac{dy}{du} \times \frac{du}{dx} = 3\cos(3x)$$

b) $y = \cos(-2x)$, so let $y = \cos u$ where $u = -2x$

$$\Rightarrow \frac{dy}{du} = -\sin(u) = -\sin(-2x), \frac{du}{dx} = -2$$

$$\frac{dy}{dx} = \frac{dy}{du} \times \frac{du}{dx} = (-2) \times (-\sin(-2x)) = 2\sin(-2x)$$

As you can see, the number at the front is always just the coefficient of x inside the trig function.

c) $\frac{dy}{dx} = \frac{dy}{du} \times \frac{du}{dx} = -\sin\frac{x}{2} \times \frac{1}{2} = -\frac{1}{2}\sin\frac{x}{2}$

d) $\frac{dy}{dx} = \frac{dy}{du} \times \frac{du}{dx} = 1 \times \cos(x + \frac{\pi}{4}) = \cos(x + \frac{\pi}{4})$

e) $\frac{dy}{dx} = \frac{dy}{du} \times \frac{du}{dx} = 6 \times \frac{1}{2} \times \sec^2\frac{x}{2} = 3\sec^2\frac{x}{2}$

f) $\frac{dy}{dx} = \frac{dy}{du} \times \frac{du}{dx} = 3 \times 5 \times \sec^2(5x) = 15\sec^2(5x)$

Q2 $f'(x) = \frac{dy}{du} \times \frac{du}{dx} = 3 \times 2 \times \sec^2(2x - 1)$
$$= 6\sec^2(2x - 1)$$

Q3 First part: $\frac{dy}{dx} = 3\sec^2 x$

Second part: $\frac{dy}{dx} = \frac{dy}{du} \times \frac{du}{dx} = 3\sec^2(3x)$

Putting it all together:

$f'(x) = 3(\sec^2 x + \sec^2(3x))$

Q4 $f'(x) = \frac{dy}{du} \times \frac{du}{dx} = 2x\cos(x^2 + \frac{\pi}{3})$

Q5 $f(x) = \sin^2 x$, so let $y = u^2$ where $u = \sin x$

$f'(x) = \frac{dy}{du} \times \frac{du}{dx} = (2\sin x) \times \cos x = 2\sin x\cos x$

Q6 $f(x) = 2\sin^3 x$, so let $y = 2u^3$ where $u = \sin x$

$f'(x) = \frac{dy}{du} \times \frac{du}{dx} = 6\sin^2 x\cos x$

Q7 **a)** $f'(x) = 3\cos x - 2\sin x$

b) $f'(x) = 0 \Rightarrow 3\cos x - 2\sin x = 0$
$$\Rightarrow 3\cos x = 2\sin x$$
$$\Rightarrow \frac{3}{2} = \tan x \Rightarrow x = \tan^{-1}\frac{3}{2} = 0.983 \text{ (3 s.f.)}$$

Remember that tan x = sin x / cos x

Q8 $y = \frac{1}{\cos x} = (\cos x)^{-1}$, so let $y = u^{-1}$ where $u = \cos x$

$$\Rightarrow \frac{dy}{du} = -u^{-2} = -\frac{1}{\cos^2 x}, \frac{du}{dx} = -\sin x$$

$$\frac{dy}{dx} = \frac{dy}{du} \times \frac{du}{dx} = -\frac{1}{\cos^2 x} \times -\sin x$$

$$= \frac{\sin x}{\cos^2 x} = \sec x\tan x$$

Remember that 1/cos x = sec x

Q9 $y = \cos^2 x$, so let $y = u^2$ where $u = \cos x$.

$$\frac{dy}{dx} = \frac{dy}{du} \times \frac{du}{dx} = (2\cos x) \times (-\sin x)$$
$$= -2\sin x\cos x$$

Q10 $\frac{dy}{dx} = \cos x$. When $x = \frac{\pi}{4}$, $\frac{dy}{dx} = \frac{1}{\sqrt{2}}$

Q11 $\frac{dy}{dx} = -2\sin(2x)$

When $x = \frac{\pi}{4}$, $y = 0$ and $\frac{dy}{dx} = -2$

So the gradient of the normal is $\frac{-1}{-2} = \frac{1}{2}$.

$y = mx + c \Rightarrow 0 = (\frac{1}{2} \times \frac{\pi}{4}) + c \Rightarrow c = -\frac{\pi}{8}$

So the equation of the normal is $y = \frac{1}{2}x - \frac{\pi}{8}$

$$\Rightarrow 8y = 4x - \pi$$

Q12 **a)** $\frac{dx}{dy} = 2\cos(2y)$, $\frac{dy}{dx} = \frac{1}{2\cos(2y)} = \frac{1}{2}\sec(2y)$

At the point $\left(\frac{\sqrt{3}}{2}, \frac{\pi}{6}\right)$, $\frac{dy}{dx} = \frac{1}{2\cos\frac{\pi}{3}} = 1$

$y = mx + c \Rightarrow \frac{\pi}{6} = \frac{\sqrt{3}}{2} + c \Rightarrow c = \frac{\pi}{6} - \frac{\sqrt{3}}{2}$

So the equation of the tangent is $y = x + \frac{\pi}{6} - \frac{\sqrt{3}}{2}$.

b) from part a), $\frac{dy}{dx} = 1$ so the normal gradient is -1.

$y = mx + c \Rightarrow \frac{\pi}{6} = -\frac{\sqrt{3}}{2} + c \Rightarrow c = \frac{\pi}{6} + \frac{\sqrt{3}}{2}$

So the equation of the normal is $y = -x + \frac{\pi}{6} + \frac{\sqrt{3}}{2}$.

Exercise 3.2 — Differentiating by using the chain rule twice

Q1 **a)** $y = \sin(\cos(2x))$, so let $y = \sin u$ where $u = \cos(2x)$

$$\frac{dy}{du} = \cos u = \cos(\cos(2x))$$

Using the chain rule again on $\frac{du}{dx}$ gives:

$u = \cos(2x) \Rightarrow \frac{du}{dx} = -2\sin(2x)$

Putting it all together:

$$\frac{dy}{dx} = \frac{dy}{du} \times \frac{du}{dx} = -2\sin(2x)\cos(\cos(2x))$$

b) $y = 2\ln f(x) \Rightarrow \frac{dy}{dx} = 2\frac{f'(x)}{f(x)}$

$f(x) = \cos(3x) \Rightarrow f'(x) = -3\sin(3x)$

$$\frac{dy}{dx} = 2\frac{-3\sin(3x)}{\cos(3x)} = -6\tan(3x)$$

c) $y = \ln(\tan^2 x) = \ln(f(x)) \Rightarrow \frac{dy}{dx} = \frac{f'(x)}{f(x)}$

$f(x) = \tan^2 x = (\tan x)^2$, so let $y = u^2$ where $u = \tan x$

$$\frac{dy}{du} = 2u = 2\tan x, \frac{du}{dx} = \sec^2 x$$

$$f'(x) = \frac{dy}{du} \times \frac{du}{dx} = 2\tan x\sec^2 x$$

Putting it all together:

$$\frac{dy}{dx} = \frac{2\tan x\sec^2 x}{\tan^2 x} = 2\sec x\,\text{cosec}\,x$$

You could've written ln (tan² x) as 2 ln (tan x) using the laws of logs and then differentiated — you'd end up with the same answer.

d) $y = e^{f(x)} \Rightarrow \dfrac{dy}{dx} = f'(x)e^{f(x)}$

$f(x) = \tan(2x)$, so let $y = \tan u$ where $u = 2x$

$\dfrac{dy}{du} = \sec^2 u = \sec^2 (2x)$, $\dfrac{du}{dx} = 2$

$\Rightarrow f'(x) = \dfrac{dy}{du} \times \dfrac{du}{dx} = 2\sec^2 (2x)$

$\Rightarrow \dfrac{dy}{dx} = 2\sec^2 (2x)\, e^{\tan (2x)}$

e) $y = \sin^4 x^2 = (\sin x^2)^4$, so let $y = u^4$ where $u = \sin x^2$

$\dfrac{dy}{du} = 4u^3 = 4\sin^3 x^2$

For $\dfrac{du}{dx}$, set up another chain rule:

$u = \sin x^2$ so let $u = \sin v$, $v = x^2$

$\dfrac{du}{dv} = \cos v = \cos x^2$, $\dfrac{dv}{dx} = 2x$

$\dfrac{du}{dx} = \dfrac{du}{dv} \times \dfrac{dv}{dx} = 2x\cos x^2$

Putting it all together:

$\dfrac{dy}{dx} = \dfrac{dy}{du} \times \dfrac{du}{dx} = 8x\sin^3 x^2\cos x^2$

f) $\dfrac{dy}{dx} = f'(x)e^{f(x)}$

$f(x) = \sin^2 x = (\sin x)^2$, so let $y = u^2$ where $u = \sin x$

$f'(x) = \dfrac{dy}{du} \times \dfrac{du}{dx} = (2\sin x) \times (\cos x)$
$\qquad = 2\sin x\cos x$

$\Rightarrow \dfrac{dy}{dx} = 2\,e^{\sin^2 x}\sin x\cos x$

g) First part:

$y = \tan^2 (3x) = (\tan (3x))^2$,

so let $y = u^2$ where $u = \tan (3x)$

$\dfrac{dy}{du} = 2u = 2\tan (3x)$

For $\dfrac{du}{dx}$ set up the chain rule again:

$u = \tan (3x)$, so let $u = \tan v$ where $v = 3x$

$\dfrac{du}{dv} = \sec^2 v = \sec^2 (3x)$, $\dfrac{dv}{dx} = 3$

$\Rightarrow \dfrac{du}{dx} = \dfrac{du}{dv} \times \dfrac{dv}{dx} = 3\sec^2 (3x)$

$\Rightarrow \dfrac{dy}{dx} = \dfrac{dy}{du} \times \dfrac{du}{dx} = 6\tan (3x)\sec^2 (3x)$

Second part:

$\dfrac{dy}{dx} = \cos x$

Putting it all together:

$$\frac{dy}{dx} = 6\tan (3x)\sec^2 (3x) + \cos x$$

With practice, you should be able to do some of the simpler chain rule calculations in your head, e.g. tan² (3x) = 6 tan (3x) sec² (3x), which will make these questions much quicker.

h) First part:

$y = e^{f(x)}$, $f(x) = 2\cos (2x) \Rightarrow \dfrac{dy}{dx} = f'(x)e^{f(x)}$

$f(x) = 2\cos (2x) \Rightarrow f'(x) = -4\sin (2x)$

So $\dfrac{dy}{dx} = -4\sin (2x)e^{2\cos (2x)}$

Second part:

$y = \cos^2 (2x) = (\cos (2x))^2$,

so let $y = u^2$ where $u = \cos (2x)$

$\dfrac{dy}{du} = 2u = 2\cos (2x)$

For $\dfrac{du}{dx}$, set up the chain rule again:

$u = \cos (2x) \Rightarrow \dfrac{du}{dx}\ -2\sin (2x)$

$\Rightarrow \dfrac{dy}{dx} = \dfrac{dy}{du} \times \dfrac{du}{dx} = -4\sin (2x)\cos (2x)$

Putting it all together:

$$\frac{dy}{dx} = -4\sin (2x)\,e^{2\cos (2x)} - 4\sin (2x)\cos (2x)$$

4. Product Rule

Exercise 4.1 — Differentiating functions multiplied together

Q1 a) $y = x(x + 2) = x^2 + 2x$

$\dfrac{dy}{dx} = 2x + 2$

b) $u = x$, $v = x + 2 \Rightarrow \dfrac{du}{dx} = 1$, $\dfrac{dv}{dx} = 1$

$\dfrac{dy}{dx} = u\dfrac{dv}{dx} + v\dfrac{du}{dx} = x + (x + 2) = 2x + 2$

Q2 a) $u = x^2$, $v = (x + 6)^3 \Rightarrow \dfrac{du}{dx} = 2x$, $\dfrac{dv}{dx} = 3(x + 6)^2$

$\dfrac{dy}{dx} = u\dfrac{dv}{dx} + v\dfrac{du}{dx} = [x^2 \times 3(x + 6)^2] + [2x(x + 6)^3]$

$= 3x^2(x + 6)^2 + 2x(x + 6)^3 = x(x + 6)^2[3x + 2(x + 6)]$

$= x(x + 6)^2(5x + 12)$

Here the chain rule was used to find $\dfrac{dv}{dx}$ — write out all the steps if you're struggling.

b) $u = x^3$, $v = (5x + 2)^4 \Rightarrow \dfrac{du}{dx} = 3x^2$, $\dfrac{dv}{dx} = 20(5x + 2)^3$

$\dfrac{dy}{dx} = u\dfrac{dv}{dx} + v\dfrac{du}{dx} = [x^3 \times 20(5x + 2)^3]$
$\qquad\qquad\qquad\qquad + [3x^2 \times (5x + 2)^4]$

$= 20x^3(5x + 2)^3 + 3x^2(5x + 2)^4$

$= x^2(5x + 2)^3[20x + 3(5x + 2)]$

$= x^2(5x + 2)^3(35x + 6)$

c) $u = x^3$, $v = e^x \Rightarrow \dfrac{du}{dx} = 3x^2$, $\dfrac{dv}{dx} = e^x$

$\dfrac{dy}{dx} = u\dfrac{dv}{dx} + v\dfrac{du}{dx} = x^3e^x + 3x^2e^x = x^2e^x(x + 3)$

d) $u = x$, $v = e^{4x} \Rightarrow \dfrac{du}{dx} = 1$, $\dfrac{dv}{dx} = 4e^{4x}$

$\dfrac{dy}{dx} = u\dfrac{dv}{dx} + v\dfrac{du}{dx} = 4xe^{4x} + e^{4x} = e^{4x}(4x + 1)$

e) $u = x$, $v = e^{x^2} \Rightarrow \dfrac{du}{dx} = 1$, $\dfrac{dv}{dx} = 2xe^{x^2}$

$\dfrac{dy}{dx} = u\dfrac{dv}{dx} + v\dfrac{du}{dx} = x \times 2xe^{x^2} + e^{x^2} = e^{x^2}(2x^2 + 1)$

f) $u = e^{2x}$, $v = \sin x \Rightarrow \dfrac{du}{dx} = 2e^{2x}$, $\dfrac{dv}{dx} = \cos x$

$\dfrac{dy}{dx} = u\dfrac{dv}{dx} + v\dfrac{du}{dx} = e^{2x}\cos x + 2e^{2x}\sin x$
$= e^{2x}(\cos x + 2\sin x)$

Q3 a) $u = x^3$, $v = (x + 3)^{\frac{1}{2}}$

$\Rightarrow \dfrac{du}{dx} = 3x^2$, $\dfrac{dv}{dx} = \dfrac{1}{2}(x + 3)^{-\frac{1}{2}}$

$f'(x) = u\dfrac{dv}{dx} + v\dfrac{du}{dx}$

$= [x^3 \times \dfrac{1}{2}(x + 3)^{-\frac{1}{2}}] + [3x^2 \times (x + 3)^{\frac{1}{2}}]$

$= \dfrac{x^3}{2\sqrt{x + 3}} + 3x^2\sqrt{x + 3}$

b) $u = x^2$, $v = (x - 7)^{-\frac{1}{2}}$

$\Rightarrow \dfrac{du}{dx} = 2x$, $\dfrac{dv}{dx} = -\dfrac{1}{2}(x - 7)^{-\frac{3}{2}}$

$f'(x) = u\dfrac{dv}{dx} + v\dfrac{du}{dx}$

$= [x^2 \times (-\dfrac{1}{2}) \times (x - 7)^{-\frac{3}{2}}] + [2x(x - 7)^{-\frac{1}{2}}]$

$= -\dfrac{x^2}{2(\sqrt{x - 7})^3} + \dfrac{2x}{\sqrt{x - 7}}$

c) $u = x^4$, $v = \ln x \Rightarrow \dfrac{du}{dx} = 4x^3$, $\dfrac{dv}{dx} = \dfrac{1}{x}$

$f'(x) = u\dfrac{dv}{dx} + v\dfrac{du}{dx} = [x^4 \times \dfrac{1}{x}] + [4x^3 \ln x]$
$= x^3 + 4x^3 \ln x = x^3(1 + 4\ln x)$

d) $u = 4x$, $v = \ln x^2 = 2\ln x \Rightarrow \dfrac{du}{dx} = 4$, $\dfrac{dv}{dx} = \dfrac{2}{x}$

$f'(x) = u\dfrac{dv}{dx} + v\dfrac{du}{dx} = [4x \times \dfrac{2}{x}] + [4\ln x^2] = 8 + 4\ln x^2$

e) $u = 2x^3$, $v = \cos x$

$\Rightarrow \dfrac{du}{dx} = 6x^2$, $\dfrac{dv}{dx} = -\sin x$

$f'(x) = u\dfrac{dv}{dx} + v\dfrac{du}{dx} = -2x^3\sin x + 6x^2\cos x$

f) $u = x^2$, $v = \cos(2x) \Rightarrow \dfrac{du}{dx} = 2x$, $\dfrac{dv}{dx} = -2\sin(2x)$

$f'(x) = u\dfrac{dv}{dx} + v\dfrac{du}{dx}$

$= [x^2 \times -2\sin(2x)] + [2x\cos(2x)]$
$= 2x\cos(2x) - 2x^2\sin(2x)$
$= 2x(\cos(2x) - x\sin(2x))$

Q4 a) $u = (x + 1)^2$, $v = x^2 - 1 \Rightarrow \dfrac{du}{dx} = 2(x + 1)$, $\dfrac{dv}{dx} = 2x$

$\dfrac{dy}{dx} = u\dfrac{dv}{dx} + v\dfrac{du}{dx}$

$= [(x + 1)^2 \times 2x] + [2(x + 1) \times (x^2 - 1)]$
$= 2x(x + 1)^2 + 2(x + 1)(x^2 - 1)$
$= 2x^3 + 4x^2 + 2x + 2x^3 + 2x^2 - 2x - 2$
$= 4x^3 + 6x^2 - 2$

b) $u = (x + 1)^3$, $v = x - 1 \Rightarrow \dfrac{du}{dx} = 3(x + 1)^2$, $\dfrac{dv}{dx} = 1$

$\dfrac{dy}{dx} = u\dfrac{dv}{dx} + v\dfrac{du}{dx}$
$= [(x + 1)^3 \times 1] + [3(x + 1)^2(x - 1)]$
$= (x + 1)^3 + 3(x + 1)^2(x - 1)$
$= (x^3 + 3x^2 + 3x + 1) + (3x^3 + 6x^2 + 3x - 3x^2 - 6x - 3)$
$= 4x^3 + 6x^2 - 2$

Use the binomial theorem to expand $(x + 1)^3$. Using Pascal's triangle you'll get the coefficients 1, 3, 3, 1.

c) $y = (x + 1)^2(x^2 - 1) = (x + 1)^2(x + 1)(x - 1)$
$= (x + 1)^3(x - 1)$

Q5 a) $u = x$, $v = e^x \Rightarrow \dfrac{du}{dx} = 1$, $\dfrac{dv}{dx} = e^x$

$\dfrac{dy}{dx} = u\dfrac{dv}{dx} + v\dfrac{du}{dx} = xe^x + e^x$

At the point $(0, 0)$, $\dfrac{dy}{dx} = 0 + 1 = 1$

$y = mx + c \Rightarrow 0 = 0 + c \Rightarrow c = 0$

So the equation of the tangent is $y = x$.

b) Gradient of the normal $= -1$
$y = mx + c \Rightarrow 0 = 0 + c \Rightarrow c = 0$
So the equation of the normal is $y = -x$

Q6 $u = \sqrt{x + 2}$, $v = \sqrt{x + 7}$

$\Rightarrow \dfrac{du}{dx} = \dfrac{1}{2\sqrt{x + 2}}$, $\dfrac{dv}{dx} = \dfrac{1}{2\sqrt{x + 7}}$

$\dfrac{dy}{dx} = u\dfrac{dv}{dx} + v\dfrac{du}{dx} = \dfrac{\sqrt{x + 2}}{2\sqrt{x + 7}} + \dfrac{\sqrt{x + 7}}{2\sqrt{x + 2}}$

At the point $(2, 6)$, $\dfrac{dy}{dx} = \dfrac{\sqrt{4}}{2\sqrt{9}} + \dfrac{\sqrt{9}}{2\sqrt{4}} = \dfrac{13}{12}$

$y = mx + c \Rightarrow 6 = (2 \times \dfrac{13}{12}) + c \Rightarrow c = \dfrac{23}{6}$

So the equation of the tangent is $y = \dfrac{13}{12}x + \dfrac{23}{6}$.

To write this in the form $ax + by + c = 0$ where a, b and c are integers, multiply by 12 and rearrange.

$y = \dfrac{13}{12}x + \dfrac{23}{6} \Rightarrow 12y = 13x + 46$

$\Rightarrow 13x - 12y + 46 = 0$

Q7 a) $u = (x - 1)^{\frac{1}{2}}$, $v = (x + 4)^{-\frac{1}{2}}$

$\Rightarrow \dfrac{du}{dx} = \dfrac{1}{2\sqrt{x - 1}}$, $\dfrac{dv}{dx} = -\dfrac{1}{2(\sqrt{x + 4})^3}$

$\dfrac{dy}{dx} = u\dfrac{dv}{dx} + v\dfrac{du}{dx}$

$= \dfrac{1}{2\sqrt{x - 1}\sqrt{x + 4}} - \dfrac{\sqrt{x - 1}}{2(\sqrt{x + 4})^3}$

When $x = 5$, $\dfrac{dy}{dx} = \dfrac{1}{2\sqrt{4}\sqrt{9}} - \dfrac{\sqrt{4}}{2(\sqrt{9})^3} = \dfrac{5}{108}$

and $y = \dfrac{\sqrt{4}}{\sqrt{9}} = \dfrac{2}{3}$

$y = mx + c \Rightarrow \dfrac{2}{3} = (5 \times \dfrac{5}{108}) + c \Rightarrow c = \dfrac{47}{108}$

So the equation of the tangent is $y = \dfrac{5}{108}x + \dfrac{47}{108}$

To write this in the form $ax + by + c = 0$ where a, b and c are integers, multiply by 108 and rearrange.

$y = \dfrac{5}{108}x + \dfrac{47}{108} \Rightarrow 108y = 5x + 47$

$\Rightarrow 5x - 108y + 47 = 0$

b) Gradient of the normal $= -\dfrac{1}{\left(\dfrac{5}{108}\right)} = -\dfrac{108}{5}$

$y = mx + c \Rightarrow \dfrac{2}{3} = (5 \times (-\dfrac{108}{5})) + c \Rightarrow c = \dfrac{326}{3}$

So the equation of the normal is

$y = -\dfrac{108}{5}x + \dfrac{326}{3}$.

To write this in the form $ax + by + c = 0$ where a, b and c are integers, multiply by 15 and rearrange.

$y = -\dfrac{108}{5}x + \dfrac{326}{3} \Rightarrow 15y = -324x + 1630$

$\Rightarrow 324x + 15y - 1630 = 0$

Q8 Stationary points occur when the gradient is 0.

$u = (x - 2)^2,\ v = (x + 4)^3$

$\Rightarrow \dfrac{du}{dx} = 2(x - 2),\ \dfrac{dv}{dx} = 3(x + 4)^2$

$\dfrac{dy}{dx} = u\dfrac{dv}{dx} + v\dfrac{du}{dx}$

$= [(x - 2)^2 \times 3(x + 4)^2] + [2(x - 2) \times (x + 4)^3]$

$= 3(x - 2)^2(x + 4)^2 + 2(x - 2)(x + 4)^3$

$= (x - 2)(x + 4)^2[3x - 6 + 2x + 8]$

$= (x - 2)(x + 4)^2(5x + 2)$

So the stationary points occur when:

$x - 2 = 0 \Rightarrow x = 2$

and $x + 4 = 0 \Rightarrow x = -4$

and $5x + 2 = 0 \Rightarrow x = -\dfrac{2}{5}$

When $x = 2,\ y = 0 \times 6^3 = 0$

When $x = -4,\ y = (-6)^2 \times 0 = 0$

When $x = -\dfrac{2}{5},\ y = (-\dfrac{12}{5})^2(\dfrac{18}{5})^3 = 268.74$ (to 2 d.p.)

So the turning points are (2, 0), (–4, 0) and (–0.4, 268.74).

Q9 First use chain rule:

$\dfrac{dy}{dx} = f'(x)e^{f(x)}$ where $f(x) = x^2\sqrt{x + 3}$.

Then use the product rule to find f'(x):

$u = x^2,\ v = \sqrt{x + 3} \Rightarrow \dfrac{du}{dx} = 2x,\ \dfrac{dv}{dx} = \dfrac{1}{2\sqrt{x + 3}}$

$\dfrac{dy}{dx} = u\dfrac{dv}{dx} + v\dfrac{du}{dx} = [x^2 \times \dfrac{1}{2\sqrt{x + 3}}] + [\sqrt{x + 3} \times 2x]$

$= \dfrac{x^2 + 4x(x + 3)}{2\sqrt{x + 3}} = \dfrac{5x^2 + 12x}{2\sqrt{x + 3}}$

Now putting it all together:

$\dfrac{dy}{dx} = \dfrac{5x^2 + 12x}{2\sqrt{x + 3}} e^{x^2\sqrt{x+3}}$

Q10 Stationary points occur when the gradient is 0. Differentiate with the product rule:

$u = x,\ v = e^{x - x^2} \Rightarrow \dfrac{du}{dx} = 1,\ \dfrac{dv}{dx} = (1 - 2x)e^{x - x^2}$

$\dfrac{dy}{dx} = u\dfrac{dv}{dx} + v\dfrac{du}{dx} = [x(1 - 2x)e^{x - x^2}] + [1 \times e^{x - x^2}]$

$= e^{x - x^2}(x - 2x^2 + 1)$

$e^{x - x^2}$ cannot be 0, so the stationary points occur when $-2x^2 + x + 1 = 0$

$\Rightarrow (2x + 1)(-x + 1) = 0 \Rightarrow x = 1$ or $x = -\dfrac{1}{2}$

When $x = 1,\ y = 1 \times e^0 = 1$.

When $x = -\dfrac{1}{2},\ y = -\dfrac{1}{2} \times e^{-\frac{3}{4}} = -\dfrac{e^{-\frac{3}{4}}}{2}$.

So the stationary points are (1, 1) and $(-\dfrac{1}{2}, -\dfrac{e^{-\frac{3}{4}}}{2})$.

5. Quotient Rule

Exercise 5.1 — Differentiating a function divided by a function

Q1 a) $u = x + 5,\ v = x - 3 \Rightarrow \dfrac{du}{dx} = 1,\ \dfrac{dv}{dx} = 1$

$\dfrac{dy}{dx} = \dfrac{v\dfrac{du}{dx} - u\dfrac{dv}{dx}}{v^2} = \dfrac{((x - 3) \times 1) - ((x + 5) \times 1)}{(x - 3)^2}$

$= -\dfrac{8}{(x - 3)^2}$

b) $u = (x - 7)^4,\ v = (5 - x)^3$

$\Rightarrow \dfrac{du}{dx} = 4(x - 7)^3,\ \dfrac{dv}{dx} = -3(5 - x)^2$

$\dfrac{dy}{dx} = \dfrac{v\dfrac{du}{dx} - u\dfrac{dv}{dx}}{v^2}$

$= \dfrac{4(5 - x)^3(x - 7)^3 + 3(x - 7)^4(5 - x)^2}{(5 - x)^6}$

$= \dfrac{(x - 7)^3[4(5 - x) + 3(x - 7)]}{(5 - x)^4}$

$= \dfrac{(x - 7)^3(-x - 1)}{(5 - x)^4}$

c) $u = e^x,\ v = x^2 \Rightarrow \dfrac{du}{dx} = e^x,\ \dfrac{dv}{dx} = 2x$

$\dfrac{dy}{dx} = \dfrac{v\dfrac{du}{dx} - u\dfrac{dv}{dx}}{v^2} = \dfrac{x^2 e^x - e^x 2x}{x^4} = \dfrac{xe^x - 2e^x}{x^3}$

d) $u = 3x,\ v = (x - 1)^2 \Rightarrow \dfrac{du}{dx} = 3,\ \dfrac{dv}{dx} = 2(x - 1)$

$\dfrac{dy}{dx} = \dfrac{v\dfrac{du}{dx} - u\dfrac{dv}{dx}}{v^2}$

$= \dfrac{3(x - 1)^2 - 6x(x - 1)}{(x - 1)^4}$

$= \dfrac{3x - 3 - 6x}{(x - 1)^3} = \dfrac{-3x - 3}{(x - 1)^3}$

Q2 $u = x^3,\ v = (x + 3)^3 \Rightarrow \dfrac{du}{dx} = 3x^2,\ \dfrac{dv}{dx} = 3(x + 3)^2$

$f'(x) = \dfrac{v\dfrac{du}{dx} - u\dfrac{dv}{dx}}{v^2}$

$= \dfrac{[(x + 3)^3 \times 3x^2] - [x^3 \times 3(x + 3)^2]}{(x + 3)^6}$

$= \dfrac{3x^2(x + 3) - 3x^3}{(x + 3)^4} = \dfrac{9x^2}{(x + 3)^4}$

Q3 $u = x^2$, $v = \sqrt{x-7} \Rightarrow \dfrac{du}{dx} = 2x$, $\dfrac{dv}{dx} = \dfrac{1}{2\sqrt{x-7}}$

$f'(x) = \dfrac{v\dfrac{du}{dx} - u\dfrac{dv}{dx}}{v^2}$

$= \dfrac{[\sqrt{x-7} \times 2x] - [x^2 \dfrac{1}{2\sqrt{x-7}}]}{x-7}$

$= \dfrac{4x(x-7) - x^2}{2(\sqrt{x-7})^3} = \dfrac{3x^2 - 28x}{2(\sqrt{x-7})^3}$

Q4 $u = e^{2x}$, $v = e^{2x} + e^{-2x} \Rightarrow \dfrac{du}{dx} = 2e^{2x}$, $\dfrac{dv}{dx} = 2e^{2x} - 2e^{-2x}$

$f'(x) = \dfrac{v\dfrac{du}{dx} - u\dfrac{dv}{dx}}{v^2}$

$= \dfrac{[(e^{2x} + e^{-2x})2e^{2x}] - [e^{2x}(2e^{2x} - 2e^{-2x})]}{(e^{2x} + e^{-2x})^2}$

$= \dfrac{2e^{4x} + 2 - 2e^{4x} + 2}{e^{4x} + e^{-4x} + 2} = \dfrac{4}{e^{4x} + e^{-4x} + 2}$

Q5 $u = x$, $v = \sin x \Rightarrow \dfrac{du}{dx} = 1$, $\dfrac{dv}{dx} = \cos x$

$f'(x) = \dfrac{v\dfrac{du}{dx} - u\dfrac{dv}{dx}}{v^2} = \dfrac{\sin x - x\cos x}{\sin^2 x}$

Q6 $u = \sin x$, $v = x \Rightarrow \dfrac{du}{dx} = \cos x$, $\dfrac{dv}{dx} = 1$

$f'(x) = \dfrac{v\dfrac{du}{dx} - u\dfrac{dv}{dx}}{v^2} = \dfrac{x\cos x - \sin x}{x^2}$

Q7 $u = x^2$, $v = \tan x \Rightarrow \dfrac{du}{dx} = 2x$, $\dfrac{dv}{dx} = \sec^2 x$

$f'(x) = \dfrac{v\dfrac{du}{dx} - u\dfrac{dv}{dx}}{v^2} = \dfrac{[\tan x \times 2x] - [x^2 \times \sec^2 x]}{\tan^2 x}$

$= \dfrac{2x\tan x - x^2\sec^2 x}{\tan^2 x}$

$= 2x\cot x - x^2\operatorname{cosec}^2 x$

Here the answer was simplified using:
sec² x/tan² x = (1/cos² x) × (cos² x/sin² x) = 1/sin² x = cosec² x

Q8 a) $u = x$, $v = \cos(2x) \Rightarrow \dfrac{du}{dx} = 1$, $\dfrac{dv}{dx} = -2\sin(2x)$

$\dfrac{dy}{dx} = \dfrac{v\dfrac{du}{dx} - u\dfrac{dv}{dx}}{v^2}$

$= \dfrac{\cos(2x) - [x \times -2\sin(2x)]}{\cos^2(2x)}$

$= \dfrac{\cos(2x) + 2x\sin(2x)}{\cos^2(2x)}$

b) $\dfrac{dy}{dx} = 0$ if $\cos(2x) + 2x\sin(2x) = 0$

$\Rightarrow -\cos(2x) = 2x\sin(2x) \Rightarrow 2x = -\cot(2x)$

$\Rightarrow x = -\dfrac{1}{2}\cot(2x)$

Remember cos x/sin x = 1/tan x = cot x.

Q9 a) $u = 1$, $v = 1 + 4\cos x \Rightarrow \dfrac{du}{dx} = 0$, $\dfrac{dv}{dx} = -4\sin x$

$\dfrac{dy}{dx} = \dfrac{v\dfrac{du}{dx} - u\dfrac{dv}{dx}}{v^2}$

$= \dfrac{[(1 + 4\cos x) \times 0] - [1 \times (-4\sin x)]}{(1 + 4\cos x)^2}$

$= \dfrac{4\sin x}{(1 + 4\cos x)^2}$

When $x = \dfrac{\pi}{2}$, $\dfrac{dy}{dx} = \dfrac{4}{(1)^2} = 4$ and $y = \dfrac{1}{1} = 1$

$y = mx + c \Rightarrow 1 = 4\dfrac{\pi}{2} + c \Rightarrow c = 1 - 2\pi$

So the equation of the tangent is $y = 4x + 1 - 2\pi$.

b) From part a), the gradient of the normal must be $-\dfrac{1}{4}$. Equation of a straight line:

$y = mx + c \Rightarrow 1 = -\dfrac{1}{4}\dfrac{\pi}{2} + c \Rightarrow c = 1 + \dfrac{\pi}{8}$

So the equation of the normal is

$y = -\dfrac{1}{4}x + 1 + \dfrac{\pi}{8}$

Q10 $u = 2x$, $v = \cos x \Rightarrow \dfrac{du}{dx} = 2$, $\dfrac{dv}{dx} = -\sin x$

$\dfrac{dy}{dx} = \dfrac{v\dfrac{du}{dx} - u\dfrac{dv}{dx}}{v^2}$

$= \dfrac{[\cos x \times 2] - [2x \times (-\sin x)]}{\cos^2 x}$

$= \dfrac{2\cos x + 2x\sin x}{\cos^2 x}$

When $x = \dfrac{\pi}{3}$, $\dfrac{dy}{dx} = \dfrac{1 + \dfrac{\pi\sqrt{3}}{3}}{(\frac{1}{2})^2} = 4 + \dfrac{4\pi\sqrt{3}}{3}$

Q11 $u = x - \sin x$, $v = 1 + \cos x$,

$\Rightarrow \dfrac{du}{dx} = 1 - \cos x$, $\dfrac{dv}{dx} = -\sin x$

$\dfrac{dy}{dx} = \dfrac{v\dfrac{du}{dx} - u\dfrac{dv}{dx}}{v^2}$

$= \dfrac{[(1 + \cos x)(1 - \cos x)] - [(x - \sin x)(-\sin x)]}{(1 + \cos x)^2}$

$= \dfrac{1 - \cos^2 x - \sin^2 x + x\sin x}{(1 + \cos x)^2}$

$= \dfrac{1 - 1 + x\sin x}{(1 + \cos x)^2} = \dfrac{x\sin x}{(1 + \cos x)^2}$

The identity sin² x + cos² x ≡ 1 was used to simplify the expression here.

Q12 Stationary points occur when the gradient is 0.

$u = \cos x$, $v = 4 - 3\cos x$, $\Rightarrow \dfrac{du}{dx} = -\sin x$, $\dfrac{dv}{dx} = 3\sin x$

$\dfrac{dy}{dx} = \dfrac{v\dfrac{du}{dx} - u\dfrac{dv}{dx}}{v^2}$

$= \dfrac{[(4 - 3\cos x)(-\sin x)] - [\cos x(3\sin x)]}{(4 - 3\cos x)^2}$

$= \dfrac{-4\sin x}{(4 - 3\cos x)^2}$

$\frac{dy}{dx} = 0 \Rightarrow -4\sin x = 0 \Rightarrow x = \sin^{-1} 0 = 0,\ \pi \text{ and } 2\pi.$

When $x = 0$, $y = \dfrac{1}{4-3} = 1$

When $x = \pi$, $y = \dfrac{-1}{4-(-3)} = -\dfrac{1}{7}$

When $x = 2\pi$, $y = \dfrac{1}{4-3} = 1$

So the stationary points are $(0, 1)$, $(\pi, -\frac{1}{7})$ and $(2\pi, 1)$

Q13 First use chain rule: $y = e^{f(x)} \Rightarrow \dfrac{dy}{dx} = f'(x)e^{f(x)}$

Then use the quotient rule to find $f'(x)$:

$u = 1 + x,\ v = 1 - x \Rightarrow \dfrac{du}{dx} = 1,\ \dfrac{dv}{dx} = -1$

$\dfrac{v\frac{du}{dx} - u\frac{dv}{dx}}{v^2} = \dfrac{[(1-x)(1)] - [(1+x)(-1)]}{(1-x)^2} = \dfrac{2}{(1-x)^2}$

So $\dfrac{dy}{dx} = f'(x)e^{f(x)} = \dfrac{2e^{\frac{1+x}{1-x}}}{(1-x)^2}$

6. More Differentiation

Exercise 6.1 — Differentiating cosec, sec and cot

Q1 a) $\dfrac{dy}{dx} = -2\operatorname{cosec}(2x)\cot(2x)$

b) $\dfrac{dy}{dx} = \dfrac{dy}{du} \times \dfrac{du}{dx} = (2\operatorname{cosec} x)(-\operatorname{cosec} x\cot x)$
$= -2\operatorname{cosec}^2 x\cot x$

c) $\dfrac{dy}{dx} = \dfrac{dy}{du} \times \dfrac{du}{dx} = -7\operatorname{cosec}^2(7x)$

d) $\dfrac{dy}{dx} = \dfrac{dy}{du} \times \dfrac{du}{dx} = (7\cot^6 x)(-\operatorname{cosec}^2 x)$
$= -7\cot^6 x\operatorname{cosec}^2 x$

e) $\dfrac{dy}{dx} = u\dfrac{dv}{dx} + v\dfrac{du}{dx} = 4x^3\cot x + x^4(-\operatorname{cosec}^2 x)$
$= 4x^3\cot x - x^4\operatorname{cosec}^2 x$
$= x^3(4\cot x - x\operatorname{cosec}^2 x)$

f) $\dfrac{dy}{dx} = \dfrac{dy}{du} \times \dfrac{du}{dx} = 2(x + \sec x)(1 + \sec x\tan x)$

g) $\dfrac{dy}{dx} = \dfrac{dy}{du} \times \dfrac{du}{dx} = 2x(-\operatorname{cosec}(x^2 + 5)\cot(x^2 + 5))$
$= -2x\operatorname{cosec}(x^2 + 5)\cot(x^2 + 5)$

h) $\dfrac{dy}{dx} = u\dfrac{dv}{dx} + v\dfrac{du}{dx} = e^{3x}\sec x\tan x + 3e^{3x}\sec x$
$= e^{3x}\sec x(\tan x + 3)$

i) $\dfrac{dy}{dx} = \dfrac{dy}{du} \times \dfrac{du}{dx} = 3(2x + \cot x)^2(2 - \operatorname{cosec}^2 x)$

Q2 $f'(x) = \dfrac{v\frac{du}{dx} - u\frac{dv}{dx}}{v^2} = \dfrac{(x+3)\sec x\tan x - \sec x}{(x+3)^2}$

Q3 $f'(x) = \dfrac{dy}{du} \times \dfrac{du}{dx} = (\sec\frac{1}{x}\tan\frac{1}{x})(-\frac{1}{x^2})$
$= -\dfrac{\sec\frac{1}{x}\tan\frac{1}{x}}{x^2}$

Q4 $f'(x) = \dfrac{dy}{du} \times \dfrac{du}{dx} = (\sec\sqrt{x}\tan\sqrt{x})(\frac{1}{2} \times \frac{1}{\sqrt{x}})$
$= \dfrac{\sec\sqrt{x}\tan\sqrt{x}}{2\sqrt{x}} = \dfrac{\tan\sqrt{x}}{2\sqrt{x}\cos\sqrt{x}}$

Q5 $f'(x) = \dfrac{dy}{du} \times \dfrac{du}{dx}$
$= 2(\sec x + \operatorname{cosec} x)(\sec x\tan x - \operatorname{cosec} x\cot x)$

Q6 $f(x) = \dfrac{1}{x\cot x} = \dfrac{\tan x}{x}$

$f'(x) = \dfrac{v\frac{du}{dx} - u\frac{dv}{dx}}{v^2} = \dfrac{x\sec^2 x - \tan x}{x^2}$

Q7 $f'(x) = u\dfrac{dv}{dx} + v\dfrac{du}{dx} = e^x(-\operatorname{cosec} x\cot x) + e^x\operatorname{cosec} x$
$= e^x\operatorname{cosec} x(1 - \cot x)$

Q8 $f'(x) = u\dfrac{dv}{dx} + v\dfrac{du}{dx} = e^{3x}\sec x\tan x + 3e^{3x}\sec x$

Q9 $f'(x) = u\dfrac{dv}{dx} + v\dfrac{du}{dx} = 3e^{3x}\cot(4x) - 4e^{3x}\operatorname{cosec}^2(4x)$

The chain rule was used here to find dv/dx — write it out in stages if you're struggling.

Q10 $f'(x) = u\dfrac{dv}{dx} + v\dfrac{du}{dx}$
$= -2e^{-2x}\operatorname{cosec}(4x) - 4e^{-2x}\operatorname{cosec}(4x)\cot(4x)$
$= -2e^{-2x}\operatorname{cosec}(4x)(1 + 2\cot(4x))$

Q11 $f'(x) = u\dfrac{dv}{dx} + v\dfrac{du}{dx} = \dfrac{\operatorname{cosec} x}{x} - \ln x\operatorname{cosec} x\cot x$

Q12 $f'(x) = \dfrac{dy}{du} \times \dfrac{du}{dx} = (\frac{1}{2}\frac{1}{\sqrt{\sec x}}) \times \sec x\tan x$
$= \dfrac{\sec x\tan x}{2\sqrt{\sec x}} = \dfrac{1}{2}\tan x\sqrt{\sec x}$

Q13 $f'(x) = g'(x)e^{g(x)} = e^{\sec x}\sec x\tan x$

Q14 a) $f'(x) = \dfrac{g'(x)}{g(x)} = \dfrac{-\operatorname{cosec} x\cot x}{\operatorname{cosec} x} = -\cot x$

b) $\ln(\operatorname{cosec} x) = \ln(\dfrac{1}{\sin x}) = \ln 1 - \ln(\sin x)$
$= -\ln(\sin x)\ (\text{as } \ln 1 = 0)$
Here you could also rearrange by saying
$\ln(1/\sin x) = \ln(\sin x)^{-1} = -\ln(\sin x)$
$f'(x) = -\dfrac{\cos x}{\sin x} = -\dfrac{1}{\tan x} = -\cot x$

Q15 $f'(x) = \dfrac{g'(x)}{g(x)} = \dfrac{1 + \sec x\tan x}{x + \sec x}$

Q16 $\dfrac{dy}{dx} = \dfrac{dy}{du} \times \dfrac{du}{dx}$
$= \dfrac{2x}{2\sqrt{x^2 + 5}} \times \sec\sqrt{x^2 + 5}\,\tan\sqrt{x^2 + 5}$
$= \dfrac{x\sec\sqrt{x^2 + 5}\,\tan\sqrt{x^2 + 5}}{\sqrt{x^2 + 5}}$

Review Exercise — Chapter 4

Q1 a) Chain rule.

b) Product rule.

c) Chain and product rules.

d) Chain and quotient rules.

e) Chain, product and quotient rules.

f) Chain, product and quotient rules.

Q2 a) $y = u^{\frac{1}{2}}$, $u = x^3 + 2x^2$

$\Rightarrow \dfrac{dy}{du} = \dfrac{1}{2}u^{-\frac{1}{2}} = \dfrac{1}{2}(x^3 + 2x^2)^{-\frac{1}{2}}$, $\dfrac{du}{dx} = 3x^2 + 4x$

$\dfrac{dy}{dx} = \dfrac{dy}{du} \times \dfrac{du}{dx} = (\dfrac{1}{2}(x^3 + 2x^2)^{-\frac{1}{2}})(3x^2 + 4x)$

$= \dfrac{3x^2 + 4x}{2\sqrt{x^3 + 2x^2}}$

b) $y = u^{-\frac{1}{2}}$, $u = x^3 + 2x^2$

$\dfrac{dy}{dx} = \dfrac{dy}{du} \times \dfrac{du}{dx} = ((-\dfrac{1}{2}) \times \dfrac{1}{(\sqrt{x^3 + 2x^2})^3}) (3x^2 + 4x)$

$= -\dfrac{3x^2 + 4x}{2(\sqrt{x^3 + 2x^2})^3}$

c) $\dfrac{dy}{dx} = f'(x)e^{f(x)} = 10xe^{5x^2}$

d) $\dfrac{dy}{dx} = \dfrac{f'(x)}{f(x)} = -\dfrac{2x}{6 - x^2}$

Q3 a) $\dfrac{dx}{dy} = 2f'(y)e^{f(y)} = 4e^{2y} \Rightarrow \dfrac{dy}{dx} = \dfrac{1}{\left(\dfrac{dx}{dy}\right)} = \dfrac{1}{4e^{2y}} = \dfrac{1}{2x}$

b) $\dfrac{dx}{dy} = \dfrac{f'(y)}{f(y)} = \dfrac{2}{2y + 3} \Rightarrow \dfrac{dy}{dx} = \dfrac{2y + 3}{2} = \dfrac{e^x}{2}$

Q4 a) $f(x) = \sin^2(x + 2) \Rightarrow y = u^2$, $u = \sin(x + 2)$

$\Rightarrow \dfrac{dy}{du} = 2u = 2\sin(x + 2)$, $\dfrac{du}{dx} = \cos(x + 2)$

$f'(x) = \dfrac{dy}{du} \times \dfrac{du}{dx} = 2\sin(x + 2)\cos(x + 2)$

b) $y = 2\cos u$, $u = 3x$

$f'(x) = \dfrac{dy}{du} \times \dfrac{du}{dx} = -6\sin(3x)$

c) $f(x) = \sqrt{\tan x} \Rightarrow y = u^{\frac{1}{2}}$, $u = \tan x$

$\Rightarrow \dfrac{dy}{du} = \dfrac{1}{2}u^{-\frac{1}{2}} = \dfrac{1}{2\sqrt{\tan x}}$, $\dfrac{du}{dx} = \sec^2 x$

$f'(x) = \dfrac{dy}{du} \times \dfrac{du}{dx} = (\dfrac{1}{2\sqrt{\tan x}})(\sec^2 x) = \dfrac{\sec^2 x}{2\sqrt{\tan x}}$

Q5 a) $u = e^{2x}$, $v = x^2 - 3 \Rightarrow \dfrac{du}{dx} = 2e^{2x}$, $\dfrac{dv}{dx} = 2x$

$\dfrac{dy}{dx} = u\dfrac{dv}{dx} + v\dfrac{du}{dx} = 2xe^{2x} + 2e^{2x}(x^2 - 3)$

$= 2e^{2x}(x + x^2 - 3)$

When $x = 0$, $\dfrac{dy}{dx} = 2 \times (-3) = -6$

b) $u = \ln x$, $v = \sin x \Rightarrow \dfrac{du}{dx} = \dfrac{1}{x}$, $\dfrac{dv}{dx} = \cos x$

$\dfrac{dy}{dx} = u\dfrac{dv}{dx} + v\dfrac{du}{dx} = \ln x\cos x + \dfrac{1}{x}\sin x$

When $x = 1$, $\dfrac{dy}{dx} = (0 \times \cos 1) + (1 \times \sin 1)$
$= 0.841$ to 3 s.f.

Q6 $u = 6x^2 + 3$, $v = 4x^2 - 1 \Rightarrow \dfrac{du}{dx} = 12x$, $\dfrac{dv}{dx} = 8x$

$\dfrac{dy}{dx} = \dfrac{v\dfrac{du}{dx} - u\dfrac{dv}{dx}}{v^2} = \dfrac{(4x^2 - 1)12x - (6x^2 + 3)8x}{(4x^2 - 1)^2}$

$= \dfrac{48x^3 - 12x - 48x^3 - 24x}{(4x^2 - 1)^2} = -\dfrac{36x}{(4x^2 - 1)^2}$

When $x = 1$, $\dfrac{dy}{dx} = \dfrac{-36 \times 1}{3^2} = -4$

$y = mx + c \Rightarrow 3 = ((-4) \times 1) + c \Rightarrow c = 7$

So the equation of the tangent is $y = 7 - 4x$

Q7 a) $y = \sqrt{\operatorname{cosec} x}$, so let $y = u^{\frac{1}{2}}$ where $u = \operatorname{cosec} x$

$\Rightarrow \dfrac{dy}{du} = \dfrac{1}{2}u^{-\frac{1}{2}} = \dfrac{1}{2\sqrt{\operatorname{cosec} x}}$, $\dfrac{du}{dx} = -\operatorname{cosec} x\cot x$

$\dfrac{dy}{dx} = \dfrac{dy}{du} \times \dfrac{du}{dx}$

$= (\dfrac{1}{2\sqrt{\operatorname{cosec} x}}) \times (-\operatorname{cosec} x\cot x)$

$= -\dfrac{\operatorname{cosec} x\cot x}{2\sqrt{\operatorname{cosec} x}} = -\dfrac{1}{2}\cot x\sqrt{\operatorname{cosec} x}$

b) $y = \cot(x^2 + 5)$, so let $y = \cot u$ where $u = x^2 + 5$

$\Rightarrow \dfrac{dy}{du} = -\operatorname{cosec}^2 u = -\operatorname{cosec}^2(x^2 + 5)$, $\dfrac{du}{dx} = 2x$

$\dfrac{dy}{dx} = \dfrac{dy}{du} \times \dfrac{du}{dx} = -2x\operatorname{cosec}^2(x^2 + 5)$

c) $u = \sec x$, $v = x^2 \Rightarrow \dfrac{du}{dx} = \sec x\tan x$, $\dfrac{dv}{dx} = 2x$

$\dfrac{dy}{dx} = \dfrac{v\dfrac{du}{dx} - u\dfrac{dv}{dx}}{v^2} = \dfrac{x\sec x\tan x - 2\sec x}{x^3}$

$= \dfrac{\sec x(x\tan x - 2)}{x^3}$

d) $u = e^{2x}$, $v = \operatorname{cosec}(5x)$

$\Rightarrow \dfrac{du}{dx} = 2e^{2x}$, $\dfrac{dv}{dx} = -5\operatorname{cosec}(5x)\cot(5x)$

$\dfrac{dy}{dx} = u\dfrac{dv}{dx} + v\dfrac{du}{dx}$

$= (e^{2x} \times -5\operatorname{cosec}(5x)\cot(5x)) + 2e^{2x}\operatorname{cosec}(5x)$

$= e^{2x}\operatorname{cosec}(5x)(-5\cot(5x) + 2)$

Q8 $y = \operatorname{cosec}(3x - 2)$, so let $y = \operatorname{cosec} u$ where $u = 3x - 2$

$\Rightarrow \dfrac{dy}{du} = -\operatorname{cosec} u\cot u = -\operatorname{cosec}(3x - 2)\cot(3x - 2)$

$\dfrac{du}{dx} = 3$

$\dfrac{dy}{dx} = \dfrac{dy}{du} \times \dfrac{du}{dx} = -3\operatorname{cosec}(3x - 2)\cot(3x - 2)$

When $x = 0$, $\dfrac{dy}{dx} = -3\operatorname{cosec}(-2)\cot(-2) = 1.51$ to 2 d.p.

Q9 Stationary points occur when the gradient is 0.

$u = e^x$, $v = \sqrt{x} \Rightarrow \dfrac{du}{dx} = e^x$, $\dfrac{dv}{dx} = \dfrac{1}{2\sqrt{x}}$

$\dfrac{dy}{dx} = \dfrac{v\dfrac{du}{dx} - u\dfrac{dv}{dx}}{v^2} = \dfrac{\sqrt{x}\,e^x - e^x\dfrac{1}{2\sqrt{x}}}{x}$

When $\dfrac{dy}{dx} = 0$, $\sqrt{x}\,e^x - e^x\dfrac{1}{2\sqrt{x}} = 0$

$\Rightarrow \sqrt{x} = \dfrac{1}{2\sqrt{x}} \Rightarrow x = \dfrac{1}{2}$

When $x = \dfrac{1}{2}$, $y = \dfrac{e^{\frac{1}{2}}}{\sqrt{\frac{1}{2}}} = \sqrt{2}\,e^{\frac{1}{2}}$

So the coordinates of the stationary point are $(\frac{1}{2},\ \sqrt{2}\,e^{\frac{1}{2}})$

Q10 $y = 3\operatorname{cosec}\dfrac{x}{4}$, so let $y = 3\operatorname{cosec} u$ where $u = \dfrac{x}{4}$

$\Rightarrow \dfrac{dy}{du} = -3\operatorname{cosec} u \cot u = -3\operatorname{cosec}\dfrac{x}{4}\cot\dfrac{x}{4}$, $\dfrac{du}{dx} = \dfrac{1}{4}$

$\dfrac{dy}{dx} = \dfrac{dy}{du} \times \dfrac{du}{dx} = -\dfrac{3}{4}\operatorname{cosec}\dfrac{x}{4}\cot\dfrac{x}{4}$

When $x = \pi$, $y = 3\sqrt{2}$

and $\dfrac{dy}{dx} = -\dfrac{3}{4} \times \sqrt{2} \times 1 = -\dfrac{3\sqrt{2}}{4}$.

So the gradient of the normal is $\dfrac{4}{3\sqrt{2}} = \dfrac{2\sqrt{2}}{3}$.

$y = mx + c \Rightarrow 3\sqrt{2} = \dfrac{2\sqrt{2}\,\pi}{3} + c$

$\Rightarrow c = 3\sqrt{2} - \dfrac{2\sqrt{2}\,\pi}{3}$

So the equation of the normal is

$y = \dfrac{2\sqrt{2}}{3}x + 3\sqrt{2} - \dfrac{2\sqrt{2}\,\pi}{3}$

Q11 $f'(x) = g'(x)e^{g(x)}$

$g(x) = \cos(3x)$, so let $y = \cos u$ where $u = 3x$

$g'(x) = \dfrac{dy}{du} \times \dfrac{du}{dx} = -3\sin(3x)$

$f'(x) = g'(x)e^{g(x)} = -3e^{\cos(3x)}\sin(3x)$

Q12 $u = \cos x^2$, $v = \ln(2x) \Rightarrow \dfrac{du}{dx} = -2x\sin x^2$, $\dfrac{dv}{dx} = \dfrac{1}{x}$

The chain rule was used here to find du/dx and dv/dx — write out each step if you need to.

$f'(x) = \dfrac{v\dfrac{du}{dx} - u\dfrac{dv}{dx}}{v^2}$

$= \dfrac{\ln(2x)(-2x\sin x^2) - \cos x^2(\frac{1}{x})}{(\ln(2x))^2}$

$= -\dfrac{2x\sin x^2}{\ln(2x)} - \dfrac{\cos x^2}{x(\ln(2x))^2}$

Q13 $u = \sin(4x)$, $v = \tan x^3$

$\Rightarrow \dfrac{du}{dx} = 4\cos(4x)$, $\dfrac{dv}{dx} = 3x^2\sec^2 x^3$

$f'(x) = u\dfrac{dv}{dx} + v\dfrac{du}{dx}$

$= 3x^2(\sec^2 x^3)(\sin(4x)) + 4\cos(4x)\tan x^3$

Q14 $u = e^{x^2}$, $v = \sqrt{x+1}$

Using the chain rule to differentiate u and v:

$\dfrac{du}{dx} = 2xe^{x^2}$

$\dfrac{dv}{dx} = \dfrac{1}{2} \times (x+1)^{-\frac{1}{2}} = \dfrac{1}{2\sqrt{x+1}}$

$\dfrac{dy}{dx} = u\dfrac{dv}{dx} + v\dfrac{du}{dx} = \dfrac{e^{x^2}}{2\sqrt{x+1}} + 2xe^{x^2}\sqrt{x+1}$

When $x = 1$, $\dfrac{dy}{dx} = \dfrac{e^1}{2\sqrt{1+1}} + (2 \times 1 \times e^1\sqrt{1+1})$

$= \dfrac{e + (2\sqrt{2})2\sqrt{2}e}{2\sqrt{2}} = \dfrac{e + 8e}{2\sqrt{2}} = \dfrac{9\sqrt{2}e}{4}$

Q15 a) $y = \sqrt{(e^x + e^{2x})} \Rightarrow y = u^{\frac{1}{2}}$, $u = e^x + e^{2x}$

$\dfrac{dy}{du} = \dfrac{1}{2}u^{-\frac{1}{2}} = \dfrac{1}{2\sqrt{u}} = \dfrac{1}{2\sqrt{e^x + e^{2x}}}$

$\dfrac{du}{dx} = e^x + 2e^{2x}$

So $\dfrac{dy}{dx} = \dfrac{dy}{du} \times \dfrac{du}{dx} = \dfrac{e^x + 2e^{2x}}{2\sqrt{e^x + e^{2x}}}$.

b) For $y = 3e^{2x+1} - \ln(1 - x^2) + 2x^3$, use the chain rule for the first 2 parts separately:

For $y = 3e^{2x+1} = 3e^{f(x)}$, $\dfrac{dy}{dx} = 3f'(x)e^{f(x)} = 6e^{2x+1}$

For $y = \ln(1 - x^2) = \ln(f(x))$, $\dfrac{dy}{dx} = \dfrac{f'(x)}{f(x)} = -\dfrac{2x}{1 - x^2}$

So putting it all together:

$\dfrac{dy}{dx} = 6e^{2x+1} + \dfrac{2x}{1 - x^2} + 6x^2$.

Q16 a) $y = (x^2 - 1)^3$, so let $y = u^3$ where $u = x^2 - 1$

$\Rightarrow \dfrac{du}{dx} = 2x$, $\dfrac{dy}{du} = 3u^2 = 3(x^2 - 1)^2$

So $\dfrac{dy}{dx} = \dfrac{dy}{du} \times \dfrac{du}{dx} = 6x(x^2 - 1)^2$

b) When $x = 2$, $y = (2^2 - 1)^3 = 27$

And from part a),

$\dfrac{dy}{dx} = 6 \times 2 \times (2^2 - 1)^2 = 12 \times 9 = 108$

The gradient of the normal is $-1 \div \dfrac{dy}{dx} = -\dfrac{1}{108}$.

The equation of the straight line is:

$y = mx + c \Rightarrow 27 = (-\dfrac{1}{108} \times 2) + c$

$\Rightarrow c = 27\frac{1}{54}$

So the equation of the normal is

$y = -\dfrac{1}{108}x + 27\frac{1}{54} \Rightarrow y + \dfrac{1}{108}x - 27\frac{1}{54} = 0$

To make a, b, and c integers, multiply by 108:

$x + 108y - 2918 = 0$

Q17 a) $u = \cos x$, $v = \ln x^2 = 2\ln x$

$\Rightarrow \dfrac{du}{dx} = -\sin x$, $\dfrac{dv}{dx} = \dfrac{2}{x}$

$\dfrac{dy}{dx} = u\dfrac{dv}{dx} + v\dfrac{du}{dx} = \dfrac{2}{x}\cos x - \ln x^2\sin x$

b) $u = e^{x^2 - x}$, $v = (x + 2)^4$

$\Rightarrow \dfrac{du}{dx} = (2x - 1)e^{x^2 - x}$, $\dfrac{dv}{dx} = 4(x + 2)^3$

$\dfrac{dy}{dx} = \dfrac{v\dfrac{du}{dx} - u\dfrac{dv}{dx}}{v^2}$

$= \dfrac{(x+2)^4(2x-1)e^{x^2-x} - 4e^{x^2-x}(x+2)^3}{(x+2)^8}$

$= \dfrac{(x+2)(2x-1)e^{x^2-x} - 4e^{x^2-x}}{(x+2)^5}$

Q18 For $y = \dfrac{\sqrt{x^2 + 3}}{\cos(3x)}$, use the quotient rule and the chain rule:

Quotient rule: $u = \sqrt{x^2 + 3}$ and $v = (\cos 3x)$.

Using the chain rule for $\dfrac{du}{dx} = \dfrac{2x}{2\sqrt{x^2 + 3}}$

$= \dfrac{x}{\sqrt{x^2 + 3}}$

Using the chain rule for $\dfrac{dv}{dx} = -3\sin(3x)$.

So $\dfrac{dy}{dx} = \dfrac{v\dfrac{du}{dx} - u\dfrac{dv}{dx}}{v^2}$

$= \dfrac{[\cos(3x) \times \dfrac{x}{\sqrt{x^2 + 3}}] - [\sqrt{x^2 + 3} \times (-3\sin(3x))]}{\cos^2(3x)}$

Then multiply top and bottom by $\sqrt{x^2 + 3}$ to get:

$\dfrac{dy}{dx} = \dfrac{x\cos(3x) + 3(x^2 + 3)\sin(3x)}{(\sqrt{x^2 + 3})\cos^2(3x)}$

$= \dfrac{x + 3(x^2 + 3)\tan(3x)}{(\sqrt{x^2 + 3})\cos(3x)}$

Exam-Style Questions — Chapter 4

Q1 a) For $y = \ln(3x + 1)\sin(3x + 1)$,

use the product rule and the chain rule:

Product rule: $u = \ln(3x + 1)$ and $v = \sin(3x + 1)$

Using the chain rule, $\dfrac{du}{dx} = \dfrac{3}{3x + 1}$ *[1 mark]*.

Using the chain rule, $\dfrac{dv}{dx} = 3\cos(3x + 1)$
[1 mark].

So $\dfrac{dy}{dx} = u\dfrac{dv}{dx} + v\dfrac{du}{dx}$

$= [\ln(3x + 1) \times 3\cos(3x + 1)] + [\sin(3x + 1) \times \dfrac{3}{3x + 1}]$
[1 mark]

$= 3\ln(3x + 1)\cos(3x + 1) + \dfrac{3\sin(3x + 1)}{3x + 1}$
[1 mark].

b) For $y = \sin^3(2x^2)$, use the chain rule twice:

$y = u^3$ where $u = \sin(2x^2)$.

$\dfrac{dy}{du} = 3u^2 = 3\sin^2(2x^2)$ *[1 mark]*.

$\dfrac{du}{dx} = 4x\cos(2x^2)$ (using chain rule)   *[1 mark]*.

So $\dfrac{dy}{dx} = 12x\sin^2(2x^2)\cos(2x^2)$ *[1 mark]*.

c) For $y = 2\text{cosec}(3x)$, use the chain rule:

$y = 2\text{cosec}\,u$ where $u = (3x)$.

$\dfrac{dy}{du} = -2\text{cosec}\,u\cot u = -2\text{cosec}(3x)\cot(3x)$.

$\dfrac{du}{dx} = 3$ *[1 mark for both]*,

so $\dfrac{dy}{dx} = -6\text{cosec}(3x)\cot(3x)$ *[1 mark]*.

Q2 $f(x) = \sec x = \dfrac{1}{\cos x}$, so using the quotient rule:

$u = 1 \Rightarrow \dfrac{du}{dx} = 0$ and $v = \cos x \Rightarrow \dfrac{dv}{dx} = -\sin x$

$\dfrac{dy}{dx} = \dfrac{v\dfrac{du}{dx} - u\dfrac{dv}{dx}}{v^2} = \dfrac{(\cos x \times 0) - (1 \times (-\sin x))}{\cos^2 x}$

$= \dfrac{\sin x}{\cos^2 x}$

Since $\tan x = \dfrac{\sin x}{\cos x}$, and $\sec x = \dfrac{1}{\cos x}$

$f'(x) = \dfrac{dy}{dx} = \dfrac{\sin x}{\cos x} \times \dfrac{1}{\cos x} = \sec x\tan x$

[4 marks available – 1 mark for correct identity for sec x, 1 mark for correct entry into quotient rule, 1 mark for correct answer from quotient rule, and 1 mark for correct rearrangement to sec x tan x.]

Q3 a) For $f(x) = 4\ln(3x)$, use the chain rule:

$y = 4\ln u$ where $u = 3x$, so

$\dfrac{dy}{du} = \dfrac{4}{u} = \dfrac{4}{3x}$ and $\dfrac{du}{dx} = 3$ *[1 mark for both]*,

so $f'(x) = \dfrac{dy}{dx} = \dfrac{12}{3x} = \dfrac{4}{x}$ *[1 mark]*.

So for $x = 1$, $f'(1) = 4$ *[1 mark]*.

b) When $x = 1$, $y = 4\ln(3 \times 1) = 4\ln 3$

Equation of a straight line (where m is the gradient):

$y = mx + c \Rightarrow 4\ln 3 = (4 \times 1) + c \Rightarrow c = 4\ln 3 - 4$

So the equation of the tangent is:

$y = 4x + 4\ln 3 - 4$

[3 marks available – 1 mark for finding y = 4ln 3, 1 mark for correct substitution of (1, 4ln 3) and gradient from (a), and 1 mark for correct final answer.]

Q4 a) For $y = e^x\sin x$, use the product rule:

$u = e^x \Rightarrow \dfrac{du}{dx} = e^x$

$v = \sin x \Rightarrow \dfrac{dv}{dx} = \cos x$

So $\dfrac{dy}{dx} = u\dfrac{dv}{dx} + v\dfrac{du}{dx} = (e^x\cos x) + (\sin x e^x)$

$= e^x(\cos x + \sin x)$ *[1 mark]*

At the turning points, $\dfrac{dy}{dx} = 0$, so:

$e^x(\cos x + \sin x) = 0$ *[1 mark]*.

$\Rightarrow$ turning points are when $e^x = 0$ or $\cos x + \sin x = 0$. e^x can't be 0, so the turning points are when $\cos x + \sin x = 0$ *[1 mark]*.

$\Rightarrow \sin x = -\cos x \Rightarrow \dfrac{\sin x}{\cos x} = -1 \Rightarrow \tan x = -1$
[1 mark]

Use the graph of tan x or the CAST diagram to help you find all the solutions.

There are two solutions for $\tan x = -1$ in the interval $-\pi \le x \le \pi$: $x = -\dfrac{\pi}{4}$ and $x = \pi - \dfrac{\pi}{4} = \dfrac{3\pi}{4}$, so the values of x at each turning point are $-\dfrac{\pi}{4}$ *[1 mark]* and $\dfrac{3\pi}{4}$ *[1 mark]*.

b) To determine the nature of the turning points, find $\frac{d^2y}{dx^2}$ at the points:

For $\frac{dy}{dx} = e^x(\cos x + \sin x)$, use the product rule:

$u = e^x \Rightarrow \frac{du}{dx} = e^x$

$v = \cos x + \sin x \Rightarrow \frac{dv}{dx} = \cos x - \sin x$, so:

$\frac{d^2y}{dx^2} = u\frac{dv}{dx} + v\frac{du}{dx} = [e^x(\cos x - \sin x)]$
$\qquad\qquad + [(\cos x + \sin x)e^x]$
$\qquad\qquad = 2e^x \cos x$ *[1 mark]*

When $x = -\frac{\pi}{4}$, $\frac{d^2y}{dx^2} > 0$ *[1 mark]*, so this is a minimum point *[1 mark]*.

When $x = \frac{3\pi}{4}$, $\frac{d^2y}{dx^2} < 0$ *[1 mark]*, so this is a maximum point *[1 mark]*.

Q5 a) For $x = \sqrt{y^2 + 3y}$, find $\frac{dx}{dy}$ first

(using the chain rule): $x = u^{\frac{1}{2}}$ where $u = y^2 + 3y$

$\frac{dx}{du} = \frac{1}{2}u^{-\frac{1}{2}} = \frac{1}{2\sqrt{u}} = \frac{1}{2\sqrt{y^2 + 3y}}$ *[1 mark]*.

$\frac{du}{dy} = 2y + 3$ *[1 mark]*.

So $\frac{dx}{dy} = \frac{2y + 3}{2\sqrt{y^2 + 3y}}$ *[1 mark]*.

(Now, flip the fraction upside down for dy/dx)

$\frac{dy}{dx} = \frac{2\sqrt{y^2 + 3y}}{2y + 3}$ *[1 mark]*.

At the point $(2, 1)$, $y = 1$, so:

$\frac{dy}{dx} = \frac{2\sqrt{1^2 + 3}}{2 + 3} = \frac{4}{5}$ $(= 0.8)$ *[1 mark]*.

b) Equation of a straight line is:

$y = mx + c \Rightarrow 1 = (0.8 \times 2) + c \Rightarrow c = -0.6$

So the equation of the tangent is:

$y = mx + c \Rightarrow y = 0.8x - 0.6$

[2 marks available – 1 mark for correct substitution of (2, 1) and gradient from a) and 1 mark for final answer.]

Q6 a) For $y = \sqrt{e^x + e^{2x}}$, use the chain rule:

$y = u^{\frac{1}{2}}$ where $u = e^x + e^{2x}$.

$\frac{dy}{du} = \frac{1}{2}u^{-\frac{1}{2}} = \frac{1}{2\sqrt{u}} = \frac{1}{2\sqrt{e^x + e^{2x}}}$ *[1 mark]*.

$\frac{du}{dx} = e^x + 2e^{2x}$ *[1 mark]*.

So $\frac{dy}{dx} = \frac{e^x + 2e^{2x}}{2\sqrt{e^x + e^{2x}}}$ *[1 mark]*.

b) For $y = 3e^{2x + 1} - \ln(1 - x^2) + 2x^3$, use the chain rule for the first 2 parts separately:

For $y = 3e^{2x+1}$, $y = 3e^u$ where $u = 2x + 1$,

so $\frac{dy}{du} = 3e^u = 3e^{2x+1}$ and $\frac{du}{dx} = 2$,

so $\frac{dy}{dx} = 6e^{2x+1}$ *[1 mark]*.

For $y = \ln(1 - x^2)$, $y = \ln u$ where $u = 1 - x^2$,

so $\frac{dy}{du} = \frac{1}{u} = \frac{1}{1 - x^2}$ and $\frac{du}{dx} = -2x$,

so $\frac{dy}{dx} = -\frac{2x}{1 - x^2}$ *[1 mark]*.

So overall: $\frac{dy}{dx} = 6e^{2x+1} + \frac{2x}{1 - x^2} + 6x^2$ *[1 mark]*.

Q7 For $y = \sin^2 x - 2\cos(2x)$, use the chain rule on each part:

For $y = \sin^2 x$, $y = u^2$ where $u = \sin x$,

so $\frac{dy}{du} = 2u = 2\sin x$ and $\frac{du}{dx} = \cos x$,

so $\frac{dy}{dx} = 2\sin x \cos x$ *[1 mark]*.

For $y = 2\cos(2x)$, $y = 2\cos u$ where $u = 2x$,

so $\frac{dy}{du} = -2\sin u = -2\sin(2x)$ and $\frac{du}{dx} = 2$,

so $\frac{dy}{dx} = -4\sin(2x)$ *[1 mark]*.

Overall $\frac{dy}{dx} = 2\sin x \cos x + 4\sin(2x)$ *[1 mark]*.

(For gradient of the tangent, put the x value into dy/dx...)

Gradient of the tangent when $x = \frac{\pi}{6}$ is:

$2\sin\frac{\pi}{6}\cos\frac{\pi}{6} + 4\sin\frac{\pi}{3}$

$= \frac{\sqrt{3}}{2} + 2\sqrt{3} = \frac{5\sqrt{3}}{2}$ *[1 mark]*.

Q8 For $y = \frac{e^x + x}{e^x - x}$, use the quotient rule:

$u = e^x + x \Rightarrow \frac{du}{dx} = e^x + 1$.

$v = e^x - x \Rightarrow \frac{dv}{dx} = e^x - 1$.

$\frac{dy}{dx} = \frac{v\frac{du}{dx} - u\frac{dv}{dx}}{v^2} =$

$\frac{(e^x - x)(e^x + 1) - (e^x + x)(e^x - 1)}{(e^x - x)^2}$

When $x = 0$, $e^x = 1$, and

$\frac{dy}{dx} = \frac{(1 - 0)(1 + 1) - (1 + 0)(1 - 1)}{(1 - 0)^2} = \frac{2 - 0}{1^2} = 2$.

[3 marks available — 1 mark for finding u, v and their derivatives, 1 mark for dy/dx (however rearranged), and 1 mark for dy/dx = 2 when x = 0.]

Q9 For $x = \sin(4y)$, $\frac{dx}{dy} = 4\cos(4y)$ (chain rule) *[1 mark]*

and so $\frac{dy}{dx} = \frac{1}{4\cos(4y)}$ *[1 mark]*.

At $(0, \frac{\pi}{4})$, $y = \frac{\pi}{4}$ and so $\frac{dy}{dx} = \frac{1}{4\cos\pi} = -\frac{1}{4}$ *[1 mark]*.

(This is the gradient of the tangent at that point, so to find the gradient of the normal do −1 ÷ gradient of tangent...)

Gradient of normal at $(0, \frac{\pi}{4}) = -1 \div -\frac{1}{4} = 4$ *[1 mark]*.

Equation of a straight line is:

$y = mx + c$, so $\frac{\pi}{4} = (4 \times 0) + c \Rightarrow c = \frac{\pi}{4}$ *[1 mark]*

So the equation of the normal is $y = 4x + \frac{\pi}{4}$ *[1 mark]*.

Chapter 5: Integration

1. Integration of $(ax + b)^n$

Exercise 1.1 — Integrating $(ax + b)^n$, $n \neq -1$

Q1 a) $\int (2x + 9)^4 \, dx = \frac{1}{2 \times 5}(2x + 9)^5 + C$

$= \frac{1}{10}(2x + 9)^5 + C$

b) $\int (x + 10)^{10} \, dx = \frac{1}{1 \times 11}(x + 10)^{11} + C$

$= \frac{1}{11}(x + 10)^{11} + C$

c) $\int (4x + 3)^5 \, dx = \frac{1}{4 \times 6}(4x + 3)^6 + C$

$= \frac{1}{24}(4x + 3)^6 + C$

d) $\int (5x)^7 \, dx = \frac{1}{5 \times 8}(5x)^8 + C = \frac{1}{40}(5x)^8 + C$

$= \frac{1}{40}5^8 x^8 + C = \frac{5^8}{40}x^8 + C = \frac{78125 x^8}{8} + C$

e) $\int (7x - 2)^{-8} \, dx = \frac{1}{7 \times -7}(7x - 2)^{-7} + C$

$= -\frac{1}{49}(7x - 2)^{-7} + C = -\frac{1}{49(7x - 2)^7} + C$

f) $\int (3 - 5x)^{-2} \, dx = \frac{1}{-5 \times -1}(3 - 5x)^{-1} + C$

$= \frac{1}{5}(3 - 5x)^{-1} + C = \frac{1}{5(3 - 5x)} + C$

g) $\int (10x - 3)^{\frac{11}{8}} \, dx = \frac{1}{10 \times \frac{19}{8}}(10x - 3)^{\frac{19}{8}} + C$

$= \frac{1}{\left(\frac{95}{4}\right)}(10x - 3)^{\frac{19}{8}} + C = \frac{4}{95}(10x - 3)^{\frac{19}{8}} + C$

h) $\int (3x - 4)^{-\frac{4}{3}} \, dx = \frac{1}{3 \times \left(-\frac{1}{3}\right)}(3x - 4)^{-\frac{1}{3}} + C$

$= \frac{1}{-1}(3x - 4)^{-\frac{1}{3}} + C = -(3x - 4)^{-\frac{1}{3}} + C$

$= \frac{-1}{\sqrt[3]{3x - 4}} + C$

Q2 a) Begin by taking the constant of 8 outside of the integration and then integrate $\int (2x - 4)^4 \, dx$ as usual.

$\int 8(2x - 4)^4 \, dx = 8 \int (2x - 4)^4 \, dx$

$= 8 \times \left(\frac{1}{2 \times 5}(2x - 4)^5 + c\right)$

$= \frac{8}{10}(2x - 4)^5 + C$

$= \frac{4}{5}(2x - 4)^5 + C$

$= \frac{4(2x - 4)^5}{5} + C$

b) *Use your answer to part a). The integral you found will be the same but without the constant of integration — it'll have limits instead.*

$\int_{\frac{3}{2}}^{\frac{5}{2}} 8(2x - 4)^4 \, dx = \frac{4}{5}[(2x - 4)^5]_{\frac{3}{2}}^{\frac{5}{2}}$

$= \frac{4}{5}\left(\left[\left(2\left(\frac{5}{2}\right) - 4\right)^5\right] - \left[\left(2\left(\frac{3}{2}\right) - 4\right)^5\right]\right)$

$= \frac{4}{5}([(1)^5] - [(-1)^5])$

$= \frac{4}{5}([1] - [-1]) = \frac{8}{5}$

Q3 $\int_0^1 (6x + 1)^{-3} \, dx = \left[\frac{1}{6 \times -2}(6x + 1)^{-2}\right]_0^1$

$= -\frac{1}{12}[(6x + 1)^{-2}]_0^1$

$= -\frac{1}{12}([(7)^{-2}] - [(1)^{-2}])$

$= -\frac{1}{12}\left(\frac{1}{49} - 1\right) = \frac{4}{49}$

Q4 You've been given that $f'(x) = (8 - 7x)^4$ and you need to find $f(x)$, so integrate with respect to x.

$f(x) = \int f'(x) \, dx = \int (8 - 7x)^4 \, dx$

$= \frac{1}{-7 \times 5}(8 - 7x)^5 + C = -\frac{1}{35}(8 - 7x)^5 + C$

Substitute in the values of x and y at the point given to find the value of C.

$\frac{3}{35} = -\frac{1}{35}(8 - (7 \times 1))^5 + C$

$\Rightarrow \frac{3}{35} = -\frac{1}{35}(1)^5 + C$

$\Rightarrow C = \frac{4}{35}$

So $f(x) = -\frac{1}{35}(8 - 7x)^5 + \frac{4}{35}$

Q5 To find the area between the curve $y = (-x - 1)^{12}$ and the x-axis for $-1 \leq x \leq 0$ you just need to integrate the curve between -1 and 0 with respect to x.

$\int_{-1}^0 (-x - 1)^{12} \, dx = \left[\frac{1}{-1 \times 13}(-x - 1)^{13}\right]_{-1}^0$

$= -\frac{1}{13}[(-x - 1)^{13}]_{-1}^0$

$= -\frac{1}{13}([(-1)^{13}] - [(0)^{13}]) = -\frac{1}{13}(-1 - 0) = \frac{1}{13}$

Q6 *Watch out — this integration is with respect to y, not x.*

$\int (9 - y)^{\frac{1}{6}} + (9 - y)^{-6} \, dy$

$= \int (9 - y)^{\frac{1}{6}} \, dy + \int (9 - y)^{-6} \, dy$

$= \frac{1}{-1 \times \frac{7}{6}}(9 - y)^{\frac{7}{6}} + \frac{1}{-1 \times -5}(9 - y)^{-5} + C$

$= -\frac{6}{7}(9 - y)^{\frac{7}{6}} + \frac{1}{5}(9 - y)^{-5} + C$

Q7 You need an integral of the form $\int (ax+b)^n\,dx$ if you want to use the formula, so write $\dfrac{-6}{(12x+5)^2}$ as $-6(12x+5)^{-2}$:

$$\int \frac{-6}{(12x+5)^2}\,dx = \int -6(12x+5)^{-2}\,dx$$

$$= -6\int (12x+5)^{-2}\,dx$$

$$= -6\left(\frac{1}{12\times -1}\times(12x+5)^{-1}+c\right)$$

$$= \frac{-6}{-12}(12x+5)^{-1}+C$$

$$= \frac{1}{2}(12x+5)^{-1}+C$$

$$= \frac{1}{2(12x+5)}+C$$

$$= \frac{1}{24x+10}+C$$

2. Integration of e^x and $\frac{1}{x}$

Exercise 2.1 — Integrating e^x and e^{ax+b}

Q1 a) $\int 2e^x\,dx = 2\int e^x\,dx = 2e^x+C$

b) $\int 4x + 7e^x\,dx = \int 4x\,dx + \int 7e^x\,dx$
$$= \int 4x\,dx + 7\int e^x\,dx = 2x^2 + 7e^x + C$$

c) $\int e^{10x}\,dx = \frac{1}{10}e^{10x}+C$

d) $\int e^{-3x}+x\,dx = \int e^{-3x}\,dx + \int x\,dx$
$$= -\frac{1}{3}e^{-3x}+\frac{1}{2}x^2+C$$

e) $\int e^{\frac{7}{2}x}\,dx = \frac{1}{\left(\frac{7}{2}\right)}e^{\frac{7}{2}x}+C = \frac{2}{7}e^{\frac{7}{2}x}+C$

f) $\int e^{4x-2}\,dx = \frac{1}{4}e^{4x-2}+C$

g) $\int \frac{1}{2}e^{2-\frac{3}{2}x}\,dx = \frac{1}{2}\int e^{2-\frac{3}{2}x}\,dx$
$$= \frac{1}{2}\times\left(\frac{1}{\left(-\frac{3}{2}\right)}e^{2-\frac{3}{2}x}+c\right) = \left(\frac{1}{2}\times -\frac{2}{3}e^{2-\frac{3}{2}x}\right)+C$$
$$= -\frac{1}{3}e^{2-\frac{3}{2}x}+C$$

h) $\int e^{4\left(\frac{x}{3}+1\right)}\,dx = \int e^{\frac{4}{3}x+4}\,dx$
$$= \frac{1}{\left(\frac{4}{3}\right)}e^{\frac{4}{3}x+4}+C = \frac{3}{4}e^{4\left(\frac{x}{3}+1\right)}+C$$

Q2 You've been given the derivative of the curve, so integrate it to get the equation of the curve.

$$y = \int \frac{dy}{dx}\,dx = \int 10e^{-5x-1}\,dx = 10\int e^{-5x-1}\,dx$$
$$= 10\times\left(\frac{1}{-5}e^{-5x-1}+c\right) = -2e^{-5x-1}+C$$

To find C, use the fact that the curve goes through the origin (0, 0). The equation of the curve is $y = -2e^{-5x-1}+C$ and substituting in $x = 0$ and $y = 0$ gives:

$0 = -2e^{-(5\times 0)-1}+C = -2e^{-1}+C = -\frac{2}{e}+C$ so $C = \frac{2}{e}$.

So the curve has equation $y = -2e^{-5x-1}+\frac{2}{e}$.

Q3 $\int e^{8y+5}\,dy = \frac{1}{8}e^{8y+5}+C$

Q4 a) $\int_2^3 e^{2x}\,dx = \frac{1}{2}[e^{2x}]_2^3 = \frac{1}{2}([e^6]-[e^4])$
$$= \frac{1}{2}(e^6-e^4)$$

b) $\int_{-1}^0 12e^{12x+12}\,dx = \left[12\times\frac{1}{12}e^{12x+12}\right]_{-1}^0$
$$= [e^{12x+12}]_{-1}^0 = e^{12}-e^0 = e^{12}-1$$

c) $\int_{-\frac{\pi}{2}}^{\frac{\pi}{2}} e^{\pi-2x}\,dx = \left[\frac{1}{-2}e^{\pi-2x}\right]_{-\frac{\pi}{2}}^{\frac{\pi}{2}}$
$$= -\frac{1}{2}[e^{\pi-2x}]_{-\frac{\pi}{2}}^{\frac{\pi}{2}}$$
$$= -\frac{1}{2}([e^{\pi-\pi}]-[e^{\pi+\pi}])$$
$$= -\frac{1}{2}(e^0-e^{2\pi}) = \frac{1}{2}(e^{2\pi}-1)$$

d) $\int_3^6 \sqrt[6]{e^x}+\frac{1}{3\sqrt[3]{e^x}}\,dx = \int_3^6 (e^x)^{\frac{1}{6}}+(e^x)^{-\frac{1}{3}}\,dx$
$$= \int_3^6 e^{\frac{x}{6}}+e^{-\frac{x}{3}}\,dx = \left[\frac{1}{\left(\frac{1}{6}\right)}e^{\frac{x}{6}}+\frac{1}{\left(-\frac{1}{3}\right)}e^{-\frac{x}{3}}\right]_3^6$$
$$= \left[6e^{\frac{x}{6}}-3e^{-\frac{x}{3}}\right]_3^6$$
$$= \left[6e^1-3e^{-2}\right]-\left[6e^{\frac{1}{2}}-3e^{-1}\right]$$
$$= 6e-\frac{3}{e^2}-6\sqrt{e}+\frac{3}{e}$$

Your answer might look a bit different if you took out a factor of 3.

Exercise 2.2 — Integrating $\frac{1}{x}$ and $\frac{1}{ax+b}$

Q1 a) $\int \frac{19}{x}\,dx = 19\int\frac{1}{x}\,dx = 19\ln|x|+C$

b) $\int \frac{1}{7x}\,dx = \frac{1}{7}\int\frac{1}{x}\,dx = \frac{1}{7}\ln|x|+C$

An equivalent answer to b) would be $\frac{1}{7}\ln|7x|+C$ if you used the general formula for integrating $\frac{1}{ax+b}$ instead.

c) There is no constant term to take out here, so use the general formula:
$$\int \frac{1}{7x+2}\,dx = \frac{1}{7}\ln|7x+2|+C$$

d) $\int \frac{1}{1-3x}\,dx = \frac{1}{-3}\ln|1-3x|+C$
$$= -\frac{1}{3}\ln|1-3x|+C$$

Q2 $\int \frac{1}{8x}-\frac{20}{x}\,dx = \frac{1}{8}\int\frac{1}{x}\,dx-20\int\frac{1}{x}\,dx$
$$= \frac{1}{8}\ln|x|-20\ln|x|+C = -\frac{159}{8}\ln|x|+C$$

You could also notice that $\frac{1}{8x}-\frac{20}{x} = \frac{1-160}{8x} = \frac{-159}{8x}$ and integrate $\frac{-159}{8x}$ using the method for $\frac{1}{x}$.

Q3 a) $\int \frac{6}{x}-\frac{3}{x}\,dx = \int\frac{3}{x}\,dx = 3\ln|x|+C$
$$= \ln|x|^3+C = \ln|x^3|+C$$

b) $\int_4^5 \frac{6}{x}-\frac{3}{x}\,dx = [\ln|x^3|]_4^5$
$$= [\ln 5^3]-[\ln 4^3] = 3\ln 5-3\ln 4$$
$$= 3(\ln 5-\ln 4) = 3\ln\left(\frac{5}{4}\right)$$

You could also have written your answer as $\ln\frac{125}{64}$.

Q4
$$\int_b^a 15(5+3x)^{-1}\,dx = \int_b^a \frac{15}{(5+3x)}\,dx$$
$$= \left[15 \times \frac{1}{3}\ln|5+3x|\right]_b^a = 5\big[\ln|5+3x|\big]_b^a$$
$$= 5(\ln|5+3a| - \ln|5+3b|)$$
$$= 5\ln\left(\frac{|5+3a|}{|5+3b|}\right) = 5\ln\left|\frac{5+3a}{5+3b}\right|$$
$$= \ln\left|\frac{5+3a}{5+3b}\right|^5$$

Q5 Integrate the derivative to find f(x).
$$f(x) = \int f'(x)\,dx = \int \frac{4}{10-9x}\,dx$$
$$= 4 \times \frac{1}{-9}\ln|10-9x| + C = -\frac{4}{9}\ln|10-9x| + C$$

Now the curve passes through the point (1, 2), so substitute these values to find C.
$$2 = -\frac{4}{9}\ln|10-(9\times1)| + C$$
$$2 = -\frac{4}{9}\ln|1| + C$$
$$2 = 0 + C$$

So C = 2 and the equation of f(x) is
$$f(x) = -\frac{4}{9}\ln|10-9x| + 2.$$

Q6 a) The area required is the shaded area below:

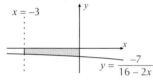

This is found by integrating the curve with respect to x between the limits x = –3 and x = 0.

So the area is expressed by the integral
$$\int_{-3}^0 \frac{-7}{16-2x}\,dx.$$

b)
$$\int_{-3}^0 \frac{-7}{16-2x}\,dx = \left[-7 \times \frac{1}{-2}\ln|16-2x|\right]_{-3}^0$$
$$= \frac{7}{2}\big[\ln|16-2x|\big]_{-3}^0$$
$$= \frac{7}{2}(\ln16 - \ln22)$$
$$= \frac{7}{2}\ln\frac{16}{22} = \frac{7}{2}\ln\frac{8}{11} = \ln\left[\left(\frac{8}{11}\right)^{\frac{7}{2}}\right]$$

Q7 Work out the integral and put in the limits to find A.
$$\int_1^A \frac{4}{6x-5}\,dx = 10$$
$$\left[4 \times \frac{1}{6}\ln|6x-5|\right]_1^A = 10$$
$$\frac{2}{3}\big[\ln|6x-5|\big]_1^A = 10$$
$$\frac{2}{3}(\ln|6A-5| - \ln|1|) = 10$$
$$\frac{2}{3}(\ln|6A-5| - 0) = 10$$
$$\frac{2}{3}\ln|6A-5| = 10$$
$$\ln|6A-5| = \frac{10}{\left(\frac{2}{3}\right)} = 15$$

Take the exponential of both sides to get rid of the ln.
$$|6A-5| = e^{15}$$
$$A = \frac{e^{15}+5}{6}$$

Note that A must be greater than or equal to 1, since it is the upper integration limit and 1 is the lower integration limit — so 6A – 5 must be greater than 6 – 5 = 1, so the modulus can be removed as it'll always be positive.

3. Integration of Trigonometric Functions
Exercise 3.1 —
Integration of sin x and cos x

Q1 a) $\int \frac{1}{7}\cos x\,dx = \frac{1}{7}\int \cos x\,dx$
$$= \frac{1}{7}\sin x + C$$

b) $\int -3\sin x\,dx = -3\int \sin x\,dx$
$$= -3(-\cos x) + C$$
$$= 3\cos x + C$$

c) $\int -3\cos x - 3\sin x\,dx = -3\int \cos x + \sin x\,dx$
$$= -3(\sin x - \cos x + c)$$
$$= -3\sin x + 3\cos x + C$$

d) $\int \sin 5x\,dx = -\frac{1}{5}\cos 5x + C$

e) $\int \cos\left(\frac{x}{7}\right)dx = \frac{1}{\left(\frac{1}{7}\right)}\sin\left(\frac{x}{7}\right) + C = 7\sin\left(\frac{x}{7}\right) + C$

f) $\int 2\sin(-3x)\,dx = 2\int \sin(-3x)\,dx$
$$= 2\left(-\left(-\frac{1}{3}\right)\cos(-3x) + c\right)$$
$$= \frac{2}{3}\cos(-3x) + C$$
An alternative solution would be $\frac{2}{3}\cos(3x) + C$ since cos(x) = cos(–x).

g) $\int 5\cos\left(3x + \frac{\pi}{5}\right)dx = 5\left(\frac{1}{3}\sin\left(3x + \frac{\pi}{5}\right) + c\right)$
$$= \frac{5}{3}\sin\left(3x + \frac{\pi}{5}\right) + C$$

h) $\int -4\sin\left(4x - \frac{\pi}{3}\right)dx = -4\left(-\frac{1}{4}\cos\left(4x - \frac{\pi}{3}\right) + c\right)$
$$= \cos\left(4x - \frac{\pi}{3}\right) + C$$

i) $\int \cos(4x+3) + \sin(3-4x)\,dx$
$$= \frac{1}{4}\sin(4x+3) + \frac{1}{-4}(-\cos(3-4x)) + C$$
$$= \frac{1}{4}\sin(4x+3) + \frac{1}{4}\cos(3-4x) + C$$

Q2 $\int \frac{1}{2}\cos 3\theta - \sin\theta\,d\theta = \frac{1}{2}\left(\frac{1}{3}\sin 3\theta\right) - (-\cos\theta) + C$
$$= \frac{1}{6}\sin 3\theta + \cos\theta + C$$

Q3 a) $\int_0^{\frac{\pi}{2}} \sin x\,dx = \big[-\cos x\big]_0^{\frac{\pi}{2}} = -\cos\frac{\pi}{2} + \cos 0$
$$= 0 + 1 = 1$$

b) $\int_{\frac{\pi}{6}}^{\frac{\pi}{3}} \sin 3x \, dx = -\frac{1}{3}[\cos 3x]_{\frac{\pi}{6}}^{\frac{\pi}{3}}$

$\qquad = -\frac{1}{3}\left(\left[\cos\left(3 \times \frac{\pi}{3}\right)\right] - \left[\cos\left(3 \times \frac{\pi}{6}\right)\right]\right)$

$\qquad = -\frac{1}{3}\left(\cos\pi - \cos\frac{\pi}{2}\right)$

$\qquad = -\frac{1}{3}(-1 - 0) = \frac{1}{3}$

c) $\int_{-1}^{2} 3\sin(\pi x + \pi) \, dx = -\frac{3}{\pi}[\cos(\pi x + \pi)]_{-1}^{2}$

$\qquad = -\frac{3}{\pi}(\cos 3\pi - \cos 0)$

$\qquad = -\frac{3}{\pi}(-1 - 1) = \frac{6}{\pi}$

Q4 Integrate the function with respect to x within the limits 1 and 2:

$\int_{1}^{2} 2\pi\cos\left(\frac{\pi x}{2}\right) dx = \frac{2\pi}{\left(\frac{\pi}{2}\right)}\left[\sin\left(\frac{\pi x}{2}\right)\right]_{1}^{2}$

$\qquad = 4\left[\sin\left(\frac{\pi x}{2}\right)\right]_{1}^{2}$

$\qquad = 4\left(\sin(\pi) - \sin\left(\frac{\pi}{2}\right)\right)$

$\qquad = 4(0 - 1) = -4$

So the area required is 4.
The integral gives a negative value for the area of the region — this means that most or all of the area is below the x-axis (if most or all of the area was above the x-axis, the integral would be positive).

If you sketch the original function, you'll see that the entire area is below the x-axis.

Q5 $\int_{\frac{\pi}{3}}^{\frac{\pi}{2}} \sin(-x) + \cos(-x) \, dx = \int_{\frac{\pi}{3}}^{\frac{\pi}{2}} - \sin x + \cos x \, dx$

$= [-(-\cos x) + \sin x]_{\frac{\pi}{3}}^{\frac{\pi}{2}}$

$= [\cos x + \sin x]_{\frac{\pi}{3}}^{\frac{\pi}{2}}$

$= \left[\cos\left(\frac{\pi}{2}\right) + \sin\left(\frac{\pi}{2}\right)\right] - \left[\cos\left(\frac{\pi}{3}\right) + \sin\left(\frac{\pi}{3}\right)\right]$

$= [0 + 1] - \left[\frac{1}{2} + \frac{\sqrt{3}}{2}\right]$

$= 1 - \frac{1}{2} - \frac{\sqrt{3}}{2} = \frac{1}{2} - \frac{\sqrt{3}}{2} = \frac{1 - \sqrt{3}}{2}$

sin(−x) = −sin(x) and cos(−x) = cos(x) are used in the first step of this solution.

Q6 Integrate the function between −2π and π:

$\int_{-2\pi}^{\pi} 5\cos\frac{x}{6} \, dx = \left[\frac{5}{\left(\frac{1}{6}\right)}\sin\left(\frac{x}{6}\right)\right]_{-2\pi}^{\pi} = 30\left[\sin\left(\frac{x}{6}\right)\right]_{-2\pi}^{\pi}$

$= 30\left(\sin\left(\frac{\pi}{6}\right) - \sin\left(-\frac{\pi}{3}\right)\right)$

$= 30\left(\frac{1}{2} - \left(-\frac{\sqrt{3}}{2}\right)\right)$

$= 30\left(\frac{1 + \sqrt{3}}{2}\right) = 15(1 + \sqrt{3})$

Exercise 3.2 — Integration of sec² x

Q1 a) $\int 2\sec^2 x + 1 \, dx = 2\tan x + x + C$

b) $\int \sec^2 9x \, dx = \frac{1}{9}\tan 9x + C$

c) $\int 20\sec^2 3y \, dy = 20 \times \frac{1}{3}\tan 3y + C$

$\qquad = \frac{20}{3}\tan 3y + C$

d) $\int \sec^2\frac{x}{7} \, dx = \frac{1}{\left(\frac{1}{7}\right)}\tan\left(\frac{x}{7}\right) + C$

$\qquad = 7\tan\left(\frac{x}{7}\right) + C$

e) $\int_{0}^{\frac{\pi}{3}} -\frac{1}{\cos^2\theta} \, d\theta = \int_{0}^{\frac{\pi}{3}} -\sec^2\theta \, d\theta = [-\tan\theta]_{0}^{\frac{\pi}{3}}$

$\qquad = -\sqrt{3} + 0 = -\sqrt{3}$

f) $\int_{0}^{\frac{\pi}{4}} 3\sec^2(-3x) \, dx = \left[\frac{3}{-3}\tan(-3x)\right]_{0}^{\frac{\pi}{4}}$

$\qquad = [-\tan(-3x)]_{0}^{\frac{\pi}{4}}$

$\qquad = \left[-\tan\left(-3 \times \frac{\pi}{4}\right)\right] - [-\tan(0)]$

$\qquad = -1 + 0 = -1$

Q2 Integrate the function between the limits:

$\int_{\frac{2}{3}\pi}^{\pi} \sec^2 x \, dx = [\tan x]_{\frac{2}{3}\pi}^{\pi} = \tan\pi - \tan\frac{2\pi}{3}$

$\qquad = 0 - (-\sqrt{3}) = \sqrt{3}$

Q3 The constants α and β do not affect the integration. You only need to worry about the coefficients of x.

$\int \sec^2(x + \alpha) + \sec^2(3x + \beta) \, dx$

$= \tan(x + \alpha) + \frac{1}{3}\tan(3x + \beta) + C$

Q4 $\int_{\frac{\pi}{12}}^{\frac{\pi}{6}} 5A\sec^2\left(\frac{\pi}{3} - 2\theta\right) d\theta = \left[-\frac{5A}{2}\tan\left(\frac{\pi}{3} - 2\theta\right)\right]_{\frac{\pi}{12}}^{\frac{\pi}{6}}$

$\qquad = -\frac{5A}{2}\left[\tan\left(\frac{\pi}{3} - 2\theta\right)\right]_{\frac{\pi}{12}}^{\frac{\pi}{6}}$

$\qquad = -\frac{5A}{2}\left(\left[\tan\left(\frac{\pi}{3} - \frac{\pi}{3}\right)\right] - \left[\tan\left(\frac{\pi}{3} - \frac{\pi}{6}\right)\right]\right)$

$\qquad = -\frac{5A}{2}\left(\tan(0) - \tan\left(\frac{\pi}{6}\right)\right)$

$\qquad = -\frac{5A}{2}\left(0 - \frac{\sqrt{3}}{3}\right)$

$\qquad = \frac{5\sqrt{3}A}{6}$

Exercise 3.3 — Integration of other trigonometric functions

Q1 a) $\int \csc^2 11x \, dx = -\frac{1}{11}\cot 11x + C$

b) $\int 5\sec 10\theta \tan 10\theta \, d\theta = 5 \times \frac{1}{10}\sec 10\theta + C$

$\qquad = \frac{1}{2}\sec 10\theta + C$

c) $\int -\csc(x + 17)\cot(x + 17) \, dx$

$\qquad = -(-\csc(x + 17)) + C$

$\qquad = \csc(x + 17) + C$

d) $\int -3\cosec 3x \cot 3x \, dx = -3\left(-\frac{1}{3}\cosec 3x\right) + C$

$$= \cosec 3x + C$$

e) $\int 13\sec\left(\frac{\pi}{4} - x\right)\tan\left(\frac{\pi}{4} - x\right) dx$

$$= 13\left(\frac{1}{-1}\sec\left(\frac{\pi}{4} - x\right)\right) + C$$

$$= -13\sec\left(\frac{\pi}{4} - x\right) + C$$

Q2 $\int 10\cosec^2\left(\alpha - \frac{x}{2}\right) - 60\sec(\alpha - 6x)\tan(\alpha - 6x)\, dx$

$$= -\frac{10}{\left(-\frac{1}{2}\right)}\cot\left(\alpha - \frac{x}{2}\right) - \frac{60}{-6}\sec(\alpha - 6x) + C$$

$$= 20\cot\left(\alpha - \frac{x}{2}\right) + 10\sec(\alpha - 6x) + C$$

Q3 $\int_{\frac{\pi}{12}}^{\frac{\pi}{8}} 6\sec 2x\tan 2x + 6\cosec 2x\cot 2x\, dx$

$$= \left[\frac{6}{2}\sec 2x - \frac{6}{2}\cosec 2x\right]_{\frac{\pi}{12}}^{\frac{\pi}{8}}$$

$$= 3\left[\sec 2x - \cosec 2x\right]_{\frac{\pi}{12}}^{\frac{\pi}{8}}$$

$$= 3\left(\left[\sec\frac{\pi}{4} - \cosec\frac{\pi}{4}\right] - \left[\sec\frac{\pi}{6} - \cosec\frac{\pi}{6}\right]\right)$$

$$= 3\left(\sqrt{2} - \sqrt{2} - \frac{2}{\sqrt{3}} + 2\right)$$

$$= 3\left(2 - \frac{2}{\sqrt{3}}\right) = 6 - 2\sqrt{3}$$

Q4 $\int_{\frac{\pi}{12}}^{\frac{\pi}{6}} \cosec^2(3x)\, dx = \left[-\frac{1}{3}\cot(3x)\right]_{\frac{\pi}{12}}^{\frac{\pi}{6}}$

$$= -\frac{1}{3}\left(\cot\left(\frac{\pi}{2}\right) - \cot\left(\frac{\pi}{4}\right)\right)$$

$$= -\frac{1}{3}(0 - 1) = \frac{1}{3}$$

The graph of y = cot x is covered in Chapter 2 — remember that it is 1 at x = $\frac{\pi}{4}$ and 0 at x = $\frac{\pi}{2}$. Or if you know your tan values of common angles, you can use these instead.

4. Integration of $\dfrac{f'(x)}{f(x)}$

Exercise 4.1 — Integrating $\dfrac{f'(x)}{f(x)}$

Q1 a) Differentiating the denominator:

$$\frac{d}{dx}(x^4 - 1) = 4x^3 = \text{numerator}$$

$$\int \frac{4x^3}{x^4 - 1}\, dx = \ln|x^4 - 1| + C$$

b) $\frac{d}{dx}(x^2 - x) = 2x - 1 = \text{numerator}$

$$\int \frac{2x - 1}{x^2 - x}\, dx = \ln|x^2 - x| + C$$

c) $\frac{d}{dx}(3x^5 + 6) = 15x^4$

$$\int \frac{x^4}{3x^5 + 6}\, dx = \frac{1}{15}\int \frac{15x^4}{3x^5 + 6}\, dx$$

$$= \frac{1}{15}\ln|3x^5 + 6| + C$$

d) $\frac{d}{dx}(x^4 + 2x^3 - x) = 4x^3 + 6x^2 - 1$

$$\int \frac{12x^3 + 18x^2 - 3}{x^4 + 2x^3 - x}\, dx = \int \frac{3(4x^3 + 6x^2 - 1)}{x^4 + 2x^3 - x}\, dx$$

$$= 3\int \frac{4x^3 + 6x^2 - 1}{x^4 + 2x^3 - x}\, dx$$

$$= 3\ln|x^4 + 2x^3 - x| + C$$

e) $\frac{d}{dx}(1 + \sin 2x) = 2\cos 2x$

$$\int \frac{2\cos 2x}{1 + \sin 2x}\, dx = \ln|1 + \sin 2x| + C$$

f) $\frac{d}{dx}(e^{2x} + 6e^x) = 2e^{2x} + 6e^x = 2(e^{2x} + 3e^x)$

$$\int \frac{2(e^{2x} + 3e^x)}{e^{2x} + 6e^x}\, dx = \ln|e^{2x} + 6e^x| + C$$

g) $\frac{d}{dx}(e^x + 3) = e^x$

$$\int \frac{e^x}{3(e^x + 3)}\, dx = \frac{1}{3}\int \frac{e^x}{(e^x + 3)}\, dx$$

$$= \frac{1}{3}\ln|e^x + 3| + C$$

h) $\frac{d}{dx}(1 + \sin 2x) = 2\cos 2x$

$$\int \frac{2\cos 2x}{1 + \sin 2x}\, dx = \ln|1 + \sin 2x| + C$$

i) $\frac{d}{dx}(\cos 3x - 1) = -3\sin 3x$

$$\int \frac{\sin 3x}{\cos 3x - 1}\, dx = -\frac{1}{3}\int \frac{-3\sin 3x}{\cos 3x - 1}\, dx$$

$$= -\frac{1}{3}\ln|\cos 3x - 1| + C$$

j) $\frac{d}{dx}(\cosec x - x^2 + 4) = -\cosec x\cot x - 2x$

$$\int \frac{3\cosec x\cot x + 6x}{\cosec x - x^2 + 4}\, dx$$

$$= \int \frac{-3(-\cosec x\cot x - 2x)}{\cosec x - x^2 + 4}\, dx$$

$$= -3\int \frac{-\cosec x\cot x - 2x}{\cosec x - x^2 + 4}\, dx$$

$$= -3\ln|\cosec x - x^2 + 4| + C$$

k) $\frac{d}{dx}(\tan x) = \sec^2 x$

$$\int \frac{\sec^2 x}{\tan x}\, dx = \ln|\tan x| + C$$

l) $\frac{d}{dx}(\sec x + 5) = \sec x\tan x$

$$\int \frac{\sec x\tan x}{\sec x + 5}\, dx = \ln|\sec x + 5| + C$$

Q2 $\frac{d}{dx}(\sin(2x + 7)) = 2\cos(2x + 7)$

$$\int \frac{4\cos(2x + 7)}{\sin(2x + 7)}\, dx = 2\int \frac{2\cos(2x + 7)}{\sin(2x + 7)}\, dx$$

$$= 2(\ln|\sin(2x + 7)| + c)$$

$$= 2(\ln|\sin(2x + 7)| + \ln k)$$

$$= 2\ln|k\sin(2x + 7)|$$

Q3 a) Using the hint, multiply the inside of the integral by a fraction which is the same on the top and bottom (it's equal to 1, so it'll make no difference).

$$\int \sec x \, dx = \int \sec x \left(\frac{\sec x + \tan x}{\sec x + \tan x}\right) dx$$
$$= \int \frac{\sec^2 x + \sec x \tan x}{\sec x + \tan x} \, dx$$

Now differentiating the denominator of this integral gives:

$$\frac{d}{dx}(\sec x + \tan x) = \sec x \tan x + \sec^2 x$$

So the numerator is the derivative of the denominator, so use the result:

$$\int \sec x \, dx = \int \frac{\sec^2 x + \sec x \tan x}{\sec x + \tan x} \, dx$$
$$= \ln|\sec x + \tan x| + C$$

b) Use the same method as part a), this time using $\frac{\csc x + \cot x}{\csc x + \cot x}$:

$$\int \csc x \, dx = \int \csc x \left(\frac{\csc x + \cot x}{\csc x + \cot x}\right) dx$$
$$= \int \frac{\csc^2 x + \csc x \cot x}{\csc x + \cot x} \, dx$$

Differentiating the denominator of this integral:

$$\frac{d}{dx}(\csc x + \cot x) = -\csc x \cot x - \csc^2 x$$
$$= -(\csc x \cot x + \csc^2 x)$$

So the numerator is minus the derivative of the denominator, so use the result:

$$\int \csc x \, dx = \int \frac{\csc^2 x + \csc x \cot x}{\csc x + \cot x} \, dx$$
$$= -\int \frac{-\csc^2 x - \csc x \cot x}{\csc x + \cot x} \, dx$$
$$= -\ln|\csc x + \cot x| + C$$

Q4 a) $\int 2 \tan x \, dx = 2 \int \frac{\sin x}{\cos x} \, dx$
$$= -2 \int \frac{-\sin x}{\cos x} \, dx$$
$$= -2 \ln|\cos x| + C$$

b) $\int \tan 2x \, dx = \int \frac{\sin 2x}{\cos 2x} \, dx$
$$= -\frac{1}{2} \int \frac{-2 \sin 2x}{\cos 2x} \, dx$$
$$= -\frac{1}{2} \ln|\cos 2x| + C$$

c) $\int 4 \csc x \, dx = 4 \int \csc x \, dx$
$$= -4 \ln|\csc x + \cot x| + C$$

d) $\int \cot 3x \, dx = \frac{1}{3} \ln|\sin 3x| + C$

e) $\int \frac{1}{2} \sec 2x \, dx = \frac{1}{2}\left(\frac{1}{2} \ln|\sec 2x + \tan 2x| + c\right)$
$$= \frac{1}{4} \ln|\sec 2x + \tan 2x| + C$$

f) $\int 3 \csc 6x \, dx = 3\left(-\frac{1}{6} \ln|\csc 6x + \cot 6x| + c\right)$
$$= -\frac{1}{2} \ln|\csc 6x + \cot 6x| + C$$

Q5 *This one looks really complicated, but if you split it into parts and use some standard results it's actually pretty simple.*

$$\int \frac{\sec^2 x}{2 \tan x} - 4 \sec 2x \tan 2x + \frac{\csc 2x \cot 2x - 1}{\csc 2x + 2x} \, dx$$
$$= \int \frac{\sec^2 x}{2 \tan x} \, dx - \int 4 \sec 2x \tan 2x \, dx$$
$$+ \int \frac{\csc 2x \cot 2x - 1}{\csc 2x + 2x} \, dx$$
$$= \frac{1}{2} \int \frac{\sec^2 x}{\tan x} \, dx - \int 4 \sec 2x \tan 2x \, dx$$
$$- \frac{1}{2} \int \frac{-2 \csc 2x \cot 2x + 2}{\csc 2x + 2x} \, dx$$
$$= \frac{1}{2} \ln|\tan x| - 2 \sec 2x - \frac{1}{2} \ln|\csc 2x + 2x| + C$$

The first and third integrals were put in the form $\int \frac{f'(x)}{f(x)} dx$, and the second one you can tackle by reversing the formula $\frac{d}{dx}(\sec x) = \sec x \tan x$ — see p.91.

5. Integrating $\frac{du}{dx} f'(u)$

Exercise 5.1 — Integrating using the reverse of the chain rule

Q1 Let $u = x^2$ so $\frac{du}{dx} = 2x$ and $f'(u) = e^u$ so $f(u) = e^u$.
Using the formula:
$$\int 2x e^{x^2} \, dx = e^{x^2} + C$$

Q2 Let $u = 2x^3$ so $\frac{du}{dx} = 6x^2$ and $f'(u) = e^u$ so $f(u) = e^u$.
Using the formula:
$$\int 6x^2 e^{2x^3} \, dx = e^{2x^3} + C$$

Q3 Let $u = \sqrt{x}$ so $\frac{du}{dx} = \frac{1}{2\sqrt{x}}$, and $f'(u) = e^u$ so $f(u) = e^u$.
Using the formula:
$$\int \frac{1}{2\sqrt{x}} e^{\sqrt{x}} \, dx = e^{\sqrt{x}} + C$$

Q4 Let $u = x^4$ so $\frac{du}{dx} = 4x^3$, and $f'(u) = e^u$ so $f(u) = e^u$.
Use the formula:
$$\int 4x^3 e^{x^4} \, dx = e^{x^4} + c$$
So divide by 4 to get the original integral:
$$\int x^3 e^{x^4} \, dx = \frac{1}{4} \int 4x^3 e^{x^4} \, dx = \frac{1}{4} e^{x^4} + C$$

Q5 Let $u = x^2 - \frac{1}{2}x$ so $\frac{du}{dx} = 2x - \frac{1}{2} = \frac{1}{2}(4x - 1)$, and $f'(u) = e^u$ so $f(u) = e^u$.
Use the formula:
$$\int \left(2x - \frac{1}{2}\right) e^{\left(x^2 - \frac{1}{2}x\right)} \, dx = e^{\left(x^2 - \frac{1}{2}x\right)} + c$$
Multiply by 2 to get the original integral:
$$\int (4x - 1) e^{\left(x^2 - \frac{1}{2}x\right)} \, dx = \int 2\left(2x - \frac{1}{2}\right) e^{\left(x^2 - \frac{1}{2}x\right)} \, dx$$
$$= 2 \int \left(2x - \frac{1}{2}\right) e^{\left(x^2 - \frac{1}{2}x\right)} \, dx$$
$$= 2 e^{\left(x^2 - \frac{1}{2}x\right)} + C$$

Q6 Let $u = x^2 + 1$ so $\dfrac{du}{dx} = 2x$, and $f'(u) = \sin u$

so $f(u) = -\cos u$.

Use the formula:

$\displaystyle\int 2x\sin(x^2 + 1)\,dx = -\cos(x^2 + 1) + C$

Q7 Let $u = x^4$ then $\dfrac{du}{dx} = 4x^3$, and $f'(u) = \cos u$

so $f(u) = \sin u$.

Use the formula:

$\displaystyle\int 4x^3\cos(x^4)\,dx = \sin(x^4) + c$

Now divide by 4 to get the original integral:

$\displaystyle\int x^3\cos(x^4)\,dx = \frac{1}{4}\int 4x^3\cos(x^4)\,dx$

$\displaystyle = \frac{1}{4}\sin(x^4) + C$

Q8 Let $u = x^2$ then $\dfrac{du}{dx} = 2x$, and $f'(u) = \sec^2 u$

so $f(u) = \tan u$.

Use the formula:

$\displaystyle\int 2x\sec^2(x^2)\,dx = \tan(x^2) + c$

Now divide by 2 to get the original integral:

$\displaystyle\int x\sec^2(x^2)\,dx = \frac{1}{2}\int 2x\sec^2(x^2)\,dx$

$\displaystyle = \frac{1}{2}\tan(x^2) + C$

Q9 *It's less obvious which function to choose as u in this one —
keep looking out for a function and its derivative. Here we
have cos x and sin x. Remember to make u the one which is
within another function, i.e. cos x.*

Let $u = \cos x$ then $\dfrac{du}{dx} = -\sin x$, and $f'(u) = e^u$

so $f(u) = e^u$.

Use the formula:

$\displaystyle\int -\sin x\, e^{\cos x}\,dx = e^{\cos x} + c$

Multiply by –1 to get the original integral:

$\displaystyle\int \sin x\, e^{\cos x}\,dx = -\int -\sin x\, e^{\cos x}\,dx = -e^{\cos x} + C$

Q10 Let $u = \sin 2x$ then $\dfrac{du}{dx} = 2\cos 2x$, and $f'(u) = e^u$

so $f(u) = e^u$.

Use the formula:

$\displaystyle\int 2\cos 2x\, e^{\sin 2x}\,dx = e^{\sin 2x} + c$

Divide by 2 to get the original integral:

$\displaystyle\int \cos 2x\, e^{\sin 2x}\,dx = \frac{1}{2}\int 2\cos 2x\, e^{\sin 2x}\,dx$

$\displaystyle = \frac{1}{2}e^{\sin 2x} + C$

Q11 Let $u = \tan x$ then $\dfrac{du}{dx} = \sec^2 x$, and $f'(u) = e^u$

so $f(u) = e^u$.

Use the formula:

$\displaystyle\int \sec^2x\, e^{\tan x}\,dx = e^{\tan x} + C$

Q12 Let $u = \sec x$ then $\dfrac{du}{dx} = \sec x \tan x$, and $f'(u) = e^u$

so $f(u) = e^u$.

Use the formula:

$\displaystyle\int \sec x \tan x\, e^{\sec x}\,dx = e^{\sec x} + C$

Exercise 5.2 — Integrating f′(x) × [f(x)]ⁿ

Q1 a) Let $f(x) = x^2 + 5$ so $f'(x) = 2x$. $n = 2$ so $n + 1 = 3$.

Using the formula:

$\displaystyle\int 3 \times 2x(x^2 + 5)^2\,dx = (x^2 + 5)^3 + C$

So $\displaystyle\int 6x(x^2 + 5)^2\,dx = (x^2 + 5)^3 + C$

b) Let $f(x) = x^2 + 7x$ so $f'(x) = 2x + 7$.

$n = 4$ so $n + 1 = 5$.

Using the formula:

$\displaystyle\int 5(2x + 7)(x^2 + 7x)^4\,dx = (x^2 + 7x)^5 + c$

Divide by 5 to get the original integral:

$\displaystyle\int (2x + 7)(x^2 + 7x)^4\,dx = \frac{1}{5}(x^2 + 7x)^5 + C$

c) Let $f(x) = x^4 + 4x^2$ so $f'(x) = 4x^3 + 8x$.

$n = 3$ so $n + 1 = 4$.

Using the formula:

$\displaystyle\int 4(4x^3 + 8x)(x^4 + 4x^2)^3\,dx = (x^4 + 4x^2)^4 + c$

Divide by 16 to get the original integral:

$\displaystyle\int (x^3 + 2x)(x^4 + 4x^2)^3\,dx$

$\displaystyle = \frac{1}{16}\int 4(4x^3 + 8x)(x^4 + 4x^2)^3\,dx$

$\displaystyle = \frac{1}{16}(x^4 + 4x^2)^4 + C$

d) Let $f(x) = x^2 - 1$, so $f'(x) = 2x$.

$n = -3$ so $n + 1 = -2$.

Using the formula:

$\displaystyle\int -2(2x)(x^2 - 1)^{-3}\,dx = (x^2 - 1)^{-2} + C$

Divide by –2 to get the original integral:

$\displaystyle\int \frac{2x}{(x^2 - 1)^3}\,dx = \int (2x)(x^2 - 1)^{-3}\,dx$

$\displaystyle = -\frac{1}{2}(x^2 - 1)^{-2} + C$

$\displaystyle = -\frac{1}{2(x^2 - 1)^2} + C$

e) Let $f(x) = e^{3x} - 5$, so $f'(x) = 3e^{3x}$.

$n = -2$ so $n + 1 = -1$.

Using the formula:

$\displaystyle\int -1(3e^{3x})(e^{3x} - 5)^{-2}\,dx = (e^{3x} - 5)^{-1} + C$

Multiply by –2 to get the original integral:

$\displaystyle\int \frac{6e^{3x}}{(e^{3x} - 5)^2}\,dx = \int 6e^{3x}(e^{3x} - 5)^{-2}\,dx$

$\displaystyle = -2\int -3e^{3x}(e^{3x} - 5)^{-2}\,dx$

$\displaystyle = -2(e^{3x} - 5)^{-1} + C$

f) $\sin x \cos^5 x = \sin x (\cos x)^5$

Let $f(x) = \cos x$ so $f'(x) = -\sin x$.

$n = 5$ so $n + 1 = 6$.

Using the formula:

$\int 6(-\sin x)(\cos x)^5 \, dx = (\cos x)^6 + c = \cos^6 x + c$

Divide by -6 to get the original integral:

$\int \sin x \cos^5 x \, dx = \dfrac{1}{-6} \int 6(-\sin x)(\cos x)^5 \, dx$

$\qquad = -\dfrac{1}{6} \cos^6 x + C$

g) *It's a bit more difficult to tell which is the derivative and which is the function here — both functions are to a power. Remember that the derivative of tan x is sec² x.*

$2\sec^2 x \tan^3 x = 2\sec^2 x (\tan x)^3$

Let $f(x) = \tan x$ so $f'(x) = \sec^2 x$. $n = 3$ so $n + 1 = 4$.

Using the formula:

$\int 4\sec^2 x (\tan x)^3 \, dx = (\tan x)^4 + c = \tan^4 x + c$

Divide by 2 to get the original integral:

$\int 2\sec^2 x \tan^3 x \, dx = \dfrac{1}{2} \int 4\sec^2 x (\tan x)^3 \, dx$

$\qquad = \dfrac{1}{2} \tan^4 x + C$

h) Let $f(x) = e^x + 4$ so $f'(x) = e^x$. $n = 2$ so $n + 1 = 3$.

Using the formula: $\int 3e^x (e^x + 4)^2 \, dx = (e^x + 4)^3 + C$

i) Let $f(x) = e^{4x} - 3x^2$ so $f'(x) = 4e^{4x} - 6x$.

$n = 7$ so $n + 1 = 8$.

Using the formula:

$\int 8(4e^{4x} - 6x)(e^{4x} - 3x^2)^7 \, dx = (e^{4x} - 3x^2)^8 + c$

So $\int 16(2e^{4x} - 3x)(e^{4x} - 3x^2)^7 \, dx = (e^{4x} - 3x^2)^8 + c$

Multiply by 2 to get the original integral:

$\int 32(2e^{4x} - 3x)(e^{4x} - 3x^2)^7 \, dx$

$= 2\int 16(2e^{4x} - 3x)(e^{4x} - 3x^2)^7 \, dx$

$= 2(e^{4x} - 3x^2)^8 + C$

j) Let $f(x) = 2 + \sin x$, so $f'(x) = \cos x$.

$n = -4$, so $n + 1 = -3$.

Using the formula:

$\int -3(\cos x)(2 + \sin x)^{-4} \, dx = (2 + \sin x)^{-3} + C$

Divide by -3 to get the original integral:

$\int \dfrac{\cos x}{(2 + \sin x)^4} \, dx = \int \cos x (2 + \sin x)^{-4} \, dx$

$= -\dfrac{1}{3}(2 + \sin x)^{-3} + C = -\dfrac{1}{3(2 + \sin x)^3} + C$

k) *Using the hint, you know that the derivative of cosec x is $-$cosec x cot x.*

Let $f(x) = \text{cosec } x$ so $f'(x) = -\text{cosec } x \cot x$.

$n = 4$ so $n + 1 = 5$.

Using the formula:

$\int 5(-\text{cosec } x \cot x)(\text{cosec } x)^4 \, dx = (\text{cosec } x)^5 + c$

Multiply by -1:

$\int 5\,\text{cosec } x \cot x \,\text{cosec}^4 x \, dx = -\text{cosec}^5 x + C$

l) *Using the hint, cot x differentiates to $-$cosec² x.*

Let $f(x) = \cot x$ so $f'(x) = -\text{cosec}^2 x$.

$n = 3$ so $n + 1 = 4$.

Using the formula:

$\int 4(-\text{cosec}^2 x)\cot^3 x \, dx = \cot^4 x + c$

Divide by -2 to get the original integral:

$\int 2\,\text{cosec}^2 x \cot^3 x \, dx = \dfrac{1}{-2} \int -4\,\text{cosec}^2 x \cot^3 x \, dx$

$= -\dfrac{1}{2}\cot^4 x + C$

Q2 a) *sec x differentiates to sec x tan x, so try to write the function as a product of sec x tan x and sec x to a power.*

$6\tan x \sec^6 x = 6\tan x \sec x \sec^5 x$

Let $f(x) = \sec x$ so $f'(x) = \sec x \tan x$.

$n = 5$ so $n + 1 = 6$.

Using the formula:

$\int 6(\tan x \sec x)(\sec^5 x) \, dx = \sec^6 x + C$

So $\int 6\tan x \sec^6 x \, dx = \sec^6 x + C$

b) *cosec x differentiates to $-$cot x cosec x so do the same as you did in part a).*

$\cot x \,\text{cosec}^3 x = \cot x \,\text{cosec } x \,\text{cosec}^2 x$

Let $f(x) = \text{cosec } x$ so $f'(x) = -\cot x \,\text{cosec } x$.

$n = 2$ so $n + 1 = 3$.

Using the formula:

$\int 3(-\cot x \,\text{cosec } x)(\text{cosec}^2 x) \, dx = \text{cosec}^3 x + c$

So $\int -3\cot x \,\text{cosec}^3 x \, dx = \text{cosec}^3 x + c$

Divide by -3 to get the original integral.

$\int \cot x \,\text{cosec}^3 x \, dx = \dfrac{1}{-3} \int -3\cot x \,\text{cosec}^3 x \, dx$

$= -\dfrac{1}{3}\text{cosec}^3 x + C$

Q3 a) *This one looks really complicated, but if you differentiate the bracket $(e^{\sin x} - 5)$ using the chain rule, you'll get the function at the front.*

Let $f(x) = e^{\sin x} - 5$ so $f'(x) = \cos x \, e^{\sin x}$.

$n = 3$ so $n + 1 = 4$.

Using the formula:

$\int 4(\cos x \, e^{\sin x})(e^{\sin x} - 5)^3 \, dx = (e^{\sin x} - 5)^4 + C$

b) Let $f(x) = e^{\cos x} + 4x$ so $f'(x) = -\sin x \, e^{\cos x} + 4$.

$n = 6$ so $n + 1 = 7$.

Using the formula:

$\int 7(-\sin x \, e^{\cos x} + 4)(e^{\cos x} + 4x)^6 \, dx$

$= (e^{\cos x} + 4x)^7 + c$

So divide by -7 to get the original integral:

$\int (\sin x \, e^{\cos x} - 4)(e^{\cos x} + 4x)^6 \, dx$

$= -\dfrac{1}{7} \int 7(-\sin x \, e^{\cos x} + 4)(e^{\cos x} + 4x)^6 \, dx$

$= -\dfrac{1}{7}(e^{\cos x} + 4x)^7 + C$

Q4 a) Start by writing the function as $\sec^2 x \tan^{-4} x$.

Let $f(x) = \tan x$ so $f'(x) = \sec^2 x$.

$n = -4$ so $n + 1 = -3$.

Using the formula:

$$\int -3\sec^2 x \tan^{-4} x \, dx = \tan^{-3} x + c$$

Divide by -3 to get the original integral:

$$\int \frac{\sec^2 x}{\tan^4 x} \, dx = -\frac{1}{3}\tan^{-3} x + C = -\frac{1}{3\tan^3 x} + C$$

b) Start by writing the function as

$\cot x \operatorname{cosec} x (\operatorname{cosec} x)^{\frac{1}{2}}$.

Let $f(x) = \operatorname{cosec} x$ so $f'(x) = -\cot x \operatorname{cosec} x$.

$n = \frac{1}{2}$ so $n + 1 = \frac{3}{2}$.

Using the formula:

$$\int \frac{3}{2}(-\cot x \operatorname{cosec} x)(\operatorname{cosec} x)^{\frac{1}{2}} \, dx = (\operatorname{cosec} x)^{\frac{3}{2}} + c$$

Divide by $-\frac{3}{2}$ to get the original integral:

$$\int \cot x \operatorname{cosec} x \sqrt{\operatorname{cosec} x} \, dx = -\frac{2}{3}(\operatorname{cosec} x)^{\frac{3}{2}} + C$$

$$= -\frac{2}{3}(\sqrt{\operatorname{cosec} x})^3 + C$$

6. Integration by Substitution
Exercise 6.1 — Integration by substitution

Q1 a) $u = x + 3 \Rightarrow \dfrac{du}{dx} = 1 \Rightarrow dx = du$

So $\int 12(x + 3)^5 \, dx = \int 12u^5 \, du$

$= 2u^6 + C$

$= 2(x + 3)^6 + C$

You could also have solved this by using the rule given on p100 — it's of the form $(ax + b)^n$.

b) $u = 11 - x \Rightarrow \dfrac{du}{dx} = -1 \Rightarrow dx = -du$

So $\int (11 - x)^4 \, dx = -\int u^4 \, du$

$= -\dfrac{1}{5}u^5 + C$

$= -\dfrac{1}{5}(11 - x)^5 + C$

c) $u = x^2 + 4 \Rightarrow \dfrac{du}{dx} = 2x \Rightarrow dx = \dfrac{1}{2x}du$

So $\int 24x(x^2 + 4)^3 \, dx = \int 24x \times u^3 \times \dfrac{1}{2x} \, du$

$= \int 12u^3 \, du$

$= 3u^4 + C$

$= 3(x^2 + 4)^4 + C$

d) $u = \sin x \Rightarrow \dfrac{du}{dx} = \cos x \Rightarrow dx = \dfrac{1}{\cos x}du$

So $\int \sin^5 x \cos x \, dx = \int u^5 \cos x \times \dfrac{1}{\cos x} \, du$

$= \int u^5 \, du$

$= \dfrac{1}{6}u^6 + C$

$= \dfrac{1}{6}\sin^6 x + C$

e) $u = x - 1 \Rightarrow \dfrac{du}{dx} = 1 \Rightarrow dx = du$

and $u = x - 1 \Rightarrow x = u + 1$

So $\int x(x - 1)^5 \, dx = \int (u + 1)u^5 \, du$

$= \int u^6 + u^5 \, du$

$= \dfrac{1}{7}u^7 + \dfrac{1}{6}u^6 + C$

$= \dfrac{1}{7}(x - 1)^7 + \dfrac{1}{6}(x - 1)^6 + C$

f) $u = \sqrt{x^2 + 1} \Rightarrow \dfrac{du}{dx} = \dfrac{x}{\sqrt{x^2 + 1}} = \dfrac{x}{u} \Rightarrow dx = \dfrac{u}{x}du$

So $\int 6x\sqrt{(x^2 + 1)} \, dx = \int 6x \times u \times \dfrac{u}{x} \, du$

$= \int 6u^2 \, du$

$= 2u^3 + C$

$= 2(\sqrt{x^2 + 1})^3 + C$

g) $u = \sqrt{4 - x^2} \Rightarrow \dfrac{du}{dx} = -\dfrac{x}{\sqrt{4 - x^2}} = -\dfrac{x}{u}$

$\Rightarrow dx = -\dfrac{u}{x}du$

So $\int \dfrac{x}{\sqrt{(4 - x^2)}} \, dx = \int \dfrac{x}{u} \times \dfrac{-u}{x} \, du$

$= \int -1 \, du$

$= -u + C$

$= -\sqrt{4 - x^2} + C$

h) $u = \ln x \Rightarrow \dfrac{du}{dx} = \dfrac{1}{x} \Rightarrow dx = x \, du$

So $\int \dfrac{15(\ln x)^4}{x} \, dx = \int \dfrac{15u^4}{x} \times x \, du$

$= \int 15u^4 \, du$

$= 3u^5 + C$

$= 3(\ln x)^5 + C$

Q2 a) Let $u = x + 2 \Rightarrow \dfrac{du}{dx} = 1 \Rightarrow dx = du$

So $\int 21(x + 2)^6 \, dx = \int 21u^6 \, du$

$= 3u^7 + C$

$= 3(x + 2)^7 + C$

b) Let $u = 5x + 4 \Rightarrow \dfrac{du}{dx} = 5 \Rightarrow dx = \dfrac{1}{5}du$

So $\int (5x + 4)^3 \, dx = \int \dfrac{1}{5}u^3 \, du$

$= \dfrac{u^4}{20} + C$

$= \dfrac{(5x + 4)^4}{20} + C$

c) Let $u = 2x + 3 \Rightarrow \dfrac{du}{dx} = 2 \Rightarrow dx = \dfrac{1}{2}du$

and $u = 2x + 3 \Rightarrow x = \dfrac{u - 3}{2}$

So $\int x(2x + 3)^3 \, dx = \int \dfrac{u - 3}{2} \times u^3 \times \dfrac{1}{2} \, du$

$= \dfrac{1}{4}\int u^4 - 3u^3 \, du$

$= \dfrac{1}{4}\left(\dfrac{1}{5}u^5 - \dfrac{3}{4}u^4\right) + C$

$= \dfrac{1}{20}u^5 - \dfrac{3}{16}u^4 + C$

$= \dfrac{1}{20}(2x + 3)^5 - \dfrac{3}{16}(2x + 3)^4 + C$

d) Let $u = x^2 - 5 \Rightarrow \dfrac{du}{dx} = 2x \Rightarrow dx = \dfrac{1}{2x}du$

So $\displaystyle\int 24x(x^2 - 5)^7\, dx = \int 24x \times u^7 \times \dfrac{1}{2x}\, du$

$\qquad\qquad\qquad\qquad = \displaystyle\int 12u^7\, du$

$\qquad\qquad\qquad\qquad = \dfrac{3}{2}u^8 + C$

$\qquad\qquad\qquad\qquad = \dfrac{3}{2}(x^2 - 5)^8 + C$

Q3 $u = \sqrt{2x - 1} \Rightarrow \dfrac{du}{dx} = \dfrac{1}{\sqrt{2x - 1}} = \dfrac{1}{u} \Rightarrow dx = u\, du$

and $u = \sqrt{2x - 1} \Rightarrow x = \dfrac{u^2 + 1}{2}$

So $\displaystyle\int \dfrac{4x}{\sqrt{(2x - 1)}}\, dx = \int 4\left(\dfrac{u^2 + 1}{2}\right) \times \dfrac{1}{u} \times u\, du$

$\qquad\qquad\qquad = \displaystyle\int 2u^2 + 2\, du$

$\qquad\qquad\qquad = \dfrac{2}{3}u^3 + 2u + C$

$\qquad\qquad\qquad = \dfrac{2}{3}(\sqrt{2x - 1})^3 + 2(\sqrt{2x - 1}) + C$

Q4 $u = 4 - \sqrt{x} \Rightarrow \dfrac{du}{dx} = -\dfrac{1}{2\sqrt{x}} \Rightarrow -2\sqrt{x}\, du = dx$

and $u = 4 - \sqrt{x} \Rightarrow x = (4 - u)^2 \Rightarrow dx$ can be written $-2(4 - u)\, du = (2u - 8)du$

So $\displaystyle\int \dfrac{1}{4 - \sqrt{x}}\, dx = \int \dfrac{1}{u}(2u - 8)\, du$

$\qquad\qquad\qquad = \displaystyle\int 2 - \dfrac{8}{u}\, du$

$\qquad\qquad\qquad = 2u - 8\ln|u| + c$

$\qquad\qquad\qquad = 2(4 - \sqrt{x}) - 8\ln|4 - \sqrt{x}| + c$

$\qquad\qquad\qquad = -2\sqrt{x} - 8\ln|4 - \sqrt{x}| + C$

Don't forget that you can leave out any constant terms that appear after you integrate (like the 8 you get out of the term $2(4 - \sqrt{x})$ here) — they just get absorbed into the constant of integration, C.

Q5 $u = 1 + e^x \Rightarrow \dfrac{du}{dx} = e^x \Rightarrow dx = \dfrac{1}{e^x}\, du$

and $u = 1 + e^x \Rightarrow e^x = u - 1$

So $\displaystyle\int \dfrac{e^{2x}}{1 + e^x}\, dx = \int \dfrac{e^{2x}}{u} \times \dfrac{1}{e^x}\, du$

$\qquad\qquad\qquad = \displaystyle\int \dfrac{e^x}{u}\, du$

$\qquad\qquad\qquad = \displaystyle\int \dfrac{u - 1}{u}\, du$

$\qquad\qquad\qquad = \displaystyle\int 1 - \dfrac{1}{u}\, du$

$\qquad\qquad\qquad = u - \ln|u| + c$

$\qquad\qquad\qquad = 1 + e^x - \ln|1 + e^x| + c$

$\qquad\qquad\qquad = e^x - \ln(1 + e^x) + C$

You can remove the modulus because e^x is always positive, so $1 + e^x > 1$.

Exercise 6.2 — Definite integrals

Q1 a) $u = 3x - 2 \Rightarrow \dfrac{du}{dx} = 3 \Rightarrow dx = \dfrac{1}{3}du$

$x = \dfrac{2}{3} \Rightarrow u = 2 - 2 = 0$

$x = 1 \Rightarrow u = 3 - 2 = 1$

So $\displaystyle\int_{\frac{2}{3}}^{1}(3x - 2)^4\, dx = \int_0^1 \dfrac{1}{3}u^4\, du$

$\qquad\qquad\qquad = \left[\dfrac{1}{15}u^5\right]_0^1 = \dfrac{1}{15}$

b) $u = 2x^3 - 1 \Rightarrow \dfrac{du}{dx} = 6x^2 \Rightarrow dx = \dfrac{1}{6x^2}du$

$x = 0 \Rightarrow u = 0 - 1 = -1$

$x = 1 \Rightarrow u = 2 - 1 = 1$

So $\displaystyle\int_0^1 x^2(2x^3 - 1)^2\, dx = \int_{-1}^1 x^2 u^2 \times \dfrac{1}{6x^2}\, du$

$\qquad\qquad\qquad = \displaystyle\int_{-1}^1 \dfrac{1}{6}u^2\, du$

$\qquad\qquad\qquad = \left[\dfrac{1}{18}u^3\right]_{-1}^1$

$\qquad\qquad\qquad = \dfrac{1}{18} - \left(-\dfrac{1}{18}\right) = \dfrac{1}{9}$

c) $u = \sin x \Rightarrow \dfrac{du}{dx} = \cos x \Rightarrow dx = \dfrac{1}{\cos x}du$

$x = 0 \Rightarrow u = \sin(0) = 0$

$x = \dfrac{\pi}{6} \Rightarrow u = \sin\dfrac{\pi}{6} = \dfrac{1}{2}$

So $\displaystyle\int_0^{\frac{\pi}{6}} 8\sin^3 x \cos x\, dx = \int_0^{\frac{1}{2}} 8u^3 \cos x \times \dfrac{1}{\cos x}\, du$

$\qquad\qquad\qquad = \displaystyle\int_0^{\frac{1}{2}} 8u^3\, du$

$\qquad\qquad\qquad = \left[2u^4\right]_0^{\frac{1}{2}}$

$\qquad\qquad\qquad = 2\left(\dfrac{1}{2}\right)^4 - 0 = \dfrac{1}{8}$

d) $u = \sqrt{x^2 + 1} \Rightarrow \dfrac{du}{dx} = \dfrac{x}{\sqrt{x^2 + 1}} = \dfrac{x}{u} \Rightarrow dx = \dfrac{u}{x}du$

$x = 0 \Rightarrow u = \sqrt{x^2 + 1} = \sqrt{1} = 1$

$x = \sqrt{3} \Rightarrow u = \sqrt{4} = 2$

So $\displaystyle\int_0^{\sqrt{3}} x\sqrt{x^2 + 1}\, dx = \int_1^2 xu \times \dfrac{u}{x}\, du$

$\qquad\qquad\qquad = \displaystyle\int_1^2 u^2\, du$

$\qquad\qquad\qquad = \left[\dfrac{1}{3}u^3\right]_1^2$

$\qquad\qquad\qquad = \dfrac{8}{3} - \dfrac{1}{3} = \dfrac{7}{3}$

Q2 a) Let $u = x^2 - 3 \Rightarrow \dfrac{du}{dx} = 2x \Rightarrow dx = \dfrac{1}{2x}du$

$x = 2 \Rightarrow u = 4 - 3 = 1$

$x = \sqrt{5} \Rightarrow u = 5 - 3 = 2$

So $\displaystyle\int_2^{\sqrt{5}} x(x^2 - 3)^4\, dx = \int_1^2 x \times u^4 \times \dfrac{1}{2x}\, du$

$\qquad\qquad\qquad = \displaystyle\int_1^2 \dfrac{1}{2}u^4\, du$

$\qquad\qquad\qquad = \left[\dfrac{1}{10}u^5\right]_1^2$

$\qquad\qquad\qquad = \dfrac{32}{10} - \dfrac{1}{10} = \dfrac{31}{10} = 3.1$

b) Let $u = 3x - 4 \Rightarrow \dfrac{du}{dx} = 3 \Rightarrow dx = \dfrac{1}{3}du$

and $u = 3x - 4 \Rightarrow x = \dfrac{u + 4}{3}$

$x = 1 \Rightarrow u = 3 - 4 = -1$

$x = 2 \Rightarrow u = 6 - 4 = 2$

So $\displaystyle\int_1^2 x(3x - 4)^3\, dx = \int_{-1}^2 \dfrac{u + 4}{3} \times u^3 \times \dfrac{1}{3}\, du$

$\qquad\qquad\qquad = \dfrac{1}{9}\displaystyle\int_{-1}^2 u^4 + 4u^3\, du$

$\qquad\qquad\qquad = \dfrac{1}{9}\left[\dfrac{u^5}{5} + u^4\right]_{-1}^2$

$\qquad\qquad\qquad = \dfrac{1}{9}\left[\left(\dfrac{32}{5} + 16\right) - \left(\dfrac{-1}{5} + 1\right)\right]$

$\qquad\qquad\qquad = \dfrac{1}{9}\left[\dfrac{108}{5}\right] = \dfrac{12}{5} = 2.4$

c) Let $u = \sqrt{x-1} \Rightarrow \dfrac{du}{dx} = \dfrac{1}{2\sqrt{x-1}} = \dfrac{1}{2u}$

$\Rightarrow dx = 2u\,du$

and $u = \sqrt{x-1} \Rightarrow x = u^2 + 1$

Using $u = \sqrt{x-1}$, $x = 2 \Rightarrow u = \sqrt{1} = 1$

and $x = 10 \Rightarrow u = \sqrt{9} = 3$

So $\displaystyle\int_2^{10} \dfrac{x}{\sqrt{x-1}}\,dx = \int_1^3 \dfrac{u^2+1}{u} \times 2u\,du$

$\displaystyle = \int_1^3 2u^2 + 2\,du$

$= \left[\dfrac{2}{3}u^3 + 2u\right]_1^3$

$= \left[(18+6) - \left(\dfrac{2}{3}+2\right)\right] = \dfrac{64}{3}$

Q3 $u = 3 - \sqrt{x} \Rightarrow \dfrac{du}{dx} = -\dfrac{1}{2\sqrt{x}} \Rightarrow dx = -2\sqrt{x}\,du$

$u = 3 - \sqrt{x} \Rightarrow x = (3-u)^2 \Rightarrow dx = (2u-6)\,du$

So $x = 1 \Rightarrow u = 3 - 1 = 2$

and $x = 4 \Rightarrow u = 3 - 2 = 1$

So area $= \displaystyle\int_1^4 \dfrac{1}{3 - \sqrt{x}}\,dx = \int_2^1 \dfrac{1}{u} \times (2u-6)\,du$

$\displaystyle = \int_2^1 2 - \dfrac{6}{u}\,du$

$= \left[2u - 6\ln|u|\right]_2^1$

$= (2 - 6\ln 1) - (4 - 6\ln 2)$

$= 2 - 0 - 4 + 6\ln 2$

$= -2 + 6\ln 2$

You could have put 2 as the upper limit and 1 as the lower limit in the integral with respect to u, and put a minus sign in front. Both methods give the right answer, but whichever you use, be careful not to lose any minus signs.

Q4 $u = 1 + e^x \Rightarrow \dfrac{du}{dx} = e^x \Rightarrow dx = \dfrac{1}{e^x}\,du$

$x = 0 \Rightarrow u = 1 + e^0 = 2$

$x = 1 \Rightarrow u = 1 + e$

So $\displaystyle\int_0^1 2e^x(1 + e^x)^3\,dx = \int_2^{1+e} 2e^x u^3 \dfrac{1}{e^x}\,du$

$\displaystyle = \int_2^{1+e} 2u^3\,du$

$= \left[\dfrac{u^4}{2}\right]_2^{1+e}$

$= \dfrac{(1+e)^4}{2} - 8 = 87.6$ to 1 d.p.

Q5 $u = \sqrt{3x+1} \Rightarrow \dfrac{du}{dx} = \dfrac{3}{2\sqrt{3x+1}} = \dfrac{3}{2u}$

$\Rightarrow dx = \dfrac{2}{3}u\,du$

and $u = \sqrt{3x+1} \Rightarrow x = \dfrac{u^2-1}{3}$

Using $u = \sqrt{3x+1}$, $x = 1 \Rightarrow u = \sqrt{4} = 2$

and $x = 5 \Rightarrow u = \sqrt{16} = 4$

So area $= \displaystyle\int_1^5 \dfrac{x}{\sqrt{3x+1}}\,dx = \int_2^4 \dfrac{u^2-1}{3u} \times \dfrac{2}{3}u\,du$

$\displaystyle = \dfrac{2}{9}\int_2^4 u^2 - 1\,du$

$= \dfrac{2}{9}\left[\dfrac{1}{3}u^3 - u\right]_2^4$

$= \dfrac{2}{9}\left[\left(\dfrac{64}{3} - 4\right) - \left(\dfrac{8}{3} - 2\right)\right]$

$= \dfrac{2}{9}\left[\dfrac{50}{3}\right] = \dfrac{100}{27}$

Exercise 6.3 — Trig identities

Q1 $x = \tan\theta \Rightarrow \dfrac{dx}{d\theta} = \sec^2\theta \Rightarrow dx = \sec^2\theta\,d\theta$

$x = 0 \Rightarrow \tan\theta = 0 \Rightarrow \theta = 0$

$x = 1 \Rightarrow \tan\theta = 1 \Rightarrow \theta = \dfrac{\pi}{4}$

So using the identity $\sec^2\theta \equiv 1 + \tan^2\theta$

$\displaystyle\int_0^1 \dfrac{1}{1+x^2}\,dx = \int_0^{\frac{\pi}{4}} \dfrac{1}{1+\tan^2\theta} \times \sec^2\theta\,d\theta$

$\displaystyle = \int_0^{\frac{\pi}{4}} \dfrac{\sec^2\theta}{\sec^2\theta}\,d\theta$

$\displaystyle = \int_0^{\frac{\pi}{4}} 1\,d\theta$

$= [\theta]_0^{\frac{\pi}{4}}$

$= \dfrac{\pi}{4}$

Q2 $x = 2\sin\theta \Rightarrow \dfrac{dx}{d\theta} = 2\cos\theta \Rightarrow dx = 2\cos\theta\,d\theta$

$x = 1 \Rightarrow \sin\theta = \dfrac{1}{2} \Rightarrow \theta = \dfrac{\pi}{6}$

$x = \sqrt{3} \Rightarrow \sin\theta = \dfrac{\sqrt{3}}{2} \Rightarrow \theta = \dfrac{\pi}{3}$

So using the identity $\sin^2\theta + \cos^2\theta \equiv 1$

$\displaystyle\int_1^{\sqrt{3}} \dfrac{1}{(4-x^2)^{\frac{3}{2}}}\,dx = \int_{\frac{\pi}{6}}^{\frac{\pi}{3}} \dfrac{1}{(4 - 4\sin^2\theta)^{\frac{3}{2}}} \times 2\cos\theta\,d\theta$

$\displaystyle = \int_{\frac{\pi}{6}}^{\frac{\pi}{3}} \dfrac{2\cos\theta}{(4 - 4(1-\cos^2\theta))^{\frac{3}{2}}}\,d\theta$

$\displaystyle = \int_{\frac{\pi}{6}}^{\frac{\pi}{3}} \dfrac{2\cos\theta}{(4\cos^2\theta)^{\frac{3}{2}}}\,d\theta = \int_{\frac{\pi}{6}}^{\frac{\pi}{3}} \dfrac{2\cos\theta}{8\cos^3\theta}\,d\theta$

$\displaystyle = \int_{\frac{\pi}{6}}^{\frac{\pi}{3}} \dfrac{1}{4}\sec^2\theta\,d\theta = \dfrac{1}{4}[\tan\theta]_{\frac{\pi}{6}}^{\frac{\pi}{3}}$

$= \dfrac{1}{4}\left(\sqrt{3} - \dfrac{1}{\sqrt{3}}\right) = \dfrac{\sqrt{3}}{6}$

Q3 $u = \sec^2 x \Rightarrow \dfrac{du}{dx} = 2\sec^2 x \tan x$

$\Rightarrow dx = \dfrac{1}{2\sec^2 x \tan x}\,du = \dfrac{1}{2u\tan x}\,du$

And using the identity

$\sec^2 x \equiv 1 + \tan^2 x \Rightarrow \tan^2 x \equiv \sec^2 x - 1 = u - 1$

$\displaystyle\int 2\tan^3 x\,dx = \int 2\tan x(u-1) \times \dfrac{1}{2u\tan x}\,du$

$\displaystyle = \int \dfrac{u-1}{u}\,du$

$\displaystyle = \int 1 - \dfrac{1}{u}\,du$

$= u - \ln|u| + C$

$= \sec^2 x - \ln(\sec^2 x) + C$

7. Integration by Parts

Exercise 7.1 — Integration by parts

Q1 a) Let $u = x$ and $\frac{dv}{dx} = e^x$.

Then $\frac{du}{dx} = 1$ and $v = e^x$.

So $\int xe^x\,dx = xe^x - \int e^x\,dx$
$$= xe^x - e^x + C$$

b) Let $u = x$ and $\frac{dv}{dx} = e^{-x}$.

Then $\frac{du}{dx} = 1$ and $v = -e^{-x}$.

So $\int xe^{-x}\,dx = -xe^{-x} - \int -e^{-x}\,dx$
$$= -xe^{-x} - e^{-x} + C$$

c) Let $u = x$ and $\frac{dv}{dx} = e^{-\frac{x}{3}}$.

Then $\frac{du}{dx} = 1$ and $v = -3e^{-\frac{x}{3}}$.

So $\int xe^{-\frac{x}{3}}\,dx = -3xe^{-\frac{x}{3}} - \int -3e^{-\frac{x}{3}}\,dx$
$$= -3xe^{-\frac{x}{3}} - 9e^{-\frac{x}{3}} + C$$

d) Let $u = x$ and $\frac{dv}{dx} = e^x + 1$.

Then $\frac{du}{dx} = 1$ and $v = e^x + x$.

So $\int x(e^x + 1)\,dx = x(e^x + x) - \int e^x + x\,dx$
$$= xe^x + x^2 - e^x - \frac{1}{2}x^2 + C$$
$$= xe^x - e^x + \frac{1}{2}x^2 + C$$

You might have spotted a pattern here — all the parts of this question had u = x and $\frac{dv}{dx}$ as a function involving e. Your answers might look a bit different if you factorised them.

Q2 a) Let $u = x$ and $\frac{dv}{dx} = \sin x$.

Then $\frac{du}{dx} = 1$ and $v = -\cos x$.

So $\int x\sin x\,dx = -x\cos x - \int -\cos x\,dx$
$$= -x\cos x + \sin x + C$$

b) Let $u = 2x$ and $\frac{dv}{dx} = \cos x$.

Then $\frac{du}{dx} = 2$ and $v = \sin x$.

So $\int 2x\cos x\,dx = 2x\sin x - \int 2\sin x\,dx$
$$= 2x\sin x + 2\cos x + C$$

c) Let $u = 3x$ and $\frac{dv}{dx} = \cos \frac{1}{2}x$.

Then $\frac{du}{dx} = 3$ and $v = 2\sin \frac{1}{2}x$.

So $\int 3x\cos\frac{1}{2}x\,dx = 6x\sin\frac{1}{2}x - \int 6\sin\frac{1}{2}x\,dx$
$$= 6x\sin\frac{1}{2}x + 12\cos\frac{1}{2}x + C$$

d) Let $u = 2x$ and $\frac{dv}{dx} = 1 - \sin x$.

Then $\frac{du}{dx} = 2$ and $v = x + \cos x$.

So $\int 2x(1 - \sin x)\,dx$
$$= 2x(x + \cos x) - \int 2(x + \cos x)\,dx$$
$$= 2x^2 + 2x\cos x - x^2 - 2\sin x + C$$
$$= x^2 + 2x\cos x - 2\sin x + C$$

Q3 a) Let $u = \ln x$ and $\frac{dv}{dx} = 2$.

Then $\frac{du}{dx} = \frac{1}{x}$ and $v = 2x$.

So $\int 2\ln x\,dx = 2x\ln x - \int 2\,dx$
$$= 2x\ln x - 2x + C$$

b) Let $u = \ln x$ and $\frac{dv}{dx} = x^4$.

Then $\frac{du}{dx} = \frac{1}{x}$ and $v = \frac{1}{5}x^5$.

So $\int x^4\ln x\,dx = \frac{1}{5}x^5\ln x - \int \frac{1}{5}x^4\,dx$
$$= \frac{1}{5}x^5\ln x - \frac{1}{25}x^5 + C$$

c) Let $u = \ln 4x$ and $\frac{dv}{dx} = 1$.

Then $\frac{du}{dx} = \frac{1}{x}$ and $v = x$.

So $\int \ln 4x\,dx = x\ln 4x - \int 1\,dx$
$$= x\ln 4x - x + C$$

d) Let $u = \ln x^3$ and $\frac{dv}{dx} = 1$.

Then $\frac{du}{dx} = \frac{3}{x}$ and $v = x$.

So $\int \ln x^3\,dx = x\ln x^3 - \int 3\,dx$
$$= x\ln x^3 - 3x + C$$

For parts a), c) and d), if the question hadn't told you to use integration by parts, you could have just used the result for integrating ln x shown on p.127 (you'd need to rewrite the logs in parts c) and d) as ln 4 + ln x and 3ln x).

Q4 a) Let $u = 20x$ and $\frac{dv}{dx} = (x + 1)^3$.

Then $\frac{du}{dx} = 20$ and $v = \frac{1}{4}(x + 1)^4$.

So $\int 20x(x + 1)^3\,dx = 5x(x + 1)^4 - \int 5(x + 1)^4\,dx$
$$= 5x(x + 1)^4 - (x + 1)^5 + C$$

b) Let $u = 30x$ and $\frac{dv}{dx} = (2x + 1)^{\frac{1}{2}}$.

Then $\frac{du}{dx} = 30$ and $v = \frac{1}{3}(2x + 1)^{\frac{3}{2}}$.

So $\int 30x\sqrt{(2x + 1)}\,dx$
$$= 10x(2x + 1)^{\frac{3}{2}} - \int 10(2x + 1)^{\frac{3}{2}}\,dx$$
$$= 10x(2x + 1)^{\frac{3}{2}} - 2(2x + 1)^{\frac{5}{2}} + C$$

Q5 a) Let $u = x$ and $\frac{dv}{dx} = 12e^{2x}$.

Then $\frac{du}{dx} = 1$ and $v = 6e^{2x}$.

So $\int_0^1 12xe^{2x}\,dx = [6xe^{2x}]_0^1 - \int_0^1 6e^{2x}\,dx$
$$= 6e^2 - [3e^{2x}]_0^1$$
$$= 6e^2 - (3e^2 - 3e^0)$$
$$= 3e^2 + 3$$

b) Let $u = x$ and $\frac{dv}{dx} = 18\sin 3x$.

Then $\frac{du}{dx} = 1$ and $v = -6\cos 3x$.

So $\int_0^{\frac{\pi}{3}} 18x\sin 3x\,dx$
$$= [-6x\cos 3x]_0^{\frac{\pi}{3}} - \int_0^{\frac{\pi}{3}} -6\cos 3x\,dx$$
$$= -2\pi\cos \pi + [2\sin 3x]_0^{\frac{\pi}{3}}$$
$$= 2\pi + [2\sin \pi - 2\sin 0]$$
$$= 2\pi$$

c) Let $u = \ln x$ and $\dfrac{dv}{dx} = \dfrac{1}{x^2}$.

Then $\dfrac{du}{dx} = \dfrac{1}{x}$ and $v = -\dfrac{1}{x}$.

So $\displaystyle\int_1^2 \dfrac{1}{x^2}\ln x \, dx = \left[-\dfrac{1}{x}\ln x\right]_1^2 - \int_1^2 -\dfrac{1}{x^2}\,dx$

$\qquad = -\dfrac{1}{2}\ln 2 + \ln 1 - \left[\dfrac{1}{x}\right]_1^2$

$\qquad = -\dfrac{1}{2}\ln 2 - \dfrac{1}{2} + 1$

$\qquad = \dfrac{1}{2} - \dfrac{1}{2}\ln 2$

Q6 Let $u = x$ and $\dfrac{dv}{dx} = e^{-2x}$.

Then $\dfrac{du}{dx} = 1$ and $v = -\dfrac{1}{2}e^{-2x}$.

So $\displaystyle\int \dfrac{x}{e^{2x}}\,dx = -\dfrac{x}{2}e^{-2x} - \int -\dfrac{1}{2}e^{-2x}\,dx$

$\qquad = -\dfrac{x}{2}e^{-2x} - \dfrac{1}{4}e^{-2x} + C$

$\qquad = -\dfrac{x}{2e^{2x}} - \dfrac{1}{4e^{2x}} + C$

Q7 Let $u = x + 1$ and $\dfrac{dv}{dx} = (x + 2)^{\frac{1}{2}}$.

Then $\dfrac{du}{dx} = 1$ and $v = \dfrac{2}{3}(x + 2)^{\frac{3}{2}}$.

So $\displaystyle\int (x + 1)\sqrt{(x + 2)}\,dx$

$\qquad = \dfrac{2}{3}(x + 1)(x + 2)^{\frac{3}{2}} - \int \dfrac{2}{3}(x + 2)^{\frac{3}{2}}\,dx$

$\qquad = \dfrac{2}{3}(x + 1)(x + 2)^{\frac{3}{2}} - \dfrac{4}{15}(x + 2)^{\frac{5}{2}} + C$

Q8 Let $u = \ln(x + 1)$ and $\dfrac{dv}{dx} = 1$.

Then $\dfrac{du}{dx} = \dfrac{1}{x + 1}$ and $v = x$.

So $\displaystyle\int \ln(x + 1)\,dx = x\ln(x + 1) - \int \dfrac{x}{x + 1}\,dx$

$\qquad = x\ln(x + 1) - \int \dfrac{x + 1 - 1}{x + 1}\,dx$

$\qquad = x\ln(x + 1) - \int 1 - \dfrac{1}{x + 1}\,dx$

$\qquad = x\ln|x + 1| - x + \ln|x + 1| + C$

$\qquad = (x + 1)\ln|x + 1| - x + C$

Exercise 7.2 — Repeated use of integration by parts

Q1 a) Let $u = x^2$ and $\dfrac{dv}{dx} = e^x$.

Then $\dfrac{du}{dx} = 2x$ and $v = e^x$.

So $\displaystyle\int x^2 e^x\,dx = x^2 e^x - \int 2xe^x\,dx$

Integrate by parts again to find $\int 2xe^x\,dx$:

Let $u = 2x$ and $\dfrac{dv}{dx} = e^x$.

Then $\dfrac{du}{dx} = 2$ and $v = e^x$.

So $\displaystyle\int 2xe^x\,dx = 2xe^x - \int 2e^x\,dx$

$\qquad = 2xe^x - 2e^x + c$

So $\displaystyle\int x^2 e^x\,dx = x^2 e^x - \int 2xe^x\,dx$

$\qquad = x^2 e^x - (2xe^x - 2e^x + c)$

$\qquad = x^2 e^x - 2xe^x + 2e^x + C$

b) Let $u = x^2$ and $\dfrac{dv}{dx} = \cos x$.

Then $\dfrac{du}{dx} = 2x$ and $v = \sin x$.

So $\displaystyle\int x^2 \cos x\,dx = x^2 \sin x - \int 2x\sin x\,dx$

Integrate by parts again to find $\int 2x\sin x\,dx$:

Let $u = 2x$ and $\dfrac{dv}{dx} = \sin x$.

Then $\dfrac{du}{dx} = 2$ and $v = -\cos x$.

So $\displaystyle\int 2x\sin x\,dx = -2x\cos x - \int -2\cos x\,dx$

$\qquad = -2x\cos x + 2\sin x + c$

So $\displaystyle\int x^2 \cos x\,dx = x^2 \sin x - \int 2x\sin x\,dx$

$\qquad = x^2 \sin x - (-2x\cos x + 2\sin x + c)$

$\qquad = x^2 \sin x + 2x\cos x - 2\sin x + C$

c) Let $u = x^2$ and $\dfrac{dv}{dx} = 4\sin 2x$.

Then $\dfrac{du}{dx} = 2x$ and $v = -2\cos 2x$.

So $\displaystyle\int 4x^2 \sin 2x\,dx = -2x^2\cos 2x + \int 4x\cos 2x\,dx$

Integrate by parts again to find $\int 4x\cos 2x\,dx$:

Let $u = x$ and $\dfrac{dv}{dx} = 4\cos 2x$.

Then $\dfrac{du}{dx} = 1$ and $v = 2\sin 2x$.

So $\displaystyle\int 4x\cos 2x\,dx = 2x\sin 2x - \int 2\sin 2x\,dx$

$\qquad = 2x\sin 2x + \cos 2x + C$

So $\displaystyle\int 4x^2 \sin 2x\,dx = -2x^2\cos 2x + \int 4x\cos 2x\,dx$

$\qquad = -2x^2\cos 2x + (2x\sin 2x + \cos 2x + C)$

$\qquad = -2x^2\cos 2x + 2x\sin 2x + \cos 2x + C$

Q2 Let $u = x^2$ and $\dfrac{dv}{dx} = (x + 1)^4$

Then $\dfrac{du}{dx} = 2x$ and $v = \dfrac{1}{5}(x + 1)^5$.

So $\displaystyle\int_{-1}^0 x^2(x + 1)^4\,dx = \left[\dfrac{x^2}{5}(x + 1)^5\right]_{-1}^0 - \int_{-1}^0 \dfrac{2}{5}x(x + 1)^5\,dx$

$\qquad = 0 - \int_{-1}^0 \dfrac{2}{5}x(x + 1)^5\,dx$

Integrate by parts again to find $\int_{-1}^0 \dfrac{2}{5}x(x + 1)^5\,dx$:

Let $u = x$ and $\dfrac{dv}{dx} = \dfrac{2}{5}(x + 1)^5$.

Then $\dfrac{du}{dx} = 1$ and $v = \dfrac{1}{15}(x + 1)^6$.

So $\displaystyle\int_{-1}^0 \dfrac{2}{5}x(x + 1)^5\,dx = \left[\dfrac{x}{15}(x + 1)^6\right]_{-1}^0 - \int_{-1}^0 \dfrac{1}{15}(x + 1)^6\,dx$

$\qquad = 0 - \left[\dfrac{1}{105}(x + 1)^7\right]_{-1}^0$

$\qquad = -\dfrac{1}{105}$

So $\displaystyle\int_{-1}^0 x^2(x + 1)^4\,dx = 0 - \int_{-1}^0 \dfrac{2}{5}x(x + 1)^5\,dx$

$\qquad = -\left(-\dfrac{1}{105}\right) = \dfrac{1}{105}$

Q3 Let $u = x^2$ and $\dfrac{dv}{dx} = e^{-2x}$.

Then $\dfrac{du}{dx} = 2x$ and $v = -\dfrac{1}{2}e^{-2x}$.

So area $= \displaystyle\int_0^1 x^2 e^{-2x}\, dx = \left[-\dfrac{x^2}{2}e^{-2x}\right]_0^1 + \displaystyle\int_0^1 x e^{-2x}\, dx$

Integrate by parts again to find $\displaystyle\int_0^1 xe^{-2x}\, dx$:

Let $u = x$ and $\dfrac{dv}{dx} = e^{-2x}$.

Then $\dfrac{du}{dx} = 1$ and $v = -\dfrac{1}{2}e^{-2x}$.

So $\displaystyle\int_0^1 xe^{-2x}\, dx = \left[-\dfrac{x}{2}e^{-2x}\right]_0^1 + \displaystyle\int_0^1 \dfrac{1}{2}e^{-2x}\, dx$

$= \left[-\dfrac{x}{2}e^{-2x}\right]_0^1 + \left[-\dfrac{1}{4}e^{-2x}\right]_0^1$

So area $= \left[-\dfrac{x^2}{2}e^{-2x}\right]_0^1 + \left[-\dfrac{x}{2}e^{-2x}\right]_0^1 + \left[-\dfrac{1}{4}e^{-2x}\right]_0^1$

$= -\dfrac{1}{2}e^{-2} - \dfrac{1}{2}e^{-2} - \dfrac{1}{4}e^{-2} + \dfrac{1}{4}$

$= \dfrac{1}{4} - \dfrac{5}{4}e^{-2}$

8. Volumes of Revolution

Exercise 8.1 — Rotating about the x-axis

Q1 a) $y^2 = 16x^2$

So $V = \pi \displaystyle\int_1^2 16x^2\, dx$

$= \pi\left[\dfrac{16}{3}x^3\right]_1^2$

$= \pi\left[\dfrac{128}{3} - \dfrac{16}{3}\right] = \dfrac{112}{3}\pi$

b) $y^2 = x + 2$

So $V = \pi \displaystyle\int_0^2 x + 2\, dx$

$= \pi\left[\dfrac{1}{2}x^2 + 2x\right]_0^2$

$= \pi\left[\left(\dfrac{1}{2}2^2 + 4\right) - 0\right] = 6\pi$

c) $y^2 = 4 - x^2$

So $V = \pi \displaystyle\int_0^2 4 - x^2\, dx$

$= \pi\left[4x - \dfrac{1}{3}x^3\right]_0^2$

$= \pi\left[\left(8 - \dfrac{8}{3}\right) - 0\right] = \dfrac{16}{3}\pi$

Q2 a) $y^2 = \dfrac{4}{x^2}$

So $V = \pi \displaystyle\int_2^8 4x^{-2}\, dx$

$= \pi\left[-\dfrac{4}{x}\right]_2^8$

$= \pi\left[-\dfrac{1}{2} - (-2)\right] = \dfrac{3}{2}\pi$

b) $y^2 = e^{2x}$

So $V = \pi \displaystyle\int_0^2 e^{2x}\, dx$

$= \pi\left[\dfrac{1}{2}e^{2x}\right]_0^2$

$= \pi\left[\dfrac{1}{2}e^4 - \dfrac{1}{2}e^0\right] = \dfrac{\pi}{2}(e^4 - 1)$

c) $y^2 = \dfrac{9}{x}$

So $V = \pi \displaystyle\int_1^2 \dfrac{9}{x}\, dx$

$= \pi\left[9\ln|x|\right]_1^2$

$= 9\pi \ln 2$

d) $y^2 = (1 + \sqrt{x})^2 = 1 + 2\sqrt{x} + x$

So $V = \pi \displaystyle\int_0^1 1 + 2x^{\frac{1}{2}} + x\, dx$

$= \pi\left[x + \dfrac{4}{3}x^{\frac{3}{2}} + \dfrac{1}{2}x^2\right]_0^1$

$= \pi\left[\left(1 + \dfrac{4}{3} + \dfrac{1}{2}\right) - 0\right] = \dfrac{17}{6}\pi$

Q3 a) $y^2 = \sin 2x$

So $V = \pi \displaystyle\int_0^{\frac{\pi}{6}} \sin 2x\, dx$

$= \pi\left[-\dfrac{1}{2}\cos 2x\right]_0^{\frac{\pi}{6}}$

$= \pi\left[\left(-\dfrac{1}{2} \times \dfrac{1}{2}\right) - \left(-\dfrac{1}{2}\right)\right] = \dfrac{\pi}{4}$

b) $y^2 = \dfrac{4}{1 + 2x}$

So $V = \pi \displaystyle\int_0^3 \dfrac{4}{1 + 2x}\, dx$

$= \pi\left[2\ln|1 + 2x|\right]_0^3$

$= 2\pi \ln 7$

c) $y^2 = \dfrac{1}{(1 + 3x)^2}$

So $V = \pi \displaystyle\int_0^1 \dfrac{1}{(1 + 3x)^2}\, dx$

$= \pi\left[-\dfrac{1}{3(1 + 3x)}\right]_0^1$

$= \pi\left[-\dfrac{1}{12} + \dfrac{1}{3}\right] = \dfrac{\pi}{4}$

d) $y^2 = 4x^2 e^{2x}$

So $V = \pi \displaystyle\int_0^1 4x^2 e^{2x}\, dx$

Use integration by parts:

Let $u = 4x^2$ and $\dfrac{dv}{dx} = e^{2x}$.

Then $\dfrac{du}{dx} = 8x$ and $v = \dfrac{1}{2}e^{2x}$.

So $V = \pi \displaystyle\int_0^1 4x^2 e^{2x}\, dx = \pi\left(\left[2x^2 e^{2x}\right]_0^1 - \displaystyle\int_0^1 4xe^{2x}\, dx\right)$

Integrate by parts again to find $\displaystyle\int_0^1 4xe^{2x}\, dx$:

Let $u = 4x$ and $\dfrac{dv}{dx} = e^{2x}$.

Then $\dfrac{du}{dx} = 4$ and $v = \dfrac{1}{2}e^{2x}$.

So $\displaystyle\int_0^1 4xe^{2x}\, dx = \left[2xe^{2x}\right]_0^1 - \displaystyle\int_0^1 2e^{2x}\, dx$

$= \left[2xe^{2x}\right]_0^1 - \left[e^{2x}\right]_0^1$

So $V = \pi\left(\left[2x^2 e^{2x}\right]_0^1 - \left[2xe^{2x}\right]_0^1 + \left[e^{2x}\right]_0^1\right)$

$= \pi(2e^2 - 2e^2 + e^2 - e^0) = \pi(e^2 - 1)$

e) $y^2 = x^2 \sin x$

So $V = \pi \displaystyle\int_0^{\frac{\pi}{4}} x^2 \sin x\, dx$

So using integration by parts:

$V = \pi\left[-x^2 \cos x + 2x \sin x + 2\cos x\right]_0^{\frac{\pi}{4}}$

$= \pi\left[-\dfrac{\pi^2}{16\sqrt{2}} + \dfrac{\pi}{2\sqrt{2}} + \dfrac{2}{\sqrt{2}} - 2\right]$

$= -\dfrac{\pi^3\sqrt{2}}{32} + \dfrac{\pi^2\sqrt{2}}{4} + \pi(\sqrt{2} - 2)$

The full working for the integration of $x^2 \sin x$ is shown in Example 1 on p.128.

Exercise 8.2 — Rotating about the y-axis

Q1 First, rearrange to make x^2 the subject: $y = x^2 + 2 \Rightarrow$ $x^2 = y - 2$.

So $V = \pi \int_3^6 y - 2 \, dy = \pi \left[\dfrac{y^2}{2} - 2y \right]_3^6$

$= \pi \left[(18 - 12) - \left(\dfrac{9}{2} - 6 \right) \right] = \dfrac{15}{2}\pi$

Q2 First, rearrange to make x^2 the subject: $y = \dfrac{x^2}{2} - 2 \Rightarrow$ $x^2 = 2y + 4$.

So $V = \pi \int_1^3 2y + 4 \, dy = \pi [y^2 + 4y]_1^3$

$= \pi[(9 + 12) - (1 + 4)] = 16\pi$

Q3 First, rearrange to make x^2 the subject: $y^2 = x \Rightarrow$ $x^2 = y^4$.

So $V = \pi \int_{-1}^2 y^4 \, dy = \pi \left[\dfrac{y^5}{5} \right]_{-1}^2$

$= \pi \left[\left(\dfrac{32}{5} \right) - \left(\dfrac{-1}{5} \right) \right] = \dfrac{33}{5}\pi$

Q4 First, rearrange to make x^2 the subject: $3y^2 + x^2 = 9 \Rightarrow$ $x^2 = 9 - 3y^2$.

So $V = \pi \int_1^2 9 - 3y^2 \, dy = \pi[9y - y^3]_1^2$

$= \pi[(18 - 8) - (9 - 1)] = 2\pi$

Q5 First, rearrange to make x^2 the subject: $y = 3x^2 - 2 \Rightarrow$ $x^2 = \dfrac{y + 2}{3}$.

So $V = \dfrac{\pi}{3} \int_{-2}^{10} y + 2 \, dy = \dfrac{\pi}{3} \left[\dfrac{y^2}{2} + 2y \right]_{-2}^{10}$

$= \dfrac{\pi}{3}[(50 + 20) - (2 - 4)] = 24\pi$

Q6 First, rearrange to make x^2 the subject: $y^2 - y = 10 - x^2$ $\Rightarrow x^2 = 10 + y - y^2$.

So $V = \pi \int_1^2 10 + y - y^2 \, dy = \pi \left[10y + \dfrac{y^2}{2} - \dfrac{y^3}{3} \right]_1^2$

$= \pi \left[\left(20 + 2 - \dfrac{8}{3} \right) - \left(10 + \dfrac{1}{2} - \dfrac{1}{3} \right) \right] = \dfrac{55}{6}\pi$

Review Exercise — Chapter 5

Q1 **a)** $\displaystyle\int \dfrac{1}{\sqrt[3]{(2 - 11x)}} \, dx = \int (2 - 11x)^{-\frac{1}{3}} \, dx$

$= \dfrac{1}{-11 \times \left(\frac{2}{3} \right)}(2 - 11x)^{\frac{2}{3}} + C$

$= -\dfrac{3}{22}(2 - 11x)^{\frac{2}{3}} + C$

b) Integrate the curve between the two limits:

$\displaystyle\int_{-\frac{123}{11}}^{-\frac{62}{11}} \dfrac{1}{\sqrt[3]{(2 - 11x)}} \, dx = -\dfrac{3}{22}[(\sqrt[3]{2 - 11x})^2]_{-\frac{123}{11}}^{-\frac{62}{11}}$

$= -\dfrac{3}{22}([(\sqrt[3]{2 + 62})^2] - [(\sqrt[3]{2 + 123})^2])$

$= -\dfrac{3}{22}((\sqrt[3]{64})^2 - (\sqrt[3]{125})^2)$

$= -\dfrac{3}{22}(16 - 25) = \dfrac{27}{22}$

Q2 To find y from $\dfrac{dy}{dx}$, integrate:

$y = \displaystyle\int \dfrac{dy}{dx} \, dx = \int (1 - 7x)^{\frac{1}{2}} \, dx$

$= \dfrac{1}{-7 \times \frac{3}{2}}(1 - 7x)^{\frac{3}{2}} + C$

$= -\dfrac{2}{21}(1 - 7x)^{\frac{3}{2}} + C$

Given that the equation goes through the point (0, 1), you can substitute in these values for x and y to get C.

$y = -\dfrac{2}{21}(1 - 7x)^{\frac{3}{2}} + C$

$1 = -\dfrac{2}{21}(1 - 0)^{\frac{3}{2}} + C$

$\Rightarrow C = \dfrac{23}{21}$

So the equation of the curve is:

$y = -\dfrac{2}{21}(1 - 7x)^{\frac{3}{2}} + \dfrac{23}{21}$

Q3 **a)** $\displaystyle\int 4e^{2x} \, dx = 4\left(\dfrac{1}{2}e^{2x} \right) + C = 2e^{2x} + C$

b) $\displaystyle\int e^{3x - 5} \, dx = \dfrac{1}{3}e^{3x - 5} + C$

c) $\displaystyle\int \dfrac{2}{3x} \, dx = \int \dfrac{2}{3} \times \dfrac{1}{x} \, dx = \dfrac{2}{3}\ln|x| + C$

d) $\displaystyle\int \dfrac{2}{2x + 1} \, dx = 2\left(\dfrac{1}{2}\ln|2x + 1| \right) + C$

$= \ln|2x + 1| + C$

You could have written this down straight away if you'd noticed that the numerator is the derivative of the denominator.

Q4 $\displaystyle\int \dfrac{8}{2 - x} - \dfrac{8}{x} \, dx = 8\left(\dfrac{1}{-1}\ln|2 - x| \right) - 8\ln|x| + C$

$= -8\ln|2 - x| - 8\ln|x| + C$

$= -8(\ln|2 - x| + \ln|x|) + C$

$= -8(\ln|x(2 - x)|) + C$

$= \ln|(2x - x^2)^{-8}| + C$

So $P = (2x - x^2)^{-8}$.

You can get rid of the modulus signs as anything raised to the power 8 will be positive.

Q5 **a)** $\displaystyle\int \cos(x + A) \, dx = \sin(x + A) + C$

b) $\displaystyle\int \sin(A - x) \, dx = \dfrac{1}{-1}(-\cos(A - x)) + C$

$= \cos(A - x) + C$

c) $\displaystyle\int \text{cosec}^2((A + B)t + A + B) \, dt$

$= \dfrac{1}{A + B}(-\cot((A + B)t + A + B)) + C$

$= -\dfrac{1}{A + B}\cot((A + B)t + A + B) + C$

Q6 **a)** $\displaystyle\int \cos 4x - \sec^2 7x \, dx = \dfrac{1}{4}\sin 4x - \dfrac{1}{7}\tan 7x + C$

b) $\displaystyle\int 6\sec 3x \tan 3x - \text{cosec}^2\dfrac{x}{5} \, dx$

$= 6\left(\dfrac{1}{3}\sec 3x \right) - \dfrac{1}{\left(\frac{1}{5} \right)}\left(-\cot\dfrac{x}{5} \right) + C$

$= 2\sec 3x + 5\cot\dfrac{x}{5} + C$

Q7 **a)** *The numerator is the derivative of the denominator so use the result* $\int \frac{f'(x)}{f(x)}\,dx = \ln|f(x)| + C$ *with* $f(x) = \sin x$.

$\int \frac{\cos x}{\sin x}\,dx = \ln|\sin x| + C$

b) Differentiating the denominator gives $5x^4 + 3x^2 - 3$. So the numerator is 4 times the derivative of the denominator.

$\int \frac{20x^4 + 12x^2 - 12}{x^5 + x^3 - 3x}\,dx = \int \frac{4(5x^4 + 3x^2 - 3)}{x^5 + x^3 - 3x}\,dx$
$$= 4\ln|x^5 + x^3 - 3x| + C$$

Q8 **a)** Let $u = x^3$ then $\frac{du}{dx} = 3x^2$, and $f'(u) = e^u$, so $f(u) = e^u$. Using the reverse chain rule formula:

$\int 3x^2 e^{x^3}\,dx = e^{x^3} + C$

b) Let $u = \sin(x^2)$ then $\frac{du}{dx} = 2x\cos(x^2)$ and $f'(u) = e^u$, so $f(u) = e^u$. Using the reverse chain rule formula:

$\int 2x\cos(x^2)e^{\sin(x^2)}\,dx = e^{\sin(x^2)} + C$

c) Let $u = \sec(4x)$ then $\frac{du}{dx} = 4\sec(4x)\tan(4x)$, and $f'(u) = e^u$, so $f(u) = e^u$.

Using the reverse chain rule formula:

$\int 4\sec 4x \tan 4x\, e^{\sec 4x}\,dx = e^{\sec 4x} + c$
$\Rightarrow \int \sec 4x \tan 4x\, e^{\sec 4x}\,dx = \frac{1}{4}e^{\sec 4x} + C$

Q9 **a)** $u = 5 - x^2 \Rightarrow \frac{du}{dx} = -2x \Rightarrow -\frac{1}{2x}du = dx$

Substituting this into the integral gives:

$\int 16x \times u^5 \times -\frac{1}{2x}\,du = \int -8u^5\,du$
$$= -\frac{4}{3}u^6 + C$$
$$= -\frac{4}{3}(5 - x^2)^6 + C$$

Make sure you reverse the substitution at the end to get your final answer in terms of x.

b) $u = \cos\theta \Rightarrow \frac{du}{d\theta} = -\sin\theta \Rightarrow -\frac{1}{\sin\theta}du = d\theta$

Substituting this into the integral gives:
$\int 3\sin\theta \times u^4 \times -\frac{1}{\sin\theta}\,du = \int -3u^4\,du$
$$= -\frac{3}{5}u^5 + C$$
$$= -\frac{3}{5}\cos^5\theta + C$$

c) $u = e^x - 1 \Rightarrow \frac{du}{dx} = e^x \Rightarrow \frac{1}{e^x}du = dx$
and $e^x + 1 = u + 2$

Substituting this into the integral gives:

$\int e^x(u + 2)u^2 \frac{du}{e^x} = \int (u + 2)u^2\,du$
$$= \int u^3 + 2u^2\,du$$
$$= \frac{1}{4}u^4 + \frac{2}{3}u^3 + C$$
$$= \frac{1}{4}(e^x - 1)^4 + \frac{2}{3}(e^x - 1)^3 + C$$

Q10 **a)** $u = x^2 - 4 \Rightarrow \frac{du}{dx} = 2x \Rightarrow \frac{du}{2x} = dx$

Change the limits:
$x = 2 \Rightarrow u = 2^2 - 4 = 0$, $x = 4 \Rightarrow u = 4^2 - 4 = 12$

Substituting into the integral gives:
$\int_0^{12} x u^3 \frac{du}{2x} = \int_0^{12} \frac{1}{2}u^3\,du$
$$= \left[\frac{1}{8}u^4\right]_0^{12}$$
$$= \frac{12^4}{8} = 2592$$

b) $u = \sec x \Rightarrow \frac{du}{dx} = \sec x \tan x \Rightarrow \frac{du}{\sec x \tan x} = dx$

Change the limits: $x = \frac{\pi}{4} \Rightarrow u = \sec\frac{\pi}{4} = \sqrt{2}$,
$x = \frac{\pi}{3} \Rightarrow u = \sec\frac{\pi}{3} = 2$

Substituting into the integral gives:

$\int_{\sqrt{2}}^{2} \sec x \tan x\, u^3 \frac{du}{\sec x \tan x} = \int_{\sqrt{2}}^{2} u^3\,du$
$$= \left[\frac{1}{4}u^4\right]_{\sqrt{2}}^{2}$$
$$= \frac{16}{4} - \frac{4}{4} = 4 - 1 = 3$$

c) $u = \sqrt{3x - 8} \Rightarrow \frac{du}{dx} = \frac{3}{2\sqrt{3x - 8}} = \frac{3}{2u}$
$\Rightarrow \frac{2}{3}u\,du = dx$ and $x = \frac{8 + u^2}{3}$

Change the limits:
$x = 3 \Rightarrow u = \sqrt{9 - 8} = 1$,
$x = 11 \Rightarrow u = \sqrt{33 - 8} = 5$

Substituting into the integral gives:

$\int_1^5 2\left(\frac{8 + u^2}{3}\right) \times \frac{1}{u} \times \frac{2}{3}u\,du = \int_1^5 \frac{4}{9}(8 + u^2)\,du$
$$= \frac{4}{9}\left[8u + \frac{1}{3}u^3\right]_1^5$$
$$= \frac{4}{9}\left[\left(40 + \frac{125}{3}\right) - \left(8 + \frac{1}{3}\right)\right] = \frac{880}{27}$$

Q11 $x = \cot\theta \Rightarrow \frac{dx}{d\theta} = -\csc^2\theta \Rightarrow dx = -\csc^2\theta\,d\theta$
Change the limits:
$x = 1 \Rightarrow \theta = \frac{\pi}{4}$, $x = \sqrt{3} \Rightarrow \theta = \frac{\pi}{6}$
Substituting into the integral and using the identity $\csc^2\theta \equiv 1 + \cot^2\theta$ gives:

$\int_{\frac{\pi}{4}}^{\frac{\pi}{6}} \frac{4\cot\theta}{\sqrt{1 + \cot^2\theta}} \times -\csc^2\theta\,d\theta$
$$= \int_{\frac{\pi}{4}}^{\frac{\pi}{6}} -\frac{4\cot\theta\csc^2\theta}{\sqrt{\csc^2\theta}}\,d\theta$$
$$= \int_{\frac{\pi}{6}}^{\frac{\pi}{4}} \frac{4\cot\theta\csc^2\theta}{\sqrt{\csc^2\theta}}\,d\theta$$
$$= \int_{\frac{\pi}{6}}^{\frac{\pi}{4}} 4\cot\theta\csc\theta\,d\theta$$
$$= \left[-4\csc\theta\right]_{\frac{\pi}{6}}^{\frac{\pi}{4}}$$
$$= -4(\sqrt{2}) - (-4(2)) = 8 - 4\sqrt{2}$$

Q12 a) Let $u = \ln x$ and let $\frac{dv}{dx} = 3x^2$.

So $\frac{du}{dx} = \frac{1}{x}$ and $v = x^3$.

Putting these into the formula gives:

$$\int 3x^2 \ln x \, dx = x^3 \ln x - \int \frac{x^3}{x} dx$$
$$= x^3 \ln x - \int x^2 dx$$
$$= x^3 \ln x - \frac{1}{3}x^3 + C$$
$$= x^3(\ln x - \frac{1}{3}) + C$$

b) Let $u = 4x$, and let $\frac{dv}{dx} = \cos 4x$.

So $\frac{du}{dx} = 4$ and $v = \frac{1}{4}\sin 4x$.

Putting these into the formula gives:

$$\int 4x \cos 4x \, dx = 4x\left(\frac{1}{4}\sin 4x\right) - \int 4\left(\frac{1}{4}\sin 4x\right)dx$$
$$= x \sin 4x - \int \sin 4x \, dx$$
$$= x \sin 4x + \frac{1}{4}\cos 4x + C$$

c) Let $u = x^2$, and let $\frac{dv}{dx} = e^{\frac{x}{2}}$.

So $\frac{du}{dx} = 2x$ and $v = 2e^{\frac{x}{2}}$.

Putting these into the formula gives:

$$\int_0^4 x^2 e^{\frac{x}{2}} dx = [2x^2 e^{\frac{x}{2}}]_0^4 - \int_0^4 4x e^{\frac{x}{2}} dx$$

Now use integration by parts again on $\int_0^4 4x e^{\frac{x}{2}} dx$:

Let $u = 4x$, and let $\frac{dv}{dx} = e^{\frac{x}{2}}$.

So $\frac{du}{dx} = 4$ and $v = 2e^{\frac{x}{2}}$.

Putting these into the formula gives:

$$\int_0^4 4x e^{\frac{x}{2}} dx = [8x e^{\frac{x}{2}}]_0^4 - \int_0^4 8 e^{\frac{x}{2}} dx$$
$$= [8x e^{\frac{x}{2}}]_0^4 - [16 e^{\frac{x}{2}}]_0^4$$

So the original integral is given by:

$$\int_0^4 x^2 e^{\frac{x}{2}} dx = [2x^2 e^{\frac{x}{2}}]_0^4 - [8x e^{\frac{x}{2}}]_0^4 + [16 e^{\frac{x}{2}}]_0^4$$
$$= 32e^2 - 32e^2 + 16e^2 - 16$$
$$= 16e^2 - 16$$

Q13 $y^2 = (2x - 1)^2 = 4x^2 - 4x + 1$

So $V = \pi \int_1^3 4x^2 - 4x + 1 \, dx$

$$= \pi\left[\frac{4}{3}x^3 - 2x^2 + x\right]_1^3$$
$$= \pi\left[(36 - 18 + 3) - (\frac{4}{3} - 2 + 1)\right] = \frac{62}{3}\pi$$

Q14 If $y = \frac{1}{x}$ then $y^2 = \frac{1}{x^2}$.

Putting this into the integral gives:

$$V = \pi \int_2^4 \frac{1}{x^2} dx = \pi\left[-\frac{1}{x}\right]_2^4 = \pi\left[(-\frac{1}{4}) - (-\frac{1}{2})\right] = \frac{\pi}{4}$$

Q15 $y^2 = 16 \ln x$

So $V = \pi \int_1^2 16 \ln x \, dx$

$$= 16\pi[x \ln x - x]_1^2$$
$$= 16\pi(2 \ln 2 - 1)$$

Remember, $\int \ln x \, dx$ was covered on p.127.

Q16 First, rearrange to make x^2 the subject: $y = x^2 + 1 \Rightarrow$
$x^2 = y - 1$.

So $V = \pi \int_1^3 y - 1 \, dy = \pi\left[\frac{y^2}{2} - y\right]_1^3$

$$= \pi\left[(\frac{9}{2} - 3) - (\frac{1}{2} - 1)\right] = 2\pi$$

Q17 First, rearrange to make x^2 the subject: $2y^3 - x^2 - 3 = 0$
$\Rightarrow x^2 = 2y^3 - 3$.

So $V = \pi \int_1^2 2y^3 - 3 \, dy = \pi\left[\frac{y^4}{2} - 3y\right]_1^2$

$$= \pi\left[(8 - 6) - (\frac{1}{2} - 3)\right] = \frac{9}{2}\pi$$

Exam-Style Questions — Chapter 5

Q1 a) $\int 3e^{(5 - 6x)} dx = \frac{3}{-6}e^{(5 - 6x)} + C$

$$= -\frac{1}{2}e^{(5 - 6x)} + C$$

[1 mark for answer in the form $ke^{(5 - 6x)}$, 1 mark for the correct value of k]

b) $\int \frac{\csc^2 x - 2}{\cot x + 2x} dx = \int \frac{-(-\csc^2 x + 2)}{\cot x + 2x} dx$

$$= -\ln|\cot x + 2x| + C$$

[1 mark for answer in the form $k\ln|f(x)|$, 1 mark for correct value of k and 1 mark for correct function f(x). Lose 1 mark if C is missed off both answers a) and b)]

Q2 Integrate the curve $y = \frac{2}{3(\sqrt[3]{5x - 2})}$ with respect to x
between 2 and 5.8 to find the shaded region:

$$\int_2^{5.8} \frac{2}{3(\sqrt[3]{5x - 2})} dx = \int_2^{5.8} \frac{2}{3}(5x - 2)^{-\frac{1}{3}} dx \text{ [1 mark]}$$

$$= \left[\frac{1}{5} \cdot \frac{2}{3} \cdot \frac{3}{2}(5x - 2)^{\frac{2}{3}}\right]_2^{5.8}$$

$$= \left[\frac{1}{5}(\sqrt[3]{5x - 2})^2\right]_2^{5.8}$$

$$= \frac{1}{5}(\sqrt[3]{27})^2 - \frac{1}{5}(\sqrt[3]{8})^2 \text{ [1 mark]}$$

$$= \frac{3^2}{5} - \frac{2^2}{5} = \frac{5}{5} = 1 \text{ [1 mark]}$$

So area $= 1$

Q3 $V = \pi \int_{\frac{\pi}{4}}^{\frac{\pi}{3}} y^2 dx = \pi \int_{\frac{\pi}{4}}^{\frac{\pi}{3}} \csc^2 x \, dx = \pi[-\cot x]_{\frac{\pi}{4}}^{\frac{\pi}{3}}$

$$= \pi\left[(-\cot\frac{\pi}{3}) - (-\cot\frac{\pi}{4})\right]$$

$$= \pi\left[-\frac{1}{\sqrt{3}} + 1\right] = 1.328 \text{ (3 d.p.)}.$$

[3 marks available — 1 mark for correct function for y^2, 1 mark for integrating, 1 mark for substituting in values of x to obtain correct answer]
Don't forget π here.

Q4 a) Let $u = x$, so $\frac{du}{dx} = 1$.

Let $\frac{dv}{dx} = \sin 4x$, so $v = -\frac{1}{4}\cos 4x$

[1 mark for both parts correct]

Using integration by parts,

$$\int x \sin 4x \, dx = -\frac{1}{4}x\cos 4x - \int -\frac{1}{4}\cos 4x \, dx$$
[1 mark]

$$= -\frac{1}{4}x\cos 4x + \frac{1}{16}\sin 4x + C \text{ [1 mark]}$$

b) Let $u = x^2$, so $\frac{du}{dx} = 2x$.

Let $\frac{dv}{dx} = \cos 4x$, so $v = \frac{1}{4}\sin 4x$

[1 mark for both parts correct]

Using integration by parts,

$$\int x^2 \cos 4x \, dx = \frac{1}{4}x^2 \sin 4x - \int \frac{1}{2}x\sin 4x \, dx$$
[1 mark]

$$= \frac{1}{4}x^2 \sin 4x - \frac{1}{2}(-\frac{1}{4}x\cos 4x + \frac{1}{16}\sin 4x) + C$$
[1 mark]

You can use the result from part a) for this stage.

$$= \frac{1}{4}x^2 \sin 4x + \frac{1}{8}x\cos 4x - \frac{1}{32}\sin 4x + C \text{ [1 mark]}$$

Q5 If $u = \ln x$, then $\frac{du}{dx} = \frac{1}{x}$, so $x\,du = dx$.

Changing the limits: when $x = 1$, $u = \ln 1 = 0$
                           when $x = 2$, $u = \ln 2$

Substituting all this into the integral gives:

$$\int_1^2 \frac{8}{x}(\ln x + 2)^3 \, dx = \int_0^{\ln 2} \frac{8}{x}(u+2)^3 x\,du = \int_0^{\ln 2} 8(u+2)^3 \, du$$
$$= [2(u+2)^4]_0^{\ln 2}$$
$$= [2(\ln 2 + 2)^4] - [2(0+2)^4]$$
$$= 105.21 - 32 = 73.21 \text{ (4 s.f.)}$$

[6 marks available — 1 mark for finding substitution for dx, 1 mark for finding correct limits, 1 mark for correct integral in terms of u, 2 marks for integration (1 mark for an answer in the form $k(u+2)^n$, 1 mark for correct values of k and n), 1 mark for final answer (to 4 s.f.)]

Q6 Let $u = \ln x$, so $\frac{du}{dx} = \frac{1}{x}$.

Let $\frac{dv}{dx} = \frac{1}{x^2}$, so $v = -\frac{1}{x}$

[1 mark for both parts correct]

Using integration by parts,

$$\int_1^4 \frac{\ln x}{x^2} \, dx = \left[-\frac{1}{x}\ln x\right]_1^4 - \int_1^4 -\frac{1}{x^2} \, dx \text{ [1 mark]}$$

$$= \left[-\frac{1}{x}\ln x\right]_1^4 - \left[\frac{1}{x}\right]_1^4 \text{ [1 mark]}$$

$$= \left[-\frac{1}{4}\ln 4 + \ln 1\right] - \left[\frac{1}{4} - 1\right] \text{ [1 mark]}$$

$$= -\frac{1}{4}\ln 4 + \frac{3}{4} \text{ [1 mark]}$$

Q7 First, rearrange the equation to get it in terms of x^2:

$y = \frac{1}{x^2} \Rightarrow x^2 = \frac{1}{y}$. Putting this into the formula:

$V = \pi \int_1^3 \frac{1}{y} \, dy = \pi[\ln y]_1^3$

$= \pi[\ln 3 - \ln 1] = \pi \ln 3$.

[5 marks available — 1 mark for rearranging equation, 1 mark for correct formula for volume, 1 mark for correct integration, 1 mark for substituting in limits, 1 mark for final answer (in terms of π and ln)]

Chapter 6: Numerical Methods

1. Location of Roots

Exercise 1.1 — Locating roots by changes of sign

Q1 $f(2) = 2^3 - 5 \times 2 + 1 = -1$
$f(3) = 3^3 - 5 \times 3 + 1 = 13$
There is a sign change (and the function is continuous in this interval) so there is a root in this interval.
They wouldn't ask you if there's a root if the function wasn't continuous in this interval, but it's worth saying anyway just to keep your answer 'strictly true'.

Q2 $f(0.9) = \sin(1.8) - 0.9 = 0.0738...$
$f(1.0) = \sin(2.0) - 1.0 = -0.0907...$
There is a sign change (and the function is continuous in this interval) so there is a root in this interval.

Q3 $f(1.2) = 1.2^3 + \ln 1.2 - 2 = -0.089...$
$f(1.3) = 1.3^3 + \ln 1.3 - 2 = 0.459...$
There is a sign change (and the function is continuous in this interval) so there is a root in this interval.

Q4 $f(2.5) = 2.5^2 + \frac{1}{2.5} - 7 = -0.35$

$f(2.6) = 2.6^2 + \frac{1}{2.6} - 7 = 0.14...$
There is a sign change (and the function is continuous in this interval) so there is a root in this interval.

Q5 $f(-0.8) = \cos(-0.8) - 0.8 = -0.10...$
$f(-0.7) = \cos(-0.7) - 0.7 = 0.06...$
There is a sign change (and the function is continuous in this interval) so there is a root in this interval.

Q6 $f(1) = e^1 + 1 - 8 = -4.28...$
$f(2) = e^2 + 2 - 8 = 1.38...$
There is a sign change (and the function is continuous in this interval) so there is a root in this interval.

Q7 $f(1.6) = (3 \times 1.6) - 1.6^4 + 3 = 1.24...$
$f(1.7) = (3 \times 1.7) - 1.7^4 + 3 = -0.25...$
There is a sign change (and the function is continuous in this interval) so there is a root in this interval.
$f(-1) = (3 \times (-1)) - (-1)^4 + 3 = -1$
$f(0) = (3 \times 0) - 0^4 + 3 = 3$
There is a sign change (and the function is continuous in this interval) so there is a root in this interval.

Q8 $f(0.01) = e^{0.01-2} - \sqrt{0.01} = 0.0366...$
$f(0.02) = e^{0.02-2} - \sqrt{0.02} = -0.0033...$
There is a sign change (and the function is continuous in this interval) so there is a root in this interval.
$f(2.4) = e^{2.4-2} - \sqrt{2.4} = -0.057...$
$f(2.5) = e^{2.5-2} - \sqrt{2.5} = 0.067...$
There is a sign change (and the function is continuous in this interval) so there is a root in this interval.

Q9 The upper and lower bounds are 2.75 and 2.85.
$f(2.75) = 2.75^3 - (7 \times 2.75) - 2 = -0.45...$
$f(2.85) = 2.85^3 - (7 \times 2.85) - 2 = 1.19...$
There is a sign change between the upper and lower bounds (and the function is continuous in this interval), so a solution to 1 d.p. is $x = 2.8$.

Q10 Upper and lower bounds are 0.65 and 0.75.

$f(0.65) = (2 \times 0.65) - \dfrac{1}{0.65} = -0.23...$

$f(0.75) = (2 \times 0.75) - \dfrac{1}{0.75} = 0.16...$

There is a sign change between the upper and lower bounds (and the function is continuous in this interval), so a solution to 1 d.p. is $x = 0.7$.

Q11 $f(0.245) = e^{0.245} - 0.245^3 - (5 \times 0.245) = 0.037...$
$f(0.255) = e^{0.255} - 0.255^3 - (5 \times 0.255) = -0.001...$
There is a sign change between the upper and lower bounds (and the function is continuous in this interval), so a solution to 2 d.p. is $x = 0.25$.

Q12 $f(2.4855) = 2.4855^3 - (2 \times 2.4855^2) - 3 = -0.00072...$
$f(2.4865) = 2.4865^3 - (2 \times 2.4865^2) - 3 = 0.0078...$
There is a sign change between the upper and lower bounds (and the function is continuous in this interval), so a solution to 3 d.p. is $x = 2.486$.

Q13 $f(-2.3) = (4 \times -2.3) - (2 \times (-2.3)^3) - 15 = 0.134$
$f(-2.2) = (4 \times -2.2) - (2 \times (-2.2)^3) - 15 = -2.504$
There is a sign change (and the function is continuous in this interval) so there is a root in this interval.

Q14 $f(0.23) = \ln(0.23 + 3) - (5 \times 0.23) = 0.022...$
$f(0.24) = \ln(0.24 + 3) - (5 \times 0.24) = -0.024...$
There is a sign change (and the function is continuous in this interval) so there is a root in this interval.

Q15 $f(0) = e^{3 \times 0}\sin 0 - 5 = -5$
$f(1) = e^{3 \times 1}\sin 1 - 5 = 11.9...$
There is a sign change (and the function is continuous in this interval) so there is a root in this interval.

Exercise 1.2 — Sketching graphs to find approximate roots

Q1 a)

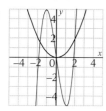

b) The graphs cross twice, so the equation has 2 roots.

c) $f(2.4) = 2.4 - \dfrac{1}{2.4} - 2 = -0.016...$

$f(2.5) = 2.5 - \dfrac{1}{2.5} - 2 = 0.1$

There is a sign change (and the function is continuous in this interval) so there is a root in this interval.

Q2 a)

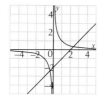

b) The graphs cross 3 times, so the equation has 3 roots.

c) $f(-2) = (2 \times (-2)^3) - (-2)^2 - (7 \times -2) = -6$
$f(-1) = (2 \times (-1)^3) - (-1)^2 - (7 \times -1) = 4$
There is a sign change (and the function is continuous in this interval) so there is a root in this interval.

Q3 a)

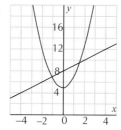

b) The graphs cross twice so the equation has 2 roots.

c) $f(1) = (2 \times 1^2) - 1 - 3 = -2$
$f(2) = (2 \times 2^2) - 2 - 3 = 3$
There is a sign change (and the function is continuous in this interval) so there is a root in this interval.

Q4 a)

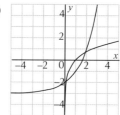

b) The graphs cross twice so the equation has 2 roots

c) $f(1.8) = \ln(1.8) - 2^{1.8} + 3 = 0.105...$
$f(2.2) = \ln(2.2) - 2^{2.2} + 3 = -0.806...$
There is a sign change (and the function is continuous in this interval), so there is a root in this interval.

$f(2.0) = \ln(2.0) - 2^{2.0} + 3 = -0.306...$
So the root is between 1.8 and 2.0

$f(1.9) = \ln(1.9) - 2^{1.9} + 3 = -0.090...$
So the root is between 1.8 and 1.9

$f(1.85) = \ln(1.85) - 2^{1.85} + 3 = 0.010...$

There is a sign change (and the function is continuous) between 1.85 and 1.9, so the root is at $x = 1.9$ (to 1 d.p.).

Q5 a)

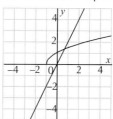

b) The graphs cross once so the equation has 1 root.

c) $f(0.6) = \sqrt{0.6 + 1} - (2 \times 0.6) = 0.064...$
$f(0.7) = \sqrt{0.7 + 1} - (2 \times 0.7) = -0.096...$

There is a sign change, so there is a root in the interval.

d) $\sqrt{x+1} = 2x \Rightarrow x + 1 = 4x^2 \Rightarrow 4x^2 - x - 1 = 0$
From quadratic formula root is $x = 0.640$ to 3 s.f.
You can ignore the other solution to this quadratic equation — you know the root is between 0.6 and 0.7.

Q6 a)

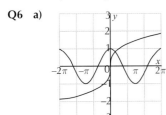

b) The graphs cross once so the equation has 1 root.

c) $f(0.5) = \cos 0.5 - \sqrt[3]{0.5} = 0.083...$
$f(0.6) = \cos 0.6 - \sqrt[3]{0.6} = -0.018...$
There is a sign change (and the function is continuous in this interval) so there is a root in this interval.

d) $f(0.55) = \cos 0.55 - \sqrt[3]{0.55} = 0.033...$
So the root is between 0.55 and 0.6.

$f(0.58) = \cos 0.58 - \sqrt[3]{0.58} = 0.002...$
So the root is between 0.58 and 0.6.

$f(0.59) = \cos 0.59 - \sqrt[3]{0.59} = -0.007...$
So the root is between 0.58 and 0.59

$f(0.585) = \cos 0.585 - \sqrt[3]{0.585} = -0.002...$
So the root is between 0.58 and 0.585, so the value to 2 significant figures is $x = 0.58$.

Q7 a)

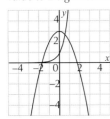

b) If the two functions are set equal to each other they can be rearranged to make $e^{2x} + x^2 = 3$. The graphs cross twice, so the equation has 2 roots.

c) Rearrange to $f(x) = 0$ so $e^{2x} + x^2 - 3 = 0$
$f(-2) = e^{(2 \times -2)} + (-2)^2 - 3 = 1.01...$
$f(-1) = e^{(2 \times -1)} + (-1)^2 - 3 = -1.86...$

There is a sign change (and the function is continuous in this interval) so there is a root in this interval.

$f(-1.5) = e^{(2 \times -1.5)} + (-1.5)^2 - 3 = -0.70...$
So the root is between −1.5 and −2

$f(-1.7) = e^{(2 \times -1.7)} + (-1.7)^2 - 3 = -0.07...$
So the root is between −1.7 and −2

$f(-1.8) = e^{(2 \times -1.8)} + (-1.8)^2 - 3 = 0.26...$
So the root is between −1.7 and −1.8

$f(-1.75) = e^{(2 \times -1.75)} + (-1.75)^2 - 3 = 0.09...$

So the root is between −1.7 and −1.75, so the value to 1 decimal place is $x = -1.7$.

2. Iterative Methods
Exercise 2.1 — Using iteration formulas

Q1 a) $f(1) = 1^3 + (3 \times 1^2) - 7 = -3$
$f(2) = 2^3 + (3 \times 2^2) - 7 = 13$
There is a sign change (and the function is continuous in this interval) so there is a root in this interval.

b) $x_1 = \sqrt{\dfrac{7 - x_0^3}{3}} = \sqrt{\dfrac{7 - 1^3}{3}} = 1.414,$
$x_2 = 1.179, \ x_3 = 1.337, \ x_4 = 1.240$

Q2 a) $x_1 = 2 + \ln x_0 = 2 + \ln 3.1 = 3.1314,$
$x_2 = 3.1415, \ x_3 = 3.1447, \ x_4 = 3.1457,$
$x_5 = 3.1460$

b) $\alpha = 3.146$ (3 d.p.)

Q3 a) $f(1.4) = 1.4^4 - (5 \times 1.4) + 3 = -0.1584$
$f(1.5) = 1.5^4 - (5 \times 1.5) + 3 = 0.5625$
There is a sign change (and the function is continuous in this interval) so there is a root in this interval.

b) $x_1 = \sqrt[3]{5 - \dfrac{3}{x_0}} = \sqrt[3]{5 - \dfrac{3}{1.4}} = 1.419,$
$x_2 = 1.424, \ x_3 = 1.425, \ x_4 = 1.425,$
$x_5 = 1.425, \ x_6 = 1.425$ (3 d.p.)

c) The last 4 iterations round to the same answer, so to 2 d.p. $x = 1.43$

Q4 a) $f(5) = 5^2 - (5 \times 5) - 2 = -2$
$f(6) = 6^2 - (5 \times 6) - 2 = 4$
There is a sign change (and the function is continuous in this interval) so there is a root in this interval.

b) $x_1 = \dfrac{2}{x_0} + 5 = \dfrac{2}{5} + 5 = 5.4,$
$x_2 = 5.370, \ x_3 = 5.372, \ x_4 = 5.372$ (4 s.f.)

Q5 $x_1 = 2 - \ln x_0 = 2 - \ln 1.5 = 1.595,$
$x_2 = 1.533, \ x_3 = 1.573, \ x_4 = 1.547, \ x_5 = 1.563,$
$x_6 = 1.553, \ x_7 = 1.560, \ x_8 = 1.555, \ x_9 = 1.558$
The iterative sequence is bouncing up and down but closing in on the correct answer.

The last three iterations round to the same answer to 2 d.p., so to 2 d.p. $x = 1.56$

Q6 a) $f(3) = e^3 - (10 \times 3) = -9.914...$
$f(4) = e^4 - (10 \times 4) = 14.598...$
There is a sign change (and the function is continuous in this interval) so there is a root in this interval.

b) Using starting value $x_0 = 3$:
$x_1 = \ln (10x_0) = \ln (10 \times 3) = 3.401$
$x_2 = 3.527, \ x_3 = 3.563, \ x_4 = 3.573$
You could have started with x_0 as anything between 3 and 4, in which case you'd get different values for $x_1 - x_4$ but it would still converge to the same root.

c) The upper and lower bounds are 3.5765 and 3.5775.
$f(3.5765) = e^{3.5765} - (10 \times 3.5765) = -0.016...$
$f(3.5775) = e^{3.5775} - (10 \times 3.5775) = 0.0089...$

There is a sign change between the upper and lower bounds (and the function is continuous in this interval), so the root to 3 d.p. is $x = 3.577$.

d) Using new iterative formula with $x_0 = 3$

$x_1 = 2.00855...$, $x_2 = 0.74525...$, $x_3 = 0.21069...$, $x_4 = 0.12345...$, $x_5 = 0.11313...$, $x_6 = 0.11197...$, $x_7 = 0.11184...$, $x_8 = 0.11183...$

The formula appears to converge to another root at $x = 0.112$ (to 3 d.p.).

Q7 a) $x_1 = \dfrac{x_0^2 - 3x_0}{2} - 5 = \dfrac{(-1)^2 - (3 \times (-1))}{2} - 5 = -3$

$x_2 = 4$, $x_3 = -3$, $x_4 = 4$

The sequence is alternating between -3 and 4.

b) Using the iterative formula given:

$x_1 = 6.32455...$, $x_2 = 6.45157...$, $x_3 = 6.50060...$, $x_4 = 6.51943...$, $x_5 = 6.52665...$, $x_6 = 6.52941...$, $x_7 = 6.53047...$, $x_8 = 6.53087...$

The last 4 iterations all round to 6.53, so the value of the root is $x = 6.53$ to 3 s.f. To verify this, check it's between the upper and lower bounds of 6.53:

$f(6.525) = 6.525^2 - (5 \times 6.525) - 10 = -0.049...$
$f(6.535) = 6.535^2 - (5 \times 6.535) - 10 = 0.031...$

There is a sign change between the upper and lower bounds (and the function is continuous in this interval) so this value is correct to 3 s.f.

Exercise 2.2 — Finding iteration formulas

Q1 a) $x^2 - 5x + 1 = 0 \Rightarrow x^2 = 5x - 1 \Rightarrow x = \sqrt{5x - 1}$

b) $x^2 - 5x + 1 = 0 \Rightarrow x^2 = 5x - 1 \Rightarrow x = 5 - \dfrac{1}{x}$

c) $x^2 - 5x + 1 = 0 \Rightarrow 5x = x^2 + 1 \Rightarrow x = \dfrac{x^2 + 1}{5}$

Q2 a) $x^4 + 7x - 3 = 0 \Rightarrow x^4 = 3 - 7x \Rightarrow x = \sqrt[4]{3 - 7x}$

b) $x^4 + 7x - 3 = 0 \Rightarrow x^4 = 3 - 7x \Rightarrow x = \dfrac{3}{x^3} - \dfrac{7}{x^2}$

c) $x^4 + 7x - 3 = 0 \Rightarrow x^4 + 5x + 2x - 3 = 0$
$\Rightarrow 2x = 3 - 5x - x^4 \Rightarrow x = \dfrac{3 - 5x - x^4}{2}$

d) $x^4 + 7x - 3 = 0 \Rightarrow x^4 = 3 - 7x$
$\Rightarrow x^2 = \sqrt{3 - 7x} \Rightarrow x = \dfrac{\sqrt{3 - 7x}}{x}$

Q3 a) $x^3 - 2x^2 - 5 = 0 \Rightarrow x^3 = 2x^2 + 5 \Rightarrow x = 2 + \dfrac{5}{x^2}$

b) $x_1 = 2 + \dfrac{5}{2^2} = 3.25$

$x_2 = 2.473...$, $x_3 = 2.817...$, $x_4 = 2.629...$, $x_5 = 2.722...$,
So $x_5 = 2.7$ to 1 d.p.

c) $f(2.65) = 2.65^3 - (2 \times 2.65^2) - 5 = -0.43...$
$f(2.75) = 2.75^3 - (2 \times 2.75^2) - 5 = 0.67...$
There is a sign change between the upper and lower bounds (and the function is continuous in this interval) so this value is correct to 1 d.p.

Q4 a) $x^2 + 3x - 8 = 0 \Rightarrow x^2 = 8 - 3x \Rightarrow x = \dfrac{8}{x} - 3$

b) $f(-5) = (-5)^2 + (3 \times -5) - 8 = 2$
$f(-4) = (-4)^2 + (3 \times -4) - 8 = -4$

There is a sign change (and the function is continuous in this interval) so there is a root in this interval.

c) $x_1 = \dfrac{a}{x_0} + b = \dfrac{8}{-5} - 3 = -4.6$
$x_2 = -4.739$, $x_3 = -4.688$, $x_4 = -4.706$,
$x_5 = -4.700$, $x_6 = -4.702$
So $x = -4.70$ to 2 d.p.

Q5 a) $2^{x-1} = 4\sqrt{x} \Rightarrow 2^{x-1} = 2^2 x^{\frac{1}{2}}$
$\Rightarrow 2^{x-1} \times 2^{-2} = x^{\frac{1}{2}} \Rightarrow 2^{x-3} = x^{\frac{1}{2}}$
$\Rightarrow (2^{x-3})^2 = x \Rightarrow x = 2^{2x-6}$

b) Using the iterative formula given:
$x_1 = 0.0625$, $x_2 = 0.0170$, $x_3 = 0.0160$, $x_4 = 0.0160$

c) $f(0.01595) = 2^{0.01595 - 1} - 4\sqrt{0.01595} = 0.00038...$
$f(0.01605) = 2^{0.01605 - 1} - 4\sqrt{0.01605} = -0.0016...$
There is a sign change between the upper and lower bounds (and the function is continuous in this interval) so this value is correct to 4 d.p.

Q6 a) $f(0.4) = \ln(2 \times 0.4) + 0.4^3 = -0.159...$
$f(0.5) = \ln(2 \times 0.5) + 0.5^3 = 0.125$

There is a sign change (and the function is continuous in this interval) so there is a root in this interval.

b) $\ln 2x + x^3 = 0 \Rightarrow \ln 2x = -x^3$
$\Rightarrow 2x = e^{-x^3} \Rightarrow x = \dfrac{e^{-x^3}}{2}$

c) Using iterative formula $x_{n+1} = \dfrac{e^{-x_n^3}}{2}$ with starting value $x_0 = 0.4$:
You know the root is between 0.4 and 0.5, so it's a good idea to use one of these as your starting value.

$x_1 = \dfrac{e^{-x_0^3}}{2} = \dfrac{e^{-0.4^3}}{2} = 0.4690...$,
$x_2 = 0.4509...$, $x_3 = 0.4561...$, $x_4 = 0.4547...$,
$x_5 = 0.4551...$, $x_6 = 0.4550...$

So the value of the root is $x = 0.455$ to 3 d.p.

Q7 a) $x^2 - 9x - 20 = 0 \Rightarrow x^2 = 9x + 20 \Rightarrow x = \sqrt{9x + 20}$
So an iterative formula is $x_{n+1} = \sqrt{9x_n + 20}$

b) $x_1 = \sqrt{9x_0 + 20} = \sqrt{(9 \times 10) + 20} = 10.488...$,
$x_2 = 10.695...$, $x_3 = 10.782...$, $x_4 = 10.818...$,
$x_5 = 10.833...$, $x_6 = 10.839...$

The last 4 iterations round to 10.8, so the value of the root is $x = 10.8$ to 3 s.f.

c) $x^2 - 9x - 20 = 0 \Rightarrow x^2 - 5x - 4x - 20 = 0$
$\Rightarrow 5x = x^2 - 4x - 20 \Rightarrow x = \dfrac{x^2 - 4x}{5} - 4$
So an iterative formula is $x_{n+1} = \dfrac{x_n^2 - 4x_n}{5} - 4$

d) $x_1 = \dfrac{x_0^2 - 4x_0}{5} - 4 = \dfrac{1^2 - (4 \times 1)}{5} - 4 = -4.6$,
$x_2 = 3.912$, $x_3 = -4.0688...$, $x_4 = 2.5661...$,
$x_5 = -4.7358...$, $x_6 = 4.2744...$, $x_7 = -3.7653...$,
$x_8 = 1.8479...$

e) The iterations seem to be bouncing up and down without converging to any particular root.

Exercise 2.3 — Sketching iterations

Q1 a)

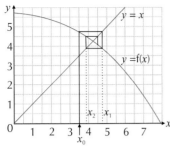

A convergent cobweb diagram.

b)

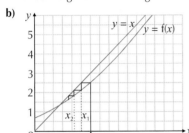

A convergent staircase diagram.

c)

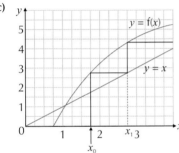

A divergent staircase diagram.

x_2 goes off the scale of the graph so you can't label it.

d)

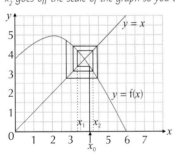

A divergent cobweb diagram.

3. Numerical Integration

Exercise 3.1 — Simpson's Rule

Q1 $h = \dfrac{2 - 1}{4} = 0.25$

$x_0 = 1,$ $y_0 = (\ln 1)^2 = 0$

$x_1 = 1.25,$ $y_1 = (\ln 1.25)^2 = 0.049793$ (6 d.p.)

$x_2 = 1.5,$ $y_2 = (\ln 1.5)^2 = 0.164402$ (6 d.p.)

$x_3 = 1.75,$ $y_3 = (\ln 1.75)^2 = 0.313170$ (6 d.p.)

$x_4 = 2,$ $y_4 = (\ln 2)^2 = 0.480453$ (6 d.p)

You want the final answer rounded to 4 d.p., so make sure you leave enough decimal places in your calculations of the y-values that you won't lose accuracy in rounding.

Using Simpson's Rule:

$$\int_1^2 (\ln x)^2 \, dx \approx \tfrac{1}{3}(0.25)[(0 + 0.480453) + 4(0.049793$$
$$+ 0.313170) + 2(0.164402)]$$
$$= 0.1884 \text{ to 4 d.p.}$$

Q2 The area under the curve $= \int_0^{\frac{\pi}{3}} \sqrt{\tan \theta} \, d\theta$.

$h = \dfrac{\frac{\pi}{3} - 0}{4} = \dfrac{\pi}{12}$

$x_0 = 0,$ $y_0 = \sqrt{\tan 0} = 0$

$x_1 = \dfrac{\pi}{12},$ $y_1 = \sqrt{\tan \dfrac{\pi}{12}} = 0.517638$ (6 d.p.)

$x_2 = \dfrac{\pi}{6},$ $y_2 = \sqrt{\tan \dfrac{\pi}{6}} = 0.759836$ (6 d.p.)

$x_3 = \dfrac{\pi}{4},$ $y_3 = \sqrt{\tan \dfrac{\pi}{4}} = 1$

$x_4 = \dfrac{\pi}{3},$ $y_4 = \sqrt{\tan \dfrac{\pi}{3}} = 1.316074$ (6 d.p)

Using Simpson's Rule,

$$\int_0^{\frac{\pi}{3}} \sqrt{\tan \theta} \, d\theta \approx \tfrac{1}{3}\left(\dfrac{\pi}{12}\right)[(0 + 1.316074) + 4(0.517638$$
$$+ 1) + 2(0.759836)]$$
$$= 0.7772 \text{ to 4 d.p.}$$

Q3 a) $h = \dfrac{3 - 1}{4} = 0.5$

$x_0 = 1,$ $y_0 = e^1 \ln 1 = 0$

$x_1 = 1.5,$ $y_1 = e^{1.5} \ln 1.5 = 1.817169$ (6 d.p.)

$x_2 = 2,$ $y_2 = e^2 \ln 2 = 5.121703$ (6 d.p.)

$x_3 = 2.5,$ $y_3 = e^{2.5} \ln 2.5 = 11.162706$ (6 d.p.)

$x_4 = 3,$ $y_4 = e^3 \ln 3 = 22.066218$ (6 d.p)

Using Simpson's Rule,

$$\int_1^3 e^x \ln x \, dx \approx \tfrac{1}{3}(0.5)[(0 + 22.066218) +$$
$$4(1.817169 + 11.162706)$$
$$+ 2(5.121703)]$$
$$= 14.0382 \text{ to 4 d.p.}$$

b) $h = \dfrac{3 - 1}{8} = 0.25$

$x_0 = 1, \quad y_0 = 0$

$x_1 = 1.25, y_1 = e^{1.25}\ln 1.25 = 0.778848$ (6 d.p.)

$x_2 = 1.5, \quad y_2 = 1.817169$ (6 d.p.)

$x_3 = 1.75, y_3 = e^{1.75}\ln 1.75 = 3.220367$ (6 d.p.)

$x_4 = 2, \quad y_4 = 5.121703$ (6 d.p.)

$x_5 = 2.25, y_5 = e^{2.25}\ln 2.25 = 7.693892$ (6 d.p.)

$x_6 = 2.5, \quad y_6 = 11.162706$ (6 d.p.)

$x_7 = 2.75, y_7 = e^{2.75}\ln 2.75 = 15.824101$ (6 d.p.)

$x_8 = 3, \quad y_8 = 22.066218$ (6 d.p)

You can get the values of y_0, y_2, y_4, y_6 and y_8 from your working for part a).

Using Simpson's Rule,

$$\int_1^3 e^x \ln x \, dx \approx \tfrac{1}{3}(0.25)[(0 + 22.066218)$$
$$+ \, 4(0.778848 + 3.220367$$
$$+ \, 7.693892 + 15.824101)$$
$$+ \, 2(1.817169 + 5.121703$$
$$+ \, 11.162706)]$$
$$= 14.0282 \text{ to 4 d.p.}$$

c) (i) The answer to b) is likely to be more accurate because more strips were used.

(ii) The answers agree to 1 decimal place (14.0).

Q4 Rearranging the equation:

$y^2 = 25 - (x + 4)^2 = 25 - x^2 - 8x - 16 = 9 - 8x - x^2$

So $y = \sqrt{9 - 8x - x^2}$ and the integral to evaluate is $\int_{-3}^0 \sqrt{9 - 8x - x^2} \, dx$.

$h = \dfrac{0 - (-3)}{6} = 0.5$

$x_0 = -3, \quad y_0 = \sqrt{9 + 24 - 9} = 4.898979$ (6 d.p.)

$x_1 = -2.5, \quad y_1 = \sqrt{9 + 20 - 6.25} = 4.769696$ (6 d.p.)

$x_2 = -2, \quad y_2 = \sqrt{9 + 16 - 4} = 4.582576$ (6 d.p.)

$x_3 = -1.5, \quad y_3 = \sqrt{9 + 12 - 2.25} = 4.330127$ (6 d.p.)

$x_4 = -1, \quad y_4 = \sqrt{9 + 8 - 1} = 4$

$x_5 = -0.5, \quad y_5 = \sqrt{9 + 4 - 0.25} = 3.570714$ (6 d.p.)

$x_6 = 0, \quad y_6 = \sqrt{9 - 0 - 0} = 3$

Using Simpson's Rule,

$$\int_{-3}^0 \sqrt{9 - 8x - x^2} \, dx \approx \tfrac{1}{3}(0.5)[(4.898979 + 3)$$
$$+ \, 4(4.769696 +$$
$$4.330127 + 3.570714)$$
$$+ \, 2(4.582576 + 4)]$$
$$= 12.6244 \text{ to 4 d.p.}$$

Q5 a) $h = \dfrac{\frac{\pi}{2} - 0}{6} = \dfrac{\pi}{12}$

$x_0 = 0, \quad y_0 = \sin 0 \cos 0 = 0$

$x_1 = \dfrac{\pi}{12}, y_1 = \sin \dfrac{\pi}{12} \cos \dfrac{\pi}{12} = 0.25$

$x_2 = \dfrac{\pi}{6}, y_2 = \sin \dfrac{\pi}{6} \cos \dfrac{\pi}{6} = 0.433013$ (6 d.p.)

$x_3 = \dfrac{\pi}{4}, y_3 = \sin \dfrac{\pi}{4} \cos \dfrac{\pi}{4} = 0.5$

$x_4 = \dfrac{\pi}{3}, y_4 = \sin \dfrac{\pi}{3} \cos \dfrac{\pi}{3} = 0.433013$ (6 d.p.)

$x_5 = \dfrac{5\pi}{12}, y_5 = \sin \dfrac{5\pi}{12} \cos \dfrac{5\pi}{12} = 0.25$

$x_6 = \dfrac{\pi}{2}, y_6 = \sin \dfrac{\pi}{2} \cos \dfrac{\pi}{2} = 0$

Using Simpson's Rule:

$$\int_0^{\frac{\pi}{2}} \sin\theta \cos\theta \, d\theta \approx \tfrac{1}{3}\left(\dfrac{\pi}{12}\right)[(0 + 0) + 4(0.25 + 0.5 +$$
$$0.25) + 2(0.433013 +$$
$$0.433013)]$$
$$= 0.5002 \text{ to 4 d.p.}$$

b) $h = \dfrac{\frac{\pi}{2} - 0}{4} = \dfrac{\pi}{8}$

$x_0 = 0, \quad y_0 = 0$ (from a))

$x_1 = \dfrac{\pi}{8}, y_1 = \sin \dfrac{\pi}{8} \cos \dfrac{\pi}{8} = 0.353553$ (6 d.p.)

$x_2 = \dfrac{\pi}{4}, y_2 = 0.5$ (from a))

$x_3 = \dfrac{3\pi}{8}, y_3 = \sin \dfrac{3\pi}{8} \cos \dfrac{3\pi}{8} = 0.353553$ (6 d.p.)

$x_4 = \dfrac{\pi}{2}, y_4 = 0$ (from a))

Using Simpson's Rule:

$$\int_0^{\frac{\pi}{2}} \sin\theta \cos\theta \, d\theta \approx \tfrac{1}{3}\left(\dfrac{\pi}{8}\right)[(0 + 0) + 4(0.353553 +$$
$$0.353553) + 2(0.5)]$$
$$= 0.5011 \text{ to 4 d.p.}$$

c) (i) $\displaystyle\int_0^{\frac{\pi}{2}} \sin\theta \cos\theta \, d\theta = \left[-\tfrac{1}{4}\cos 2\theta\right]_0^{\frac{\pi}{2}}$

$$= \left(-\tfrac{1}{4}\cos \pi\right) - \left(-\tfrac{1}{4}\cos 0\right)$$
$$= 0.5$$

(ii) a) is accurate to 3 d.p. while b) is accurate to 2 d.p.

The answer to a) used 6 strips, whereas the answer to b) used 4 strips, so you'd expect a) to be more accurate.

Exercise 3.2 — The Mid-Ordinate Rule

Q1 $h = \dfrac{5-1}{4} = 1$

$x_{0.5} = 1.5, y_{0.5} = \sqrt{1.5^3 + 1.5^2} = 2.371708$ (6 d.p.)

$x_{1.5} = 2.5, y_{1.5} = \sqrt{2.5^3 + 2.5^2} = 4.677072$ (6 d.p.)

$x_{2.5} = 3.5, y_{2.5} = \sqrt{3.5^3 + 3.5^2} = 7.424621$ (6 d.p.)

$x_{3.5} = 4.5, y_{3.5} = \sqrt{4.5^3 + 4.5^2} = 10.553435$ (6 d.p.)

Using the Mid-Ordinate Rule:

$$\int_1^5 \sqrt{x^3 + x^2}\, dx \approx 1[2.371708 + 4.677072 + \\ 7.424621 + 10.553435]$$
$$= 25.0268 \text{ to 4 d.p.}$$

Q2 $h = \dfrac{5-2}{6} = 0.5$

$x_{0.5} = 2.25, y_{0.5} = (2.25^2 + 2.25)^{-1} = 0.136752$ (6 d.p.)

$x_{1.5} = 2.75, y_{1.5} = (2.75^2 + 2.75)^{-1} = 0.096970$ (6 d.p.)

$x_{2.5} = 3.25, y_{2.5} = (3.25^2 + 3.25)^{-1} = 0.072398$ (6 d.p.)

$x_{3.5} = 3.75, y_{3.5} = (3.75^2 + 3.75)^{-1} = 0.056140$ (6 d.p.)

$x_{4.5} = 4.25, y_{4.5} = (4.25^2 + 4.25)^{-1} = 0.044818$ (6 d.p.)

$x_{5.5} = 4.75, y_{5.5} = (4.75^2 + 4.75)^{-1} = 0.036613$ (6 d.p.)

Using the Mid-Ordinate Rule:

$$\int_2^5 (x^2 + x)^{-1} dx \approx 0.5[0.136752 + 0.096970 + \\ 0.072398 + 0.056140 + \\ 0.044818 + 0.036613]$$
$$= 0.2218 \text{ to 4 d.p.}$$

Q3 a) Rearrange to give $y^2 = 16 - x^2 + 8x - 16 = 8x - x^2$
then $y = \sqrt{8x - x^2}$.

This then rearranges to give $y^2 = x(8 - x)$.
So when $y = 0$, $x(8 - x) = 0$, so $x = 0$ or $x = 8$.

So the area to be found is $\int_0^8 \sqrt{8x - x^2}\, dx$.

$h = \dfrac{8-0}{4} = 2$

$x_{0.5} = 1, y_{0.5} = \sqrt{8 - 1} = 2.646$ (3 d.p.)

$x_{1.5} = 3, y_{1.5} = \sqrt{24 - 9} = 3.873$ (3 d.p.)

$x_{2.5} = 5, y_{2.5} = \sqrt{40 - 25} = 3.873$ (3 d.p.)

$x_{3.5} = 7, y_{3.5} = \sqrt{56 - 49} = 2.646$ (3 d.p.)

Using the Mid-Ordinate Rule:

$$\int_0^8 \sqrt{8x - x^2}\, dx \approx 2[2.646 + 3.873 + 3.873 \\ + 2.646]$$
$$= 26.1 \text{ to 1 d.p.}$$

b) The area of a circle radius r is πr^2, so the area of the semicircle radius 4 =
$\dfrac{1}{2}\pi r^2 = 0.5 \times \pi \times 4^2 = 25.1$ to 1 d.p.

c) % error $= \left| \dfrac{25.1 - 26.1}{25.1} \right| \times 100\%$

$= 3.98\%$ (to 2 d.p.).
You could improve the estimate by using more strips / increasing the value of n.

Q4 a) $h = \dfrac{2-0}{4} = 0.5$

$x_{0.5} = 0.25, y_{0.5} = e^{0.25} \cos 0.25 = 1.244108$ (6 d.p.)

$x_{1.5} = 0.75, y_{1.5} = e^{0.75} \cos 0.75 = 1.548985$ (6 d.p.)

$x_{2.5} = 1.25, y_{2.5} = e^{1.25} \cos 1.25 = 1.100583$ (6 d.p.)

$x_{3.5} = 1.75, y_{3.5} = e^{1.75} \cos 1.75 = -1.025735$ (6 d.p.)

$$\int_0^2 e^x \cos x\, dx \approx 0.5[1.244108 + 1.548985 + \\ 1.100583 - 1.025735]$$
$$= 1.4340 \text{ to 4 d.p.}$$

b) $h = \dfrac{2-0}{8} = 0.25$

$x_{0.5} = 0.125, y_{0.5} = 1.124307$ (6 d.p.)

$x_{1.5} = 0.375, y_{1.5} = 1.353881$ (6 d.p.)

$x_{2.5} = 0.625, y_{2.5} = 1.515079$ (6 d.p.)

$x_{3.5} = 0.875, y_{3.5} = 1.537672$ (6 d.p.)

$x_{4.5} = 1.125, y_{4.5} = 1.328117$ (6 d.p.)

$x_{5.5} = 1.375, y_{5.5} = 0.769451$ (6 d.p.)

$x_{6.5} = 1.625, y_{6.5} = -0.275134$ (6 d.p.)

$x_{7.5} = 1.875, y_{7.5} = -1.953204$ (6 d.p.)

$$\int_0^2 e^x \cos x\, dx \approx 0.25[1.124307 + 1.353881 + \\ 1.515079 + 1.537672 + \\ 1.328117 + 0.769451 - \\ 0.275134 - 1.953204]$$
$$= 1.3500 \text{ to 4 d.p.}$$

c) The results agree to 1 decimal place. The answer to b) using 8 strips is the most accurate.

Q5 a) You need to find $\int_2^{10} \sqrt{\ln x + 2x}\, dx$.

$h = \dfrac{10-2}{4} = 2$

$x_{0.5} = 3, y_{0.5} = \sqrt{\ln 3 + 6} = 2.664$ (3 d.p.)

$x_{1.5} = 5, y_{1.5} = \sqrt{\ln 5 + 10} = 3.407$ (3 d.p.)

$x_{2.5} = 7, y_{2.5} = \sqrt{\ln 7 + 14} = 3.993$ (3 d.p.)

$x_{3.5} = 9, y_{3.5} = \sqrt{\ln 9 + 18} = 4.494$ (3 d.p.)

You're told that $y \geq O$, so you only need the positive square root.

$$\int_2^{10} \sqrt{\ln x + 2x}\, dx \approx \\ 2[2.664 + 3.407 + 3.993 + 4.494]$$
$$= 29.12 \text{ to 2 d.p.}$$

b) $h = \dfrac{10-2}{8} = 1$

$x_{0.5} = 2.5, y_{0.5} = \sqrt{\ln 2.5 + 5} = 2.432$ (3 d.p.)

$x_{1.5} = 3.5, y_{1.5} = \sqrt{\ln 3.5 + 7} = 2.873$ (3 d.p.)

$x_{2.5} = 4.5, y_{2.5} = \sqrt{\ln 4.5 + 9} = 3.241$ (3 d.p.)

$x_{3.5} = 5.5, y_{3.5} = \sqrt{\ln 5.5 + 11} = 3.564$ (3 d.p.)

$x_{4.5} = 6.5, y_{4.5} = \sqrt{\ln 6.5 + 13} = 3.856$ (3 d.p.)

$x_{5.5} = 7.5, y_{5.5} = \sqrt{\ln 7.5 + 15} = 4.125$ (3 d.p.)

$x_{6.5} = 8.5, y_{6.5} = \sqrt{\ln 8.5 + 17} = 4.375$ (3 d.p.)

$x_{7.5} = 9.5, y_{7.5} = \sqrt{\ln 9.5 + 19} = 4.610$ (3 d.p.)

$$\int_2^{10} \sqrt{\ln x + 2x}\, dx \approx 1[2.432 + 2.873 + 3.241 + \\ 3.564 + 3.856 + 4.125 + \\ 4.375 + 4.610]$$
$$= 29.08 \text{ to 2 d.p.}$$

c) The answer to b) should be more accurate as it uses more strips.

Review Exercise — Chapter 6

Q1 There are 2 roots (the graph crosses the x-axis twice in this interval).

Q2 **a)** $f(3) = \sin(2 \times 3) = -0.2794...$
$f(4) = \sin(2 \times 4) = 0.9893...$
There is a sign change (and the function is continuous in this interval) so there is a root in this interval.

b) $f(2.1) = \ln(2.1 - 2) + 2 = -0.3025...$
$f(2.2) = \ln(2.2 - 2) + 2 = 0.3905...$

There is a sign change (and the function is continuous in this interval) so there is a root in this interval.

c) First rearrange so that $f(x) = 0$:
$x^3 - 4x^2 = 7 \Rightarrow x^3 - 4x^2 - 7 = 0$

$f(4.3) = 4.3^3 - 4 \times 4.3^2 - 7 = -1.453$
$f(4.5) = 4.5^3 - 4 \times 4.5^2 - 7 = 3.125$

There is a sign change (and the function is continuous in this interval) so there is a root in this interval.

Q3 If 1.2 is a root to 1 d.p. then there should be a sign change for $f(x)$ between upper and lower bounds:

$f(1.15) = 1.15^3 + 1.15 - 3 = -0.3291...$
$f(1.25) = 1.25^3 + 1.25 - 3 = 0.2031...$

There is a sign change (and the function is continuous) between the upper and lower bounds, so the answer must be between them and so be rounded to 1.2 to 1 d.p.

Q4 $x_1 = -\frac{1}{2}\cos(-1) = -0.2701...$

$x_2 = -\frac{1}{2}\cos(-0.2701...) = -0.4818...$

$x_3 = -\frac{1}{2}\cos(-0.4818...) = -0.4430...$

$x_4 = -\frac{1}{2}\cos(-0.4430...) = -0.4517...$

$x_5 = -\frac{1}{2}\cos(-0.4517...) = -0.4498...$

$x_6 = -\frac{1}{2}\cos(-0.4498...) = -0.4502...$

x_4, x_5 and x_6 all round to -0.45, so to 2 d.p. $x = -0.45$.

Q5 $x_1 = \sqrt{\ln 2 + 4} = 2.1663...$
$x_2 = \sqrt{\ln 2.1663... + 4} = 2.1847...$
$x_3 = \sqrt{\ln 2.1847... + 4} = 2.1866...$
$x_4 = \sqrt{\ln 2.1866... + 4} = 2.1868...$
$x_5 = \sqrt{\ln 2.1868... + 4} = 2.1868...$
x_3, x_4 and x_5 all round to 2.187, so to 3 d.p.
$x = 2.187$.

Q6 **a)** **(i)** $2x^2 - x^3 + 1 = 0 \Rightarrow 2x^2 - x^3 = -1$
$\Rightarrow x^2(2 - x) = -1 \Rightarrow x^2 = \dfrac{-1}{2 - x}$
$\Rightarrow x = \sqrt{\dfrac{-1}{2 - x}}$

(ii) $\Rightarrow 2x^2 - x^3 + 1 = 0 \Rightarrow x^3 = 2x^2 + 1$
$\Rightarrow x = \sqrt[3]{2x^2 + 1}$.

(iii) $2x^2 - x^3 + 1 = 0 \Rightarrow 2x^2 = x^3 - 1$
$\Rightarrow x^2 = \dfrac{x^3 - 1}{2} \Rightarrow x = \sqrt{\dfrac{x^3 - 1}{2}}$

b) Using $x_{n+1} = \sqrt{\dfrac{-1}{2 - x_n}}$ with $x_0 = 2.3$ gives:

$x_1 = \sqrt{\dfrac{-1}{2 - 2.3}} = 1.8257...$

$x_2 = \sqrt{\dfrac{-1}{2 - 1.8257...}}$ has no real solution
so this formula does not converge to a root.

Using $x_{n+1} = \sqrt[3]{2x_n^2 + 1}$ with $x_0 = 2.3$ gives:
$x_1 = \sqrt[3]{2 \times (2.3)^2 + 1} = 2.2624...$
$x_2 = \sqrt[3]{2 \times (2.2624...)^2 + 1} = 2.2398...$
$x_3 = \sqrt[3]{2 \times (2.2398...)^2 + 1} = 2.2262...$
$x_4 = \sqrt[3]{2 \times (2.2262...)^2 + 1} = 2.2180...$
$x_5 = \sqrt[3]{2 \times (2.2180...)^2 + 1} = 2.2131...$
$x_6 = \sqrt[3]{2 \times (2.2131...)^2 + 1} = 2.2101...$
$x_7 = \sqrt[3]{2 \times (2.2101...)^2 + 1} = 2.2083...$
x_5, x_6 and x_7 all round to 2.21,
so to 2 d.p. $x = 2.21$ is a root.

Using $x_{n+1} = \sqrt{\dfrac{x_n^3 - 1}{2}}$ with $x_0 = 2.3$ gives:

$x_1 = \sqrt{\dfrac{2.3^3 - 1}{2}} = 2.3629...$

$x_2 = \sqrt{\dfrac{2.3629...^3 - 1}{2}} = 2.4691...$

$x_3 = \sqrt{\dfrac{2.4691...^3 - 1}{2}} = 2.6508...$

$x_4 = \sqrt{\dfrac{2.6508...^3 - 1}{2}} = 2.9687...$

This sequence is diverging so does not converge to a root. The only formula that converges to a root is $x_{n+1} = \sqrt[3]{2x_n^2 + 1}$.

Q7 **a)**

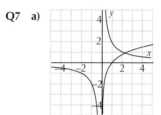

1 crossing point and therefore 1 root.

b) $f(2) = \ln 2 - \dfrac{2}{2} = -0.306...$

$f(3) = \ln 3 - \dfrac{2}{3} = 0.431...$

There is a sign change (and the function is continuous in this interval) so there is a root in this interval.

Q8 **a)**

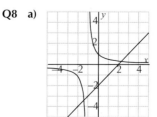

b) $f(-1.4) = \dfrac{1}{-1.4 + 1} - (-1.4) + 2 = 0.9$

$f(-1.3) = \dfrac{1}{-1.3 + 1} - (-1.3) + 2 = -0.033..$

There is a sign change (and the function is continuous in this interval) so there is a root in this interval.

c) $\dfrac{1}{x + 1} - x + 2 = 0 \Rightarrow 1 - x(x + 1) + 2(x + 1) = 0$

$\Rightarrow 1 - x^2 - x + 2x + 2 = 0 \Rightarrow -x^2 + x + 3 = 0$

$\Rightarrow x^2 - x - 3 = 0$

Q9 a) $f(1.5) = 1.5^{1.5} - 3 = -1.16..., \quad f(2) = 2^2 - 3 = 1$

There is a sign change (and the function is continuous in this interval) so there is a root in this interval.

b) Using $x_0 = 1.5$ (though anything between 1.5 and 2 is fine):

$x_1 = 3^{\frac{1}{x_0}} = 3^{\frac{1}{1.5}} = 2.08008...,$

$x_2 = 1.69580..., x_3 = 1.91140..., x_4 = 1.77671...,$

$x_5 = 1.85584..., x_6 = 1.80755..., x_7 = 1.83636...,$

$x_8 = 1.81893...,$

x_6 to x_8 round to give $x = 1.8$ to 1 d.p.

c) Using the iterative formula given:

$x_1 = 2.44948..., x_2 = 0.81876..., x_3 = 2.89323...,$

$x_4 = 0.40143..., x_5 = 1.73724...$

The formula appears to be bouncing up and down without converging to a root.

Q10 a) $f(1.1) = 2 \times 1.1 - 5 \times \cos 1.1 = -0.06...$

$f(1.2) = 2 \times 1.2 - 5 \times \cos 1.2 = 0.58...$

There is a sign change (and the function is continuous in this interval) so there is a solution in this interval.

b) $2x - 5\cos x = 0 \Rightarrow 2x = 5\cos x$

$\Rightarrow x = \dfrac{5}{2}\cos x$ so $p = \dfrac{5}{2}$

c) Using the iterative formula $x_{n+1} = \dfrac{5}{2}\cos x_n$:

$x_1 = \dfrac{5}{2}\cos x_0 = \dfrac{5}{2}\cos 1.1 = 1.1340$

$x_2 = 1.0576, x_3 = 1.2274, x_4 = 0.8418,$

$x_5 = 1.6653, x_6 = -0.2360, x_7 = 2.4307,$

$x_8 = -1.8945$

The sequence at first looks like it might converge to the root in part a) but then it continues to jump up and down.

d) $2x - 5\cos x = 0$

$5\cos x = 2x$

$\cos x = 0.4x$

$x = \cos^{-1} 0.4x$

So the iterative formula is $x_{n+1} = \cos^{-1} 0.4x_n$

$x_0 = 1.1, \; x_1 = 1.1151..., \; x_2 = 1.1084...,$

$x_3 = 1.1114..., \; x_4 = 1.1100...$ So $x = 1.11$ to 3 s.f.

$f(1.105) = (2 \times 1.105) - 5\cos 1.105 = -0.035...$

$f(1.115) = (2 \times 1.115) - 5\cos 1.115 = 0.029...$

There is a sign change (and the function is continuous in this interval) so there is a root in this interval. The root is $x = 1.11$ correct to 3 s.f.

Q11

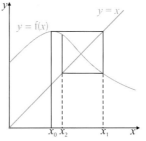

Convergent cobweb diagram.

Q12

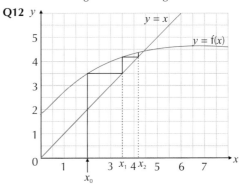

Convergent staircase diagram.

Q13 a) $h = \dfrac{4 - 1}{6} = 0.5$

$x_0 = 1, \qquad y_0 = 1.0986$ (4 d.p.)

$x_1 = 1.5, \qquad y_1 = 1.1709$ (4 d.p.)

$x_2 = 2, \qquad y_2 = 1.2279$ (4 d.p.)

$x_3 = 2.5, \qquad y_3 = 1.2757$ (4 d.p.)

$x_4 = 3, \qquad y_4 = 1.3170$ (4 d.p.)

$x_5 = 3.5, \qquad y_5 = 1.3535$ (4 d.p.)

$x_6 = 4, \qquad y_6 = 1.3863$ (4 d.p.)

Using Simpson's Rule:

$\displaystyle\int_1^4 \ln(\sqrt{x} + 2)\,dx \approx \dfrac{1}{3}(0.5)[(1.0986 + 1.3863)$
$+ 4(1.1709 + 1.2757$
$+ 1.3535) + 2(1.2279$
$+ 1.3170)]$
$= 3.80$ (2 d.p.).

b) Simpson's Rule only works with an even number of strips.

c) $h = \dfrac{4 - 1}{6} = 0.5$

$x_{0.5} = 1.25, \; y_{0.5} = 1.1372$ (4 d.p.)

$x_{1.5} = 1.75, \; y_{1.5} = 1.2008$ (4 d.p.)

$x_{2.5} = 2.25, \; y_{2.5} = 1.2528$ (4 d.p.)

$x_{3.5} = 2.75, \; y_{3.5} = 1.2970$ (4 d.p.)

$x_{4.5} = 3.25, \; y_{4.5} = 1.3357$ (4 d.p.)

$x_{5.5} = 3.75, \; y_{5.5} = 1.3703$ (4 d.p.)

Using the Mid-Ordinate Rule:

$\displaystyle\int_1^4 \ln(\sqrt{x} + 2)\,dx \approx 0.5[1.1372 + 1.2008 +$
$1.2528 + 1.2970 + 1.3357 + 1.3703]$
$= 3.80$ (2 d.p.).

Q14 a) $h = \dfrac{4-2}{4} = 0.5$

$x_{0.5} = 2.25$, $y_{0.5} = 6.5004$ (4 d.p.)
$x_{1.5} = 2.75$, $y_{1.5} = 16.0098$ (4 d.p.)
$x_{2.5} = 3.25$, $y_{2.5} = 36.8667$ (4 d.p.)
$x_{3.5} = 3.75$, $y_{3.5} = 80.9241$ (4 d.p.)

Using the Mid-Ordinate Rule:
$\displaystyle\int_2^4 x^2 e^{x-2}\,dx \approx 0.5[6.5004 + 16.0098 + 36.8667$
$+ 80.9241]$
$= 70.15$ (2 d.p.).

b) $h = \dfrac{4-2}{4} = 0.5$

$x_0 = 2$, $y_0 = 4$
$x_1 = 2.5$, $y_1 = 10.3045$ (4 d.p.)
$x_2 = 3$, $y_2 = 24.4645$ (4 d.p.)
$x_3 = 3.5$, $y_3 = 54.9007$ (4 d.p.)
$x_4 = 4$, $y_4 = 118.2249$ (4 d.p.)

Using Simpson's Rule:
$\displaystyle\int_2^4 x^2 e^{x-2}\,dx \approx \frac{1}{3}(0.5)[(4 + 118.2249) + 4(10.3045$
$+ 54.9007) + 2(24.4645)]$
$= 72.00$ (2 d.p.)

Exam-Style Questions — Chapter 6

Q1 a) There will be a change of sign between f(0.7) and f(0.8) if p lies between 0.7 and 0.8.

$f(0.7) = (2 \times 0.7 \times e^{0.7}) - 3 = -0.1807...$ *[1 mark]*

$f(0.8) = (2 \times 0.8 \times e^{0.8}) - 3 = 0.5608...$ *[1 mark]*

f(x) is continuous, and there is a change of sign, so $0.7 < p < 0.8$ *[1 mark]*.

b) If $2xe^x - 3 = 0$, then $2xe^x = 3 \Rightarrow xe^x = \dfrac{3}{2}$
$\Rightarrow x = \dfrac{3}{2e^x} \Rightarrow x = \dfrac{3}{2}e^{-x}$.

[2 marks available — 1 mark for partial rearrangement, 1 mark for correct final answer.]

c) $x_{n+1} = \dfrac{3}{2}e^{-x_n}$ and $x_0 = 0.7$, so:

$x_1 = \dfrac{3}{2}e^{-0.7} = 0.74487... = 0.7449$ to 4 d.p.

$x_2 = \dfrac{3}{2}e^{-0.74487...} = 0.71218... = 0.7122$ to 4 d.p.

$x_3 = \dfrac{3}{2}e^{-0.71218...} = 0.73585... = 0.7359$ to 4 d.p.

$x_4 = \dfrac{3}{2}e^{-0.73585...} = 0.71864... = 0.7186$ to 4 d.p.

[3 marks available — 1 mark if x_1 is correct, 1 mark if x_2 is correct, 1 mark if all 4 are correct.]

d) If the root of f(x) = 0, p, is 0.726 to 3 d.p. then there must be a change of sign in f(x) between the upper and lower bounds of p.

Lower bound = 0.7255.
$f(0.7255) = (2 \times 0.7255 \times e^{0.7255}) - 3 = -0.0025...$

Upper bound = 0.7265.
$f(0.7265) = (2 \times 0.7265 \times e^{0.7265}) - 3 = 0.0045...$

f(x) is continuous, and there's a change of sign, so $p = 0.726$ to 3 d.p.

[3 marks available — 1 mark for identifying upper and lower bounds, 1 mark for finding value of the function at both bounds, 1 mark for indicating that the change in sign and the fact that it's a continuous function shows the root is correct to the given accuracy.]

Q2 a) Where $y = \sin 3x + 3x$ and $y = 1$ meet,
$\sin 3x + 3x = 1 \Rightarrow \sin 3x + 3x - 1 = 0$ *[1 mark]*

$x = a$ is a root of this equation, so if $x = 0.1$ and $x = 0.2$ produce different signs, then a lies between them. So for the continuous function $f(x) = \sin 3x + 3x - 1$:

$f(0.1) = \sin (3 \times 0.1) + (3 \times 0.1) - 1 = -0.4044...$
[1 mark]

$f(0.2) = \sin (3 \times 0.2) + (3 \times 0.2) - 1 = 0.1646...$
[1 mark]

There is a change of sign, so $0.1 < a < 0.2$
[1 mark]

b) $\sin 3x + 3x = 1 \Rightarrow 3x = 1 - \sin 3x$
$\Rightarrow x = \dfrac{1}{3}(1 - \sin 3x)$.
[2 marks available — 1 mark for partial rearrangement, 1 mark for correct final answer.]

c) $x_{n+1} = \dfrac{1}{3}(1 - \sin 3x_n)$ and $x_0 = 0.2$:
$x_1 = \dfrac{1}{3}(1 - \sin (3 \times 0.2)) = 0.1451...$ *[1 mark]*

$x_2 = \dfrac{1}{3}(1 - \sin (3 \times 0.1451...)) = 0.1927...$

$x_3 = \dfrac{1}{3}(1 - \sin (3 \times 0.1927...)) = 0.1511...$

$x_4 = \dfrac{1}{3}(1 - \sin (3 \times 0.1511...)) = 0.1873...$

So $x_4 = 0.187$ to 3 d.p. *[1 mark]*.

Q3 a) $x_{n+1} = \sqrt[3]{x_n^2 - 4}$, $x_0 = -1$:
$x_1 = \sqrt[3]{(-1)^2 - 4} = -1.44224...$
$= -1.4422$ to 4 d.p.

$x_2 = \sqrt[3]{(-1.4422...)^2 - 4} = -1.24287...$
$= -1.2429$ to 4 d.p.

$x_3 = \sqrt[3]{(-1.2428...)^2 - 4} = -1.34906...$
$= -1.3491$ to 4 d.p.

$x_4 = \sqrt[3]{(-1.3490...)^2 - 4} = -1.29664...$
$= -1.2966$ to 4 d.p.

[3 marks available — 1 mark if x_1 is correct, 1 mark if x_2 is correct, 1 mark if all 4 are correct.]

b) If b is a root of $x^3 - x^2 + 4 = 0$, then $x^3 - x^2 + 4 = 0$ will rearrange to form $x = \sqrt[3]{x^2 - 4}$, the iteration formula used in (a).
(This is like finding the iteration formula in reverse...)
$x^3 - x^2 + 4 = 0 \Rightarrow x^3 = x^2 - 4 \Rightarrow x = \sqrt[3]{x^2 - 4}$,
and so b must be a root of $x^3 - x^2 + 4 = 0$.

[2 marks available — 1 mark for stating that b is a root if one equation can be rearranged into the other, 1 mark for correct demonstration of rearrangement.]

c) If the root of $f(x) = x^3 - x^2 + 4 = 0$, b, is -1.315 to 3 d.p. then there must be a change of sign in $f(x)$ between the upper and lower bounds of b, which are -1.3145 and -1.3155.

$f(-1.3145) = (-1.3145)^3 - (-1.3145)^2 + 4$
$= 0.00075...$

$f(-1.3155) = (-1.3155)^3 - (-1.3155)^2 + 4$
$= -0.00706...$

$f(x)$ is continuous, and there's a change of sign, so $b = -1.315$ to 3 d.p.

[3 marks available — 1 mark for identifying upper and lower bounds, 1 mark for finding value of the function at both bounds, 1 mark for indicating that the change in sign and the fact that it's a continuous function shows the root is correct to the given accuracy.]

Q4 a) For $f(x) = \ln(x + 3) - x + 2$, there will be a change in sign between $f(3)$ and $f(4)$ if the root lies between those values.

$f(3) = \ln(3 + 3) - 3 + 2 = 0.7917...$ *[1 mark]*
$f(4) = \ln(4 + 3) - 4 + 2 = -0.0540...$ *[1 mark]*

There is a change of sign, and the function is continuous for $x > -3$, so the root, m, must lie between 3 and 4 *[1 mark]*.

b) $x_{n+1} = \ln(x_n + 3) + 2$, and $x_0 = 3$, so:
$x_1 = \ln(3 + 3) + 2 = 3.7917...$
$x_2 = \ln(3.7917... + 3) + 2 = 3.9157...$
$x_3 = \ln(3.9157... + 3) + 2 = 3.9337...$
$x_4 = \ln(3.9337... + 3) + 2 = 3.9364...$
$x_5 = \ln(3.9364... + 3) + 2 = 3.9367...$

So $m = 3.94$ to 2 d.p.

[3 marks available — 1 mark for correct substitution of x_0 to find x_1, 1 mark for evidence of correct iterations up to x_5, 1 mark for correct final answer to correct accuracy.]

c) From b), $m = 3.94$ to 2 d.p. If this is correct then there will be a change of sign in $f(x)$ between the upper and lower bounds of m, which are 3.935 and 3.945.

$f(3.935) = \ln(3.935 + 3) - 3.935 + 2 = 0.00158...$
$f(3.945) = \ln(3.945 + 3) - 3.945 + 2$
$= -0.00697...$

$f(x)$ is continuous for $x > -3$, and there's a change of sign, so $m = 3.94$ is correct to 2 d.p.

[3 marks available — 1 mark for identifying upper and lower bounds, 1 mark for finding value of the function at both bounds, 1 mark for indicating that the change in sign and the fact that it's a continuous function shows the root is correct to the given accuracy.]

d)

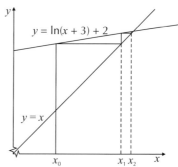

[2 marks available — 1 mark for converging staircase, 1 mark for correct positions of x_1 and x_2]

Q5 $h = \dfrac{5 - 1}{4} = 1$

$x_0 = 1, y_0 = 0.25$
$x_1 = 2, y_1 = 0.1,$
$x_2 = 3, y_2 = 0.0556$
$x_3 = 4, y_3 = 0.0357$
$x_4 = 5, y_4 = 0.025$

Using Simpson's Rule:
$$\int_1^5 \frac{1}{x^2 + 3x}\, dx \approx \frac{1}{3}(1)[(0.25 + 0.025) + 4(0.1 + 0.0357) + 2(0.0556)]$$
$= 0.310$ (3 s.f.).

[4 marks available — 1 mark for correct x-values, 1 mark for correct y-values, 1 mark for correct use of formula, 1 mark for final answer]

Q6 $h = \dfrac{3 - 1}{4} = 0.5$

$x_{0.5} = 1.25, y_{0.5} = 2.3784$ (5 s.f.)
$x_{1.5} = 1.75, y_{1.5} = 3.3636$ (5 s.f.)
$x_{2.5} = 2.25, y_{2.5} = 4.7568$ (5 s.f.)
$x_{3.5} = 2.75, y_{3.5} = 6.7272$ (5 s.f.)

Using the Mid-Ordinate Rule:
$$\int_1^3 2^x\, dx \approx 0.5[2.3784 + 3.3636 + 4.7568 + 6.7272]$$
$= 8.613$ (4 s.f.).

[3 marks available — 1 mark for calculating y-values for the midpoint of each strip, 1 mark for correct use of formula, 1 mark for correct answer]

Chapter 7: Proof

1. Proof

Exercise 1.1 — Different types of proof

Q1 **a)** Take two even numbers, $2j$ and $2k$ (where j and k are integers), then their product is $2j \times 2k = 4jk = 2(2jk) =$ even.

b) Take one even number, $2l$ and one odd number $2m + 1$ (where l and m are integers), then their product is $2l \times (2m + 1) = 4lm + 2l = 2(2lm + l) =$ even.

Q2 Proof by exhaustion:
Take three consecutive integers $(n - 1)$, n and $(n + 1)$. Their product is $(n - 1)n(n + 1) = n(n^2 - 1) = n^3 - n$. Consider the two cases — n even and n odd. For n even, n^3 is even (as even × even = even) so $n^3 - n$ is also even (as even – even = even). For n odd, n^3 is odd (as odd × odd = odd) so $n^3 - n$ is even (as odd – odd = even). So $n^3 - n$ is even when n is even and when n is odd, and n must be either odd or even, so the product of three consecutive integers is always even.
Another approach to this proof is to take the product of three consecutive integers n(n + 1)(n + 2) and consider n odd and n even. If n is odd:
n(n + 1)(n + 2) = (odd × even) × odd = even × odd = even.
If n is even:
n(n + 1)(n + 2) = (even × odd) × even = even × even = even.

Q3 The simplest way to disprove the statement is to find a counter-example. Try some values of n and see if the statement is true for them:
$n = 3 \Rightarrow n^2 - n - 1 = 3^2 - 3 - 1 = 5$ — prime
$n = 4 \Rightarrow n^2 - n - 1 = 4^2 - 4 - 1 = 11$ — prime
$n = 5 \Rightarrow n^2 - n - 1 = 5^2 - 5 - 1 = 19$ — prime
$n = 6 \Rightarrow n^2 - n - 1 = 6^2 - 6 - 1 = 29$ — prime
$n = 7 \Rightarrow n^2 - n - 1 = 7^2 - 7 - 1 = 41$ — prime
$n = 8 \Rightarrow n^2 - n - 1 = 8^2 - 8 - 1 = 55$ — not prime
$n^2 - n - 1$ is not prime when $n = 8$.
So the statement is false.

Sometimes good old trial and error is the easiest way to find a counter-example. Don't forget, if you've been told to disprove a statement like this, then a counter-example must exist.

Q4 Proof by contradiction:
Suppose that the statement is not true, that is, the graph has a turning point. That means that there is at least one value of x for which $\frac{dy}{dx} = 0$. $\frac{d}{dx}(\ln x) = \frac{1}{x}$ but there is no value of x for which $\frac{1}{x} = 0$, so we've contradicted the statement that the graph has a turning point, hence the original statement is true.

Q5 Find a counter-example for which the statement isn't true. Take $x = -1$ and $y = 2$. Then
$\sqrt{x^2 + y^2} = \sqrt{(-1)^2 + 2^2} = \sqrt{1 + 4} = \sqrt{5} = 2.236...$
and $x + y = -1 + 2 = 1$. $2.236... > 1$, so the statement is not true.

Q6 Direct proof:
Replace $1 + \tan^2 \theta$ with $\sec^2 \theta$ in the LHS and rearrange:
$$\cos^2\theta(1 + \tan^2\theta) \equiv \cos^2\theta(\sec^2\theta)$$
$$\equiv \cos^2\theta\left(\frac{1}{\cos^2\theta}\right)$$
$$\equiv 1$$

This is the same as the RHS so the identity is true.
This proof used the 'known facts' $1 + \tan^2 \theta \equiv \sec^2 \theta$ and $\sec \theta \equiv \frac{1}{\cos \theta}$.

Q7 **a)** Proof by exhaustion:
Consider the two cases — n even and n odd.
Let n be even.
$n^2 - n = n(n - 1)$.
If n is even, $n - 1$ is odd so $n(n - 1)$ is even (as even × odd = even). This means that $n(n - 1) - 1$ is odd.
Let n be odd. If n is odd, $n - 1$ is even, so $n(n - 1)$ is even (as odd × even = even). This means that $n(n - 1) - 1$ is odd.
As any integer n has to be either odd or even, $n^2 - n - 1$ is odd for any value of n.

b) As $n^2 - n - 1$ is odd, $n^2 - n - 2$ is even. The product of even numbers is also even, so as $(n^2 - n - 2)^3$ is the product of 3 even numbers, it will always be even.

Glossary

A

Absolute value
Another name for the **modulus**.

Asymptote
A straight line that a graph approaches (but never touches).

C

Chain rule
A method for **differentiating** a function of a function.

Cobweb diagram
A diagram showing an **iteration sequence**, where the terms spiral towards or away from the **root**. Terms alternate between being above and below the root.

Coefficient
The constant multiplying the variable(s) in an algebraic term.

Composite function
A combination of two or more functions acting on a value or set of values.

Continuous
A function is continuous if its graph contains no breaks or jumps.

Convergence
A sequence converges if the terms get closer and closer to a single value.

Cos⁻¹
The **inverse** of the cosine function, also written as arccosine or arccos.

Cosec
The **reciprocal** of the sine function, sometimes written as cosecant.

Cot
The **reciprocal** of the tangent function, sometimes written as cotangent.

D

Definite integral
An **integral** which is evaluated over an interval given by two **limits**.

Derivative
The result after **differentiating** a function.

Differentiation
A method of finding the rate of change of a function with respect to a variable — the opposite of **integration**.

Direct proof
Using known facts to build up an argument to prove that a statement is true or false.

Disproof by counter-example
Finding one example of where a statement doesn't hold, hence showing that it is false.

Divergence
A sequence diverges if the terms get further and further apart.

Domain
The set of values that can be input into a **mapping** or **function**. Usually given as the set of values that x can take.

E

e
An **irrational number** for which the gradient of $y = e^x$ is equal to e^x.

Exponential function
A function of the form $y = a^x$. $y = e^x$ is known as 'the' exponential function.

F

Function
A type of **mapping** which maps every number in the **domain** to only one number in the **range**.

I

Identity
An equation that is true for all values of a variable, usually denoted by the '≡' sign.

Indefinite integral
An **integral** which contains a constant of integration that comes from integrating without limits.

Integer
A whole number, including 0 and negative numbers. The set of integers has the notation $\mathbb{Z}$.

Integral
The result you get when you **integrate** a function.

Integration
Process for finding the equation of a function, given its **derivative** — the opposite of **differentiation**.

Integration by parts
A method for **integrating** a product of two functions. The reverse process of the **product rule**.

Integration by substitution
A method for **integrating** a function of a function. The reverse process of the **chain rule**.

Inverse function
An inverse function, written as $f^{-1}(x)$, reverses the effect of the function $f(x)$.

Irrational number
A number that can't be written as a fraction of two integers.

Iteration
A numerical method for solving equations that allows you to find the approximate value of a **root** by repeatedly using an iteration formula.

Iteration sequence
The list of results x_1, x_2... etc. found with an iteration formula.

Limits
The numbers between which you integrate to find a **definite integral**.

Logarithm
The logarithm to the base a of a number x (written $\log_a x$) is the power to which a must be raised to give that number.

Lower bound
The lowest value a number could take and still be rounded up to the correct answer.

Many-to-one function
A function where some values in the **range** correspond to more than one value in the **domain**.

Mapping
An operation that takes one number and transforms it into another.

Mid-Ordinate rule
A way of estimating the area under a curve by dividing it up into a number of rectangular strips.

Modulus
The modulus of a number is its positive numerical value.
The modulus of a function, f(x), makes every value of f(x) positive by removing any minus signs.

Natural logarithm
The **inverse function** of $\mathbf{e}^x$, written as $\ln x$ or $\log_e x$.

Natural number
A positive integer, not including 0. The set of natural numbers has the notation $\mathbb{N}$.

Normal
A straight line that crosses a curve at a given point and is perpendicular to the curve at that point.

O

One-to-one function
A function where each value in the **range** corresponds to one and only one value in the **domain**.

Percentage error
The difference between a value and its approximation, as a percentage of the real value.

Product rule
A method for **differentiating** a product of two functions.

Proof
Using mathematical arguments to show that a statement is true or false.

Proof by contradiction
Assuming that a statement is false, then showing that this assumption is impossible, to prove that the statement is true.

Proof by exhaustion
Splitting a situation into separate cases that cover all possible scenarios, then showing that the statement is true for each case, hence true overall.

Quotient rule
A method of **differentiating** one function divided by another.

Range
The set of values output by a **mapping** or **function**. Usually given as a set of values that y or f(x) can take.

Rational number
A number that can be written as a fraction of two integers, where the denominator is non-zero.

Real number
Any positive or negative number (or 0) including all **rational** and **irrational numbers**, e.g. fractions, decimals, integers and surds. The set of real numbers has the notation $\mathbb{R}$.

Reciprocal
The reciprocal of a number or function is 1 divided by the number or function.

Root
A value of x at which a function is equal to 0.

S

Sec
The **reciprocal** of the cosine function, sometimes written as secant.

Second order derivative
The result of **differentiating** a function twice.

Simpson's rule
A way of estimating the area under a curve by dividing it up into an even number of strips.

Sin⁻¹
The **inverse** of the sine function, also written as arcsine or arcsin.

Staircase diagram
A diagram showing an **iteration sequence**, where the terms climb or descend towards or away from a **root**. Terms are all either above or below the root.

Stationary point
A point on a curve where the gradient is 0.

Tan⁻¹
The **inverse** of the tangent function, also written as arctangent or arctan.

Tangent
A straight line which just touches a curve at a point, without going through it and that has the same **gradient** as the curve at that point.

Turning point
A **stationary point** that is a (local) maximum or minimum point.

Upper bound
The upper limit of the values that a number could take and still be rounded down to the correct answer.

Volume of revolution
The volume of the 3D solid shape formed by rotating an area, bounded by a curve and straight lines, through 2π radians about the x- or y-axis.

Index

C3 Formula Sheet

The formulas below will be included in the formula book for your exams — make sure you know exactly **when you need them** and **how to use them**. These are the formulas relating specifically to the C3 module, but remember you might also need any formulas relevant to C1 and C2 in C3.

Differentiation

f(x)	f'(x)
$\tan kx$	$k\sec^2 kx$
$\sec x$	$\sec x \tan x$
$\cot x$	$-\text{cosec}^2 x$
$\text{cosec } x$	$-\text{cosec } x \cot x$
$\dfrac{f(x)}{g(x)}$	$\dfrac{f'(x)g(x) - f(x)g'(x)}{(g(x))^2}$

Logs and Exponentials

$$e^{x \ln a} = a^x$$

Integration

$$\int u \frac{dv}{dx}\,dx = uv - \int v\frac{du}{dx}\,dx$$

f(x)	$\int$ f(x) dx
$\sec^2 kx$	$\frac{1}{k}\tan kx + C$
$\tan x$	$\ln|\sec x| + C$
$\cot x$	$\ln|\sin x| + C$
$\text{cosec } x$	$\begin{cases} -\ln|\text{cosec } x + \cot x| + C \\ \ln|\tan (\frac{1}{2}x)| + C \end{cases}$
$\sec x$	$\begin{cases} \ln|\sec x + \tan x| + C \\ \ln|\tan (\frac{1}{2}x + \frac{1}{4}\pi)| + C \end{cases}$

Numerical Integration

The Mid-Ordinate Rule:

$$\int_a^b y\,dx \approx h(y_{0.5} + y_{1.5} + \ldots + y_{n-1.5} + y_{n-0.5}), \text{ where } h = \frac{b-a}{n}$$

Simpson's Rule:

$$\int_a^b y\,dx \approx \frac{1}{3}h\{(y_0 + y_n) + 4(y_1 + y_3 + \ldots + y_{n-1}) + 2(y_2 + y_4 + \ldots + y_{n-2})\},$$

where $h = \frac{b-a}{n}$, n is even

MAC3T61